MW00441390

ACKNOWLEDGMENTS

All praises due to the Father, thanking Him
always for His grace and for keeping me.

To my parents and my great family,
thank you for not giving up on me.

Special thanks and appreciation to my friend, RWJ,
for his unyielding support in this project.

Thanks Renee—you came through.

I want to say to all the women who have
fallen due to "The Life," it ain't over!!

And in special remembrance to the
victims of the Green River killer.

Peace.

Preface

People always say, "Sharell, you should write a book." Sometimes my past would slip out in conversation or I would reflect on certain experiences, then my brothers or my confidant would just look in amazement. My brother, Kenny, would laugh in disbelief, but he knew all too well it was true. "Girl, write a book," he would say. I couldn't do that, then everybody would see my skeletons.

My friend would just look with admiration that I've come out of the murk without any outward blemishes. He would say, "you need, (emphasis on need), to tell your story." Although he really does not know that much. (I hate for him to read this book). I always thought some secrets should be kept secret. You just do not tell everything, so I kept silent. People would know about me. No! That could never happen.

I am really afraid of what my children will say if they read what I've done. My sons think I walk on water. I could never let them read the truth about me. My goodness, I kept so much from them. They were young during most of my adventures.

Oh Lord, my church members, what in the world would they think of me. They are my friends and I love them dearly. They might look at me differently. I hope not. People change. Their attitudes change. They whisper things when they find out your little secrets. I did trust my Pastor with one truth—not all. I believe he got the picture. Gosh! I was really out there.

One childhood friend expressed, "Sharell, for the life you've lived, it's a wonder you still look the way you do." I've been blessed in that area. Maybe it was all the years of dancing for a living or moving fast—awake all night, or maybe it's true what they say, "The Lord takes care of babies and fools." I was both. I don't believe in luck. After everything I've been through, one would be stupid not to give God the glory. Oh yes, I thank Him because He never let me go. How wonderful is my Father in heaven, to love even me.

It has been a long road to get back to Sharell. To really look at myself . . . didn't happen.

My friend finally convinced me that I may be able to help someone by telling my experiences and how I escaped or was rescued. What really convinces me was the sister that spoke at my church on Women's Day. She just let it all hang out and was bold with her story. She asked, "Why on earth did she survive if not to let others know, they too can find their way back home." Praise God!

It's something about living the life. There's a residue that we sometimes recognize in others with similar backgrounds. We think because we know it and recognize some parts in others, that everyone can see our grit. No one knows. It's your secret. Unless you are outwardly projecting your experiences, no one can tell. It's not stamped across our forehead.

It took so long for me to feel okay about myself. I hope no one ever takes as long as I did to get a grip and wake up. To know that you are good and worth more than gold. I kept myself down longer than anybody, because I just thought I wasn't good enough. Twenty-five years lost. Don't do that.

So, I want to share some of my experiences with the hope that someone will read it and will recognize when they are approached by a liar coming to entice them, or to destroy and abuse their life. Or, maybe it's the only life you know. You can change it. If your plans change, look for positive alternatives. It's not the end of the world. There's always something else, just as good. Seek God's guidance and pray. If you fall, get up and keep stepping. Stay up!

Yours in Love,
Sharell

Chapter 1

The 70's were exciting times in Oklahoma City. Everybody was doing something. Everybody seemed to be a professional. The word professional was thrown around in every circle—professional this and professional that. There was so much talent around. People were excellent at their trade. Whatever it was, they were thoroughly competent. There was movement in the air and it smelled good. It was a rush. Nonstop parties everywhere that ended only when daybreak eased in without warning. Treva's Club, Kidnapp's Offbeat Club and Bryant Center were the spots. The Top Hat Club, the Pink Elephant—you couldn't beat the food and fun.

Every weekend was anticipated and pre-planned 'cause I had to beg Momma for hours to go and we had to get our story straight. Times were fast and classy and I was right there in it. I loved Oklahoma City. It's a beautiful town. There are no ghettos here; people are cool and kind. No sir, there are no ghettos in Oklahoma City.

People were sharp back then and we could dress with the best of them—thanks to my best friend, Phyl, who boosted our clothes. At seventeen, we were graduating from high school and wearing $500 outfits. Knits and leathers were in, and we had to look good, because we were the stars. We were too cool to be seen in the same outfit too many times.

Phyllis, Connie, Vicki and me, Sharell—four beautiful, classy, seniors, ready for the world, with change, challenge and fate waiting. Who would make it, fake it, choose it or lose it. You could tell something was going to happen. Nothing stays the same, at least not this good. We were in fairytale land.

"Girl, you know we are going to be the Queens our senior year. I can't believe we were all nominated. You know we're gonna win over Karla and that stuck up bunch." I bragged.

Phyl chimed in, "Don't worry, they won't beat us, we're way more popular. Everybody likes us. Anyway, we're having the after party. They better pick us . . . Guess what? I got us three, brand new convertible Cadillacs to drive around the football stadium when we win."

I couldn't believe what I was hearing. "You are lying Phyl."

Phyl was so excited, she continued to give us the details.

"Yes, I do! I got a red one, a baby blue one and a white convertible for us to ride around the stadium at the Homecoming game tonight."

"How did you get it?"

"You know that guy, Finley, on 23rd and Lottie, he gave them to me."

"He what?" I couldn't believe it. Phyl has connections. I never could get over the connections she had. She always had the hook ups.

Phyl continued to explain. "I was just messing with him and I asked him if we could sport three of his Cadillacs and he said okay."

"Right on! We'll have them all day?"

"Naw girl, but we're gonna be styling around the stadium in brand new convertible Cadillacs at the Homecoming game tonight. We're going to be sharp," Phyl said laughing loud.

"I got a three finger lid of weed, I'm going to pass joints around like we're at a concert." I wanted to contribute on something cool, too.

"You ought to keep that for us. Don't give away the weed."

"I got it for our party. Anyway, I only paid a dime for it, so ... this is our party." We were all jumping and screaming by then. So much happening.

I was always amazed at Phyl. Everybody loved Phyllis. People just wanted to impress her for some reason. She planned on becoming a nurse. Phyl would take over an accident scene, hold down the fort until the police or ambulance arrived. Wouldn't let you touch or move the victims—being professional. She kept blankets in her car trunk, just in case of an emergency. She was a natural. Always prepared.

Phyl loved Gerald Hilton. They had been going together since Kindergarten. Gerald didn't like me too much. I did the unthinkable. I was at his house with Phylis one day and saw a letter from some girl and gave it to her. She didn't speak to Gerald for months. Gerald could have killed me and I hate I did that. I just didn't understand real love then and they really loved each other.

"Did you get your gown for the Homecoming program yet?" Phyl asked.

"I'm going today with Momma. Girl, she bought me this glittering pantsuit to wear to the game tonight. Can you believe Momma? You know it would be tight if we had a live band at the party. Is Mark Stafford and Walter gonna come through for us with their band?"

We use to give parties all of the time at our friend, Billy's apartment complex, in the Hospitality room. After the clubs closed, people came to our little high school party. We were barely seventeen and selling alcohol at our parties. We made money.

"Girl yes. He's glad to play, he's playing for free. Mark just wants a chance to play and sing for somebody and he's good. Well, good enough. I can't wait." Phyl said.

"Girl, we're going to be like Melva Jean." I said.

Melva is Connie's older sister. She is six feet tall and she is a fox. Melva could have any man she wanted and she ruled. Melva was like Cleopatra Jones—her afro was perfect. She was Homecoming Queen in 1972. I remember when she was announced as the Queen. They were lowering her down from the ceiling in a swing. She really made a statement. It was great. We all looked up to Melva.

"I bought gallons of alcohol for the after party. We're charging two dollars at the door and three dollars for drinks. Girl we are going to make some money," Phyl said laughing. She was always scheming and making things happen. We called the local radio station and had the party announced at no cost. We said it was to raise money for the Black Student Union at Northeast High School—a free public service announcement. Of course, it was aired.

Phyllis was nominated for 1974 Homecoming Queen, I was nominated for Football Queen and Connie was nominated for Miss Northeast. Vicki was helping us get dressed and just hanging out. She was the model of the bunch. We were a team—best friends and ready to wear our crowns. We were gorgeous that night. Pure and anyone would have been proud to escort us down the school aisle. Larry was my escort. He was ready and licking his lips to give me that winning kiss. I was scared to death that he was going to stick his tongue in my mouth.

"Girl, can you believe they picked them over us?" Phyl asked. We were all disappointed.

"They wanted Karla over me. That was rigged. That had to be rigged," I complained. We were defeated? Us? We were sitting around in the girl's gym trying to make sense of everything.

"Mrs. Johnson asked if they could use our cars to ride around the stadium tonight." Phyl said.

"Tell her no." I really wasn't in the mood to be nice. I felt cheated.

"I can't do that. I said yeah, but they're only going to ride around one time." That was Phyl—too kind. They rode in our convertibles, waving and grinning only once around the stadium. Afterward, we hurried them out as we got into our convertibles. With the tops still down and us sitting on the back dash headed to the after party, a trail of cars followed behind us blowing the horns with the music playing loud, people screaming, "We won, we won!" We were happy teenagers, having fun, kicking it.

School was out and it's our last summer together. I planned on Hampton Institute in Virginia. Vicki and Connie were moving to Colorado with Melva Jean. Phyllis was planning on Oklahoma University. Then the unthinkable happened. Phyllis was pregnant. We were all numb. This was something new for us. We were too young and had too many things to do. But, we were going to have a baby.

Momma brought me luggage for my graduation present and I was ready to fly the coop. Get away from the guarded nest. I wanted to break and be free. I also wanted to study law. I've always been interested in political science and law. I just wasn't sure what to do next. That summer I enrolled in a shorthand class, I could already write over eighty words a minute. I sometimes would write what the news commentators reported at night. It was good practice. I thought I could be a courtroom stenographer, if nothing else.

My mom was something. She had four children when she met Marzett. He was my stepfather. Marzett never said too much and I never said too much to him. He married Momma and us; then they added the identical twins. With six kids they never looked back. Marzett was a real man. He loved my Momma deeply, because my Momma was a fox. My mom was one of the most beau-

C. Oakes

tiful women you ever want to see. Not because she is my mother but because it's true. My mother was mesmerizing—it was her eyes. She was confident and the boss and Marzett let her have her way.

Momma was so protective. I never really had a boyfriend. They were all too scared of Momma. She had a way of looking at you that would intimidate any normal human being and maybe some not so normal. She would drill and pick before she decided if I could go anywhere with anybody. She had me so nervous, no telling what was coming out of Momma's mouth. It was too much trouble for boys. I didn't even have male friends like Vicki, Connie and Phyllis. They had regular boys who could come to their house, who were just friends. Guys would hang out at their houses and it was okay. I thought that was so cool. I learned to keep my distance until I was free. I couldn't wait to fly the coup.

Chapter 2

Connie and Vicki saw him first. They were at an apartment, swimming and they told us about this fine guy that they met.

"Girl, we got to go back swimming, tonight," Connie said.

"What did he look like?" I was curious because they seemed so excited.

"He is fine. He's from California. Come on, we're going back to that pool. He said his name was Mike and asked if we would come back again tonight. We told him we would be there." Connie was giving me the scoop.

"Girl, wait till you see him." Vicki said.

I had a white bikini. It was cute and I was cute in it. Vicki, Connie and I were there to see Mike again. I finally saw him looking from an upstairs apartment window. They were right. He sure was fine. But there was something else about him. He was different. He came down, looking at me, smiling, with all the confidence in the world on his shoulders. I was grinning back, talking, while wading around in the water.

"Are you going to be here for a while?" Mike asked.

"Yes," I nodded.

"Well, I'll be right back, I'm getting my trunks so I can join you," Mike said.

"Okay!" I said. Vicki and Connie were in the water laughing, cracking up. I didn't know why, I thought they were just being silly and acting young. He left to get his trunks and then they told me.

"Sharell, your top is down." Connie laughed. I looked down and there they were, wading freely in the water, too. I was so upset.

"Why didn't you say something. You're supposed to be my friends. That's why he was looking at me like that. Nobody said anything. How long was my top down?" I was upset.

"Girl, you are so stupid, you didn't know your top was down?" Vicki asked.

"Noooo. I'm embarrassed, y'all could have said something." I was hurt that my friends didn't let me know. They just laughed.

Soon, he was back and in swim trunks, looking great.

"I'm Mike, what's your name?"

"Sharell," I said.

"You sure are cute. I'd like to call you sometime. Can I get your telephone number," Mike asked.

"That'll be okay. My friends stated you're from California. How long are you in the City." My eyes were flirting. I couldn't stop smiling.

"Well, I don't know. I have some business I'm doing now," Mike said.

"What do you do?" I asked. I wanted to know more about him.

"I'm a artist," Mike said shyly.

"What kind of artist?" I asked. An artist . . my curiosity was in high gear.

"I'll have to show you sometime. I'd like to get to know you better. Is that ok?" Mike asked. He wasn't giving me too much to work on. I needed more information but getting information from him was like pulling teeth. We talked most the night. I forgot all about Vicki and Connie. It was a dark and beautiful summer night. The sky was lit up—sparkling. The weather warm and the water was cool. I was with this very handsome and mysterious man. I've never felt so excited about anyone. He reeled me in like an expert. I was definitely a catch.

When Mike arrived for our first date, I was ready. My afro was together. I kept it trimmed perfectly and my makeup was perfect, as well. I was looking good. But why did he bring some-one with him? What is that about? I felt disappointed that he brought a friend with him. They were dressed alike! What is that high school stuff about. My friends and I would never dress alike. This seemed strange, but there he was, taking pictures of me. Treating me like I was the only person in the universe. I enjoyed his attention. Still there was something fun and mysterious about this guy. I didn't know what it was about him, but I wanted to know more.

It was such an unusual thing to be the center of attraction. I was always in the shadow of my friends. Each one had their unique quality that put them on center stage. This time it was my turn. Things were happening so fast.

C. Oakes

We were finally alone at his apartment. He had fixed dinner—grilled fish. We were sipping wine. I never had an evening like this. He was rapping to me, blowing my mind.

"I'm going to make love to you through your mind, first. Then your body. I'm going to take you slow. Would you like that." Mike was smacking to me. If this was a line, I wanted every word. Don't miss nothing. I was floating away. I've never, ever had conversation like this. There I was in a beautiful apartment, candlelight, and body oil being rubbed on me—through me.

"Turn over so I can massage your back." He whispered so close to my ear, I got a chill. I turned over and took another drink of my wine. I was on cloud nine. I was absorbing every minute and purring like a cat. Definitely and completely seduced. My young mind was blown.

Mike came to get me everyday. I was introduced to his world which included a group of followers. They were jealous of the attention I got from him. He was in charge so it didn't matter. He didn't dress that good, but this had to be the cleanest man I've ever met. He was crazy clean. All his followers would jump to attention and wait on his next instructions. What was wrong with this bunch?

Then it happened, Mike brought me home too late. Momma went ballistic. She was kicking my ass. What really impressed me about the whole ass-whipping is, Mike didn't run. He watched every lick I got and stayed till the ass kicking was over. After the whipping, Momma looked at him and he was still there. What was this, she didn't kick his ass out the house and tell him not to ever come back. Well now. He could stay?

"Are you alright?" Mike asked.

"Yeah, I'm really embarrassed. I don't know why she acts like that. Nobody else goes through this with their momma. I finished school. I was good in school. I'm going to college," I said sniffling.

"Well, I'll call you tomorrow. It's okay. You got me," Mike said walking toward me. He gave me a light kiss, wiped away my tears and left.

Well, I stayed out late again and Momma whipped my ass again. This time she tried to strangle me. I was holding her off. She told Mike he could take care of me since I didn't want to mind her and obey her rules. He was too happy and I was too mad. With only a month left through the summer, I left with Mike to join his entourage. He called it The Family.

Momma would come by the apartment crying, begging me to come back home, but by then it was too late. Mike had me— mind, body and soul. I was his. He would try to convince Momma that he would take care of me.

"Sharell is on her way to school. Are you going to throw that all away?" Momma asked as she begged me to come home.

"No, Momma, I'm still going to school."

"I'll take care of her. She's going to go to college." Mike said trying to convince Momma, but Momma wasn't buying it.

"Well, since y'all gonna live together, then why don't you marry her," Momma said, thinking he would back out of that deal.

"Okay, I'll marry her," Mike said too quickly. This was my first love. Wild horses couldn't drag me away from Mike. My attachment to Mike was hard as cement.

Slowly, I got the picture about Mike. He was an artist alright, a con-artist. He had so many ways of conning people. His smile would woo anybody. I watched Mike go through towns and banks talking and conning his way through thousands of dollars.

"Sharell, as long as there's a town, banks and stores we'll have money. I'll never be broke." Mike explained our plight. I had never seen anything like it. Mike said he was plucking a note. That's what he called short changing. He could talk his way, smile his way through any situation or transaction. He was like Phyl— people loved him. Mike could charm a snake.

We would travel through all the little towns; he would short change and con people. He tried to teach me, but I was too square. I couldn't get it straight. I just wasn't slick. His gang would be in the back seat, looking mad about me sitting next to him, having all his attention, but they tolerated me. I really didn't care. We were captivated by each other.

Effie was Mike's cousin. She came from California with him. She was alright. She had pretty hair but, she was just a zombie. She did whatever Mike asked. Mike told me he had been taking care of Effie since she was a little girl. Marvin was Effie's cousin. He was from McAlester, OK. He tried to be like Mike. Dressed like him, acted like him, except, he hated me.

LaPonz was his homeboy. LaPonz was so much fun, he sure was extreme. LaPonz liked me. We would laugh for hours. We would dance. *Party Time* by Willie Hutch was the song. Mike danced better than anybody. We'd party all night.

"Sharell, we're going to California. Get packed." Mike said.

"Okay!" I said apprehensively. I didn't know why I felt so nervous. I made sure I had money to call Momma, just in case. Mike and LaPonz were deep in conversation, talking in riddles—I was use to that. I rarely knew what they were talking about. I had book smarts but I wasn't street smart at all. Effie was happy to be getting away from Oklahoma. She was buzzing around. Excited. She would tell me how great Cali was. She talked about all the different restaurants—Little Mesa and the sorts.

"Things are different in California. It's a whole new world out there. You ready, Sharell?" Effie laughed. Marvin was even walking with more pep in his step. California was something to look forward to, I guess. Everybody was acting fishy. They would let me in on the big deal sooner or later. Effie lived in Pittsburg, CA. I never heard of Pittsburg, CA. I tried to share her enthusiasm. Just wasn't feeling it, though. What is going on, I thought. Something, I couldn't put a finger on it. LaPonz sat up front with Mike during this trip. They were deep in conversation. I didn't try to keep up, I was just staying focused on what I needed to do—my escape plan, if something weird happened. We drove to Pittsburg.

"This is Pittsburg?" I asked. I couldn't believe it. What was the big deal. We drove straight to Effie's house. Her mom was so happy to see everybody.

"She's a nice lady," I said to Mike. She started hugging and making sleeping arrangements, accommodating everybody.

"Okay, Sharell you can sleep here on the sofa bed with me. Mike, you and Effie can take my bed," Effie's mother said.

"What is she talking about?" I asked.

"You ready for the truth?" Mike whispered to me

"What truth, Mike? What are you talking about? Mike what's going on?" I questioned. I was confused. I was trying to understand what exactly was happening. Why was Effie's mother telling them to sleep together.

"The truth about me and Effie—that truth," Mike whispered.

I was sucker punched in the gut. I was sick. Effie looked at me with this ugly slick-ass, crooked teeth smile. I couldn't believe what I was hearing. My innocence, trust, morals and values, took a hard blow. Real people don't do this.

"Mike, she's not your cousin?" I asked. I couldn't believe she went along with deceiving me like this. I would never let my man bring another woman in my house and I act like a cousin. She's stupid. . . a good dog obeying her master. These people are lowdown. They're sick. I was devastated. I couldn't talk, I couldn't cry. All I need to do is get back to Oklahoma City.

I was stuck for now. I couldn't call Momma, because she would tell me this and that, and be right. I had to be cool and get back home. I didn't talk too much to anybody. They were all dirty, crazy people. Mike tried to touch me—I slapped him hard. That was the first time I've ever been hit by a man. He knocked me on the ground. I saw stars. My mouth was bleeding and he came over and grabbed me up and started whispering something. I didn't hear a word. It was like slow motion. I was trying to get myself together. I held my head up, dusted myself off, and pulled myself away from his ugly hands. I never wanted him to touch me again.

"Don't ever touch me again, Mike," I said.

"You better be cool, you don't tell me what to do. Do you understand me? Just be cool, Sharell." Mike was still talking in a low voice. I had to be cool, because I was in a real bind. I would say to myself, they're not going to kill you. At least that's what I hoped. Get home and it'll be okay.

Mike left Effie at her mom's house, the rest of us went to Oakland. I guess he was showing me the big Bay Area. Acting like nothing happened. Effie was really his girl. I was so hurt and blind. I must have been really green not to have recognized this bullshit. I was getting good at holding my peace. Um palm trees— it's starting to look like California.

I wasn't talking much.

"Sharell let's go for a ride," Mike said, still in charge. I got up to head for the car. He wanted to talk to me alone. Does he really think I would forgive him after this shit? One thing about it, Effie wasn't getting back in the same car with me, if I could help it. She was lowdown. These people didn't have any class. They're gut

C. Oakes

bucket low.

"When are we going back home, Mike," I asked.

"What's wrong? You don't like it here in California?" Mike asked.

"No, Mike. I don't like it here—not at all. I'm going home."

"What if I don't let you go?" Mike asked.

"What are you talking about?" I was trying to be cool, like nothing was bothering me.

"Sharell, I don't want to let you go. You think I'm going to take you back to Oklahoma City so you can leave me. All you're going to do is find another man and be with him," Mike argued. I thought I should soften up a bit. I didn't want any trouble getting home.

"Mike, I'm going to school." I had to play it just right.

"Well, I'm not going to let you leave me. You are going to be mine. You're going to be my wife, Sharell." Mike said. He had that little smirk that he always uses when he's playing somebody. I guess he's playing me now. He has lost what little sense he had left. He's really crazy now.

"What are you talking about. You're crazy, I'm not ready to marry anybody. You're going to take me home and I'm going to join the military or something. I'm getting away from everybody 'cause I got to get on track, Mike. I need to get myself together," I said as slowly and thoroughly as I could. I wanted to get my point across.

"I'm going to marry you and take care of you, Sharell," Mike said.

"That's alright, you take care of Effie, Mike, that's what you do." I blurted out. I was mad now. Was he paying attention to what I said. Did he understand?

"Fuck Effie. She was just somebody that helped me. You are going to be my wife." Then he finally let it go. Mike stayed at my heels during the rest of the trip. He didn't try to push himself on me and I was glad of that. I just wanted to get away.

We finally left California. Mike wouldn't let me out of his sight for months. Everywhere he went I was right there. I was too embarrassed to tell anybody about what happened in California. One morning in 1975, I was 18, we got up and did the quickie marry thing at the courthouse in Oklahoma City.

I don't know what I expected once I got married. Our relationship started out with another woman. Was the women suppose to go away? Mike was a straight whore. I couldn't have any friends. He would eventually be with them. Then he would let me know.

"Sharell, I don't want Princess back in our house," Mike spouted out as he was coming home one morning. Damn, I told her about him and not to do it. When she saw him, I noticed how she looked at him, how they looked at each other, I warned that cow about my husband.

"I guess you fucked her, too. I can't have any friends," I cried. I felt sorry that he would use my friends like that.

"They're not your damn friends. You ain't got no friends. Just don't bring the bitch back in here, smiling in your face," Mike shouted. I know he didn't want to see her anymore. He got what he wanted 'cause he's a dog.

C. Oakes

Chapter 3

My cousin Tammy moved to Oklahoma City from Memphis. It's hard to describe Tammy. She had long, thick, curly hair, a beautiful body and beautiful face but, she had an unusual thing for sex. Tammy was a sex addict. I wondered what it was like to enjoy sex that much. She was something. Tammy could out drink any man. She's sweet, fun loving, beautiful—all that, but she had serious issues.

"Sharell girrrrl, Guess what I've been doing. Wait 'till you hear. I met this lady and she took me to this club where you get paid to dance. I've been dancing," Tammy said.

"What are you talking about," I asked.

"Girl, look at all this money I made. Now, look at that," Tammy said.

"You made all that? All you did was dance?" I asked. I couldn't believe it.

"Yeah, this is what I made in one week," She replied. Tammy showed me a $350 dollar check. In 1975, especially in Oklahoma City, that was a lot of money for one week.

"What are you doing?" I asked.

"Stripping. Sharell, I'm stripping and I like it. It's fun," Tammy said defending her new found joy.

"What! Tammy, are you crazy? What are you doing stripping?" I shouted at Tammy. I couldn't believe she was telling me this.

"Shoot! Girl, I'm making more money than I ever made in my life and, it's easy," Tammy said, still defending herself for engaging in this family tabu.

"Girl, you better not let Momma and them know what you're doing. Momma will have you on the next bus out of here back to Memphis. You know Momma don't play," I warned Tammy. I didn't want Momma to send her back. I was glad Tammy was here with us in Oklahoma.

"Well, I'll get my own place. I'm making enough money now. Anyway, I need a ride to work. You think Mike will give me a ride to work?" Tammy asked. She just ignored everything I said . . . being a smart ass.

"He'll give you a ride. Ask him!" I said.

Mike and I were together and not doing too much. He would pluck a note here and there, enough to pay the bills. Mike knew I would never move with him to California, so he stayed here, in Oklahoma, with me. His entourage had basically left and it was finally, just me and him.

"Mike, will you give me a ride to work tonight?" Tammy asked.

"A ride where? I don't have gas to be going too far," Mike said.

"I got a job at this club, downtown. I'll give you ten dollars to take me to work," Tammy said. That night Mike gave Tammy a ride downtown to the strip club. It was in a dinky smoky little upstairs room. Dark and not too pretty. Curiosity definitely wasn't going to get the best of Mike. He was checking it out.

"Sharell, you should see that place. Those girl are cleaning up. I sat there and watched for a while. It's pretty neat what was going on. I know one thing, it's easy money," Mike said.

"What are they doing?" I asked.

"They dance on stage. They ask the guys to buy them a drink. I guess they make money when they sit with a guy and he buys them a drink. Oh, I told her I would pick her up tonight if she needs a ride," Mike said.

The next day, Mike was waiting to take Tammy to work. I rode with them. Tammy liked what she was doing a lot. Matter of fact, she was proud and wanted us to see.

"Why don't y'all come up and see me dance?"

"Girl, I'm not going in that place. I'm not going in a place like that." I was kind of pissed. Tammy knew better than that. I have enough problems with Mike and women—I really don't need him looking at Tammy's naked ass.

"Why not?" Tammy asked, knowing full well I wouldn't be caught dead in a place like that.

"'cause I'm not and that's all I have to say. I don't have to explain anything to you. I don't feel comfortable being in a place like that . . . that's why."

"Tammy, she's too good for that," Mike said, being as sarcastic as he knows how to be.

"It's not that I'm too good . . . Well, yes it is. You're right, I am too damn good for a place like that and so are you, Tammy.

Are you crazy, girl? What if your mom finds out what you're doing? Don't you care? I'm not going inside." I looked at Tammy, trying to make her understand what she was doing and the ramifications that she would face if Momma finds out. That news would spread through our family like wildfire.

"Sharell, come on and check it out. Come on cuz and watch me dance." Tammy begged me to come inside and check her out.

"I don't want to see you dance naked." I reluctantly gave up the fight and followed Tammy inside the strip club. I slowly followed as Mike and Tammy took me up the dark narrow stairway to the dinky little smoky room. I was surprised that it was mostly black girls dancing for old white men. The girls would go pick a song off an old rusty jukebox and they would go to the old ragedy stage and dance. *I believe in Miracles. . . you sexy thang, you sexy thang. I believe in Miracles.* Tammy was working that song out. After she got dressed, she would approach men and ask for a drink. They were too happy to oblige. Mike and I quietly left the premises.

"You know that wasn't bad what they were doing. They just dance on stage, then talk with the customers," Mike said.

"No, I guess it wasn't that bad. She sure is making money. You know Tammy likes that kind of stuff anyway." I tried to justify her actions.

"Sharell, why don't you get you a job doing it. She's not doing nothing that bad," Mike said with his little smirk . . . he knows better.

"I'm not going to do that." I couldn't believe he asked me something like that.

"Why not. I take penitentiary chances for you, for us everyday," Mike said. He was getting irritated and I didn't want to make him mad, but I was getting irritated, too.

"You can get a regular job if you want."

"That white man isn't going to give me a job making enough money to live on," Mike said. That was always his excuse not to do the right thing.

"Why do you always want to blame everything on "the white man." My momma had six kids and raised them, just working a regular job. No white man stopped her from doing what she needed to do." I wasn't in the mood for his stupid excuses.

Mike didn't want me to work a regular job for some reason. He would create a disturbance or he would just say I wasn't going to work today. I would eventually get fired. He was jealous of me working, going to school, and making an honest living.

"Sharell, you're going to do it. You think you are all that, don't you? I could go to jail tomorrow, but I still do what it takes for us. You're not willing to do anything for us. You're going to get a job dancing tomorrow. We need the money," Mike said in his whispering voice. That's the way he talks when he's ready to fight and I didn't want to start anything.

The next day I thought it would be a showdown. I was not dancing in that dirty, little club. Mike finally stopped talking about it. Then one day out of the clear blue, we were out riding down 10th Street near MacArthur Blvd., he stopped. There was this little building and we pulled into the parking lot.

"What's this place?" I asked. There was a neon sign outside flashing, The Cherry Tree.

"Come on, get out the car," Mike ordered. I got out of the car and followed him inside. My heart was pounding. He went straight to the manager and he said I was there to try out. Mike had been busy. There were strip clubs up and down 10th Street. Next thing I know, I was on stage dancing. I didn't have to strip to try out.

At the Cherry Tree, it was mostly white girls. You had to dance three songs. Cherry Tree was more or less the burlesque style strip club. They stripped piece by piece. Each song, they'd take a little more off or the girls would have a different costume altogether. On the last song, you were expected to be nearly nude. The girls would have sheer robes, boas, scarfs, but they were showing everything. Husbands and boyfriends were not allowed in the club. There were no dating customers either. We were expected to ask for drinks. The drinks were five dollars and we received half. There was champagne, too, that range from $25 to $500 a bottle. We received half on all drinks. Plus, we were paid $25 per day. This club was a whole lot better than the one downtown. I wasn't ready.

I'll never forget the first time I was on stage. I danced on *You Ain't Seen Nothing Yet*. This club was mostly country and western, so I was happy to get a little rock music. I was the new girl so they wanted to get to know me. There was only one other black girl. She wasn't cute but she made lots of money. Most of the girls had routines and little show props. One girl had puppets. She would be standing on her head and the puppets would put baby powder between her legs. That lady was old and wrinkled—she had a good routine. I did alright. I got the hang of it pretty fast. At the end of the night, the bouncers walked all the girls to their cars, so I was safe. They didn't play about dating the customers. That was an automatic fire. It really made me feel better about the place. They said if you have sex with any of the customers, he would not spend money on you anymore, and he would eventually go to a different club. I guess it made sense. They didn't have to worry about me no way. Mike was always waiting when I walked out the door.

My first paycheck was good. I made $450. I was excited about my money and how I was going to spend it.

"Look at my paycheck. I did good. I guess dancing wasn't that bad. I sure like the money." I rattled on about my money.

"Give it to me," Mike said.

With my hands on my hips I replied "What are you talking about, I'm not giving you my money." He hit me without warning . . . so hard . . . I was dazed. Why did he do that?

"Let me tell you something. You give me all the money. I handle the money in this household. Do you understand that?" Mike whispered, talking between his teeth.

I was crying now, "Yeah, but you didn't have to hit me like that, Mike. What's wrong with you?"

"You need to understand that I'm the man and you don't talk to me any kind of way. Do you understand, do you understand me, Sharell?" Mike continued his little speech. He's getting bad. Real bad and I was getting real scared of him. I cried all night.

I graduated from the Cherry Tree and went to Swizzle Sticks, where I met Ron Boscoe. Ron was a real hands-on manager. At Swizzle Sticks you didn't sit with a guy at all unless he buys a drink, period. Ron didn't play that. He would embarrass the girl or the guy. I really learned to hustle while working for him. I understood Ron. He was all business. Anyway, I really appreciated him because I took his game with me a long way. He'd send me to open his other clubs. I became a main attraction and I had some good routines. I grew a good customer base for myself that I could count on every week.

I had to work on my conversation. In fact, I didn't have a conversation. I would go home at night and write out conversations. I would work out different scenario's and study them, just to have something to talk about. My conversation couldn't be too deep, because the customers didn't want to really think about anything, but they wanted to be entertained. On the other hand, I had to keep their attention so their minds wouldn't drift.

Thanks to the costume lady, I had some nice outfits. She would come every Wednesday. She had leathers and feathers. My favorite was the I Dream of Genie outfit. I'd wear my long genie ponytail wig. It was pretty sexy. My routines started getting better. I still had to work on my conversation.

C. Oakes

Chapter 4

Mike was getting use to fighting me. He would fight me, want sex, then decorate me with jewelry or clothes that he had purchased off the streets. I got beat whenever we went out. He said I was smiling too much or he'd imagine someone was talking to me too long. Sometimes he would sneak in the club and watch me dance, then I really got beat and abused. It would be so embarrassing because I still had to work with marks and bruises all over me. I was scared to death of him. It had gotten so bad that any movement he made, I would duck or flinch.

Phyllis said I must like it or I would leave him.

"You know some people like that shit, Sharell," She explained, like that was my condition. Like I was some kind of sicko.

"Phyllis, I don't like getting beat up. You need to stop saying that."

"Then why are you still with him. Leave his ass," Phyl said. She was talking common sense—I couldn't relate to this. I felt trapped.

"I can't. He said he would kill me and my momma if I ever left him. You don't know him Phyl, he'll hurt my family."

"Girl, he ain't going to do shit. You're just scared. I'll tell you what, if a man hit on me like that, I'll kill his ass," Phyl continued with her look on things.

"I just don't want anything to happen to my family. You don't know him, Phyl. He'll kill me. Mike's not like normal people. He's dangerous." I continued to try to make her understand my circumstances. Phyl wasn't buying it.

"Sharell, he just has his bluff on you. Look at you, he's been beating on you. You got scars all over your back. What has he been hitting you with? Look at your arms. You got to get away from his crazy ass," Phyl argued. I was too ashamed to tell her what was really happening to me. Mike's been beating me with wires and hangers, tying me up with rope, leaving me tied up in the closet all day. He was careful not to leave scars on my face or any where that someone might see them. I was so scared of him. I was beaten down in every way. Now, I was the zombie!

My Mom would asked what was wrong with me. I would ignore her. She knew he was abusing me and she hated Mike. Somehow, I didn't hate him. After he'd fight me, he would cry and beg me to forgive him. He swore he'll never do it again and he loved me. I would have more jewelry and clothes. I was so wounded and belittled. My self esteem was gone. I thought I would die sooner or later.

I did try to run away. I went straight over to Connie's house. I felt that he wouldn't go there starting shit. So I packed my suitcases and left to hide out a few days. To my surprise, there he was over Connie's house. When Mike saw my bags, he started jumping on me right there. Connie and Vicki had never been in a fight in their lives but that night, we were all fighting Mike.

"Don't you hit her. Stop it, Stop it. Stop him, Vicki," Connie screamed. We were all fighting back. Seems like we were in a circle being slung around, then getting up, jumping back in. I didn't put it together at the time, but the dog was hitting on my best friend. I couldn't have any friends. Connie felt bad for me. After that, Connie and Vicki moved to Colorado for good.

Then another time, I left the city and was on the outskirts of town. I was asleep and was feeling a little good about myself, a clean get-a-way, then it happened. He snuffed me out, Mike was coming through the window of my hotel room.

"You know I'm going to kick your ass don't you," Mike said, as he climbed through the hotel window.

"Mike you don't have to fight me. Please don't. You're going to hate that you fought me afterwards." I begged Mike not to fight me.

"You have to be taught a lesson, Sharell." Mike stated. He was glad he was going to beat me.

"You going to beat me while I'm pregnant?" I begged him not to hit me.

"I got to do something to you. I can't let you get away with this. You got to be punished," Mike explained like he was doing it for my own good. After that beating I didn't try anymore. Mike had friends everywhere, they told him I was there. I couldn't run. I had no hope.

Phyllis and Gerald had a daughter. She was beautiful. They looked like the happiest couple you ever wanted to see. They lived on the eastside in a cute little house with a big yard. They even had a goldfish pond in the backyard. We were over there everyday. Mike and Gerald were good friends. Gerald even started liking me. Gerald always had Phyl laughing. He was crazy about Phyllis. He sure wasn't abusive to her. They were about the same size so she'd probably give him a run for his money if he ever tried.

One day we were driving down Eastern Avenue, (it's now called Martin L. King Avenue) close to Northeast 16th Street, when Gerald flagged us down. He really was trying to get us to stop. When we stopped, we were too far away, so we kept going.

"Look at Gerald, he's dressed in black like he's going to rob somebody," Mike stated.

"Is that how you dress when you're going to rob something?" I asked.

"Yeah, I hope he's not going to do something crazy. I should have backed up for him. I guess he'll be alright," Mike said. That evening we got the news that Gerald had been shot. Mike felt guilty.

"I should have stopped. It's my fault, I should have stopped," Mike cried that night. Gerald was shot in the head, but he was still alive. Phyl visited him everyday, all day. We really thought he would pull through, but after about a week, Gerald died. It's funny how certain songs come along at that right time. Gerald's song was by the OJays, *Stairway to Heaven. Here we go, climbing the stairway to heaven. . .*That song was just right. It was so soothing. We were walking around singing it, feeling it, couldn't believe it. Phyl took it pretty good. Well, not really. She was devastated. Only nineteen, a widow with child.

Phyl was determined to continue school. She was in college studying to be a nurse. I was so proud of her. She wasn't letting anything stop her from her goals. I wasn't doing anything. Mike wouldn't let me go to school. I tried a couple times, but he would create a scene and I would be too embarrassed to go back.

After about a year, Phyl met Keith. Keith was fun. He and Phyl acted like they had known each other for years. I don't believe Phyl was ready for a man yet, but Keith wouldn't leave her alone. Keith fit right in.

Vicki came back home from Colorado. To everybody's surprise, she was getting married. I have never known Vicki to have a real boyfriend. I never knew who she liked. Vicki was so classy, she didn't tell. She dressed perfect. She had a cool flavor and she never let any man get too close to her. Vicki was very pretty, but out of all of us, she was the homebody. We would go to the club or go to the college party, Vicki would go home. Every year, she got a new car. That's how her parent's treated her and her siblings. One thousand guesses wouldn't have prepared me for this shocker. Vicki and my older brother, Kenny, were getting married.

Kenny looks exactly like my dad. He is a knockout. Kenny's the perfect pretty boy that lives next door. He's definitely my Momma's favorite. I didn't mind that. Kenny would laugh so much on such corny jokes, he'd make anybody laugh because we'd would try to figure out what was so funny.

"When did y'all start seeing each other, Vicki," I grilled her. I wanted to know everything—what, definitely when, and how did this got started? What was going on? This was totally unexpected.

"Girl, I've always had a thing for your brother. Sharell, you want to know something? Kenny has been my one and only. He's the only man I've ever slept with." Vicki let the cat out of the bag. The sneaky dog . . . Kenny never said a word about he and Vicki. I never thought she had a boyfriend. Vicki could rap on the phone better than any of us, but in person, she would completely shut down. I never would have put her with my brother. But then, it kind of makes sense. They do kind of fit.

"Um, ain't that something, and I thought you were my friend, hanging out with me, all the time you liked my brother. Well, I hope you're happy with him. Girl, Kenny's a trip. You know Kenny has his own idea about things. He's pretty old fashioned. I hope you know what you're getting into," I told Vicki, because Kenny's so old fashion. But he's really a great guy. He's a catch. He always wanted to do the right thing.

"Sharell, I love Kenny. I always have," Vicki asserted to me.

"You just wanted to be my sister, didn't you, Vicki," I laughed, hoping they would forever be happy. Kenny and Vicki got married in her mother's courtyard. It was a beautiful wedding. My real daddy married them. It was great.

C. Oakes

Before long, Mike started selling drugs—heroine. He always wore a mask over his face when he worked with drugs. He didn't want to get it in his system, he'd say. Mike acted like he had a license to sell narcotics.

"I can't believe you. You're use to California but this is Oklahoma, Mike. You will go to jail in this town. You're too wild." I didn't want anything to happen to him.

"I don't keep anything here . . . at home, so they won't be finding anything on me. I don't put anything in anybody's hands. That's why I got all these women, so they can sell the drugs for me. All I have to do is give them a little something," Mike said as he tried to assure me it was alright.

"Mike, all they have to do is watch you, those police know everything you're doing. You better be careful."

"Yeah, I know you'll be happy so you can get with another man. If you ever get with somebody else, I'm going to kill you and that nigga." Mike was getting deeper and deeper in the drug life. Plucking a note was getting old and we had a couple of close calls. He bought a new Cadillac and would go to California to pick up drugs to sell in Oklahoma. There was a brand new entourage hanging around, too. These weren't any home boys. They couldn't be trusted. I couldn't believe how lowdown the women were that hung around. Mike was getting more and more disrespectful to me and let everybody else disrespect me, too. He would hit me in front of his new girlfriends. They thought I was nothing.

Mike and Keith were good friends now. Keith kept the drugs at their house. Phyl's house. One day he came home and said he believed he sold drugs to an undercover snitch.

"Well Mike, if you believe that, why are you still here in Oklahoma." I kept trying to get Mike to leave. Then it happened. The police kicked the doors in. I opened my eyes to this big shining new sawed off shotgun in my face. Police were everywhere. They tore up the house. Mike was so calm. I really thought nothing was at the house. Then they found it.

"Give me that dope." Mike snatched it out of their hands and they beat his ass. They arrested him and left me at home. Police kicked in Phyl's house, too. I can't believe Mike had drugs at her house. They didn't arrest Phyl but they charged her with possession. This was terrible. A drug case for a medical student. Now

Phyl could never be what she was called to be, a nurse. Healing was definitely her calling. Phyl's life was ruined.

Everybody bailed out of jail and they continued to do what they were doing. It cost most of our savings to get Mike out and hire an attorney. I was so confused because had it been me, I would have left the state way before this happened. Mike was too worried about someone getting me to leave Oklahoma. I sure wasn't going to California so he could nut up with me 2,500 miles away from home.

In 1976, I had a son. He was the most beautiful baby boy you want to see. Mike was deep into his women and drugs. He had to sell drugs now to pay the lawyers fees. It was getting so weird. Mike was so disrespectful. He had his women living with us. My son and I would stay in the bedroom and not come out. It was like he knew it was his last leg.

Then I got another shocker. Mike got the call first.

"Sharell, you need to go home. It's an emergency," Mike said. When I got there, Kenny, my brother met me on the front porch.

"Sharell, Marzett had a heart attack," Kenny announced as I approached the steps.

I got ready to run in the house. He stopped me before I entered the house.

"Sharell, he died."

His eyes were bucked wide opened. He was shaking. I was staggered.

"What, what . . .?"

It was one of those blank moments. Marzett looked strong as a horse. He wasn't overweight or old, he was young. Nothing would have prepared me for this. That very same morning, Marzett was playing with my son, Matt—he was crazy about him. Laughing, calling him a papoose.

"Marzett, will you take me to Phyl's house?" I asked.

"Are you ready now, because I'm on my way to Boley," Marzett replied, while as he was putting his hunting equipment in his truck. Boley's a little town in Oklahoma where most of the Marzett's live. His father, Papa, lived there and they had planned a hunting trip that day. I jumped in the truck. It was about nine o'clock in the morning.

Marzett and I were riding down the street, going to Phyl's

C. Oakes

house the very morning he died. That's when I first heard the voice. The voice was trying to let me know.

"Sharell, tell Marzett thank you," the voice said. It was clear as a bell, calm and easy.

"Tell Marzett, thank you." Again, I heard it.

Then, I got this overwhelming feeling that I can't describe. I tried to say thank you, Marzett for all you've done for us, for being a father to us . . . but it wouldn't come out. It was like it stuck in my throat. I remember trying. I couldn't express myself. After all those years never really talking to Marzett, I just didn't know how to come out with it. I truly appreciated Marzett, especially after I married Mike. I saw what he was—a real man—an example of what I needed in my life. My eyes were opened. How many young men would marry a woman with four kids in the first place. He truly loved Momma, I wish I could say, thank you, Marzett. I really do. My chance was gone forever.

Mike had a terrible secret. I didn't figure it out until it was way too late. I don't know if he would have let me help him anyway. We got into a terrible argument because he couldn't spell my name.

"Mike, we've been married two years and you can't spell my name. What is wrong with you?" I thought that was a sure sign that he just neglected me so severely and he didn't care. Then he let it out.

'Sharell, I can't read."

I was shocked. Who can't read in this day and time. I didn't believe it. Mike couldn't read? He wheeled and dealt, but couldn't read. This is crazy. Mike talked to lawyers, insurance companies, banks, real estate brokers and couldn't read. Scamming everybody. He hid it well, very well. I didn't know what to do. That's why he was so jealous of me working and going to school. He should have let me know or asked for help. He continued to get worse.

We were at it again, I ran to my mother's house. Mike was behind me, threatening me. I begged Momma not to answer the door. I was scared. He told Momma he was going to kill me.

"I'm going to kill Sharell and come back and kill you, too."

He never would have said that while Marzett was alive. Marzett didn't talk much, but he didn't play, and he sure wasn't a punk. Mike wouldn't say anything like that while Marzett was alive. My mother talked with my uncles and brothers about Mike's threats. He was threatening to kill everybody. Swearing on his life to kill me. There was no choice. Mike had to go.

About a couple of days later, Mike went to traffic court to pay a speeding fine—I and the baby rode with him. This was the first time that I truly recognized it. The Holy Spirit at work. It was plain as day the way it happened. How else could you explain the circumstances. Sooner or later, one of us would be hurt, or even killed. I didn't want to drag my family in my mess, but I needed help. To my surprise, while he was standing in front of the judge for a traffic ticket, they handcuffed Mike. On the spot, he proceeded to serve a 20-year prison sentence. It was divine intervention for Mike, my family and for me.

C. Oakes

Chapter 5

I was in a state of bewilderment. I was completely lost with a two-month old son. Car note due, bills due—I'd never handled money or paid any bills. I never made decisions or even worried about running the household. That was Mike's job. He made that plain and clear. What should I to do first? After the drug bust, money was tight, we received an eviction notice, so I had to move. On top of all this other stuff, I was now on three years probation. Earlier I had found an apartment, but didn't have anybody to help me move. All this was running through my mind. What was I going to do? What to do first?

People never cease to amaze me. Those lowdown women that were disrespecting me, Mike's other women, came with a moving truck and moved me lock, stock and barrel. I didn't have the energy to refuse, plus, I needed the help. They didn't stop till the last towel was folded and put on the shelf. Everything in place before nightfall. I was grateful for their help, and gave them a little more respect for their loyalty to Mike—they wanted to do the right thing. I know they hated me, I guess they hated me. I wouldn't treat a dog like they treated me. Coming into my home, not giving a damn about my feelings, in my house. I couldn't have any of my family over because of what may be going on there. Hell, I stayed locked down in my bedroom. I couldn't stand the way they made themselves at home in my house. Mike had many women.

I hadn't danced in months. While Mike was selling drugs, I didn't have to work. It was work keeping the peace. People would tell me I was lucky to have a man like Mike—just let him do his thang. Don't worry about what he's doing on the street. Stop arguing with him about those women. They're making it easier for your man to have money to buy you all those beautiful dresses and things. Be cool.

"Yeah, right." Easier said than done.

After all the dark clouds faded away, I went back to dancing. I could always make a living doing that. Checkmate was the club where I decided to work. It was a little classy place; they had a stage with a mic and sound system just in case you could sing. Even if the girls couldn't sing, they would try, putting on the charm in full force. Getting guys to fall in love and spend all their money buying drinks and champagne. It was fun singing and dancing at the Checkmate. The girls there had nice props and some were straight showgirls that traveled the dance circuit—coming from Vegas. They were always talking about where the money was. They talked a lot about Prudhoe Bay, Alaska. They said that's where they were building a pipeline and people were making fifty to a hundred dollars an hour. They talked about the fishermen coming off the boat with thousands of dollars just waiting to throw it away on the lucky girl for the evening. They also talked about girls disappearing, being kept captives and becoming sex slaves. I wanted to go somewhere. I thought I would stay in Oklahoma until Mike was close to getting out, then leave before he was released.

Now, that's what I need to do if I'm going to dance. Be a showgirl. Get out of Oklahoma. Start fresh. Meet knew people and all. But I had a little boy. Momma was such a big help. She adored the little fella. Her first grand.

My son and I visited Mike at Big Mac at least a couple times a month. That's the main penitentiary in Oklahoma. This is where all the rapist, child molesters, and murderers reside and it's where they administer the death penalty. Momma thought I was crazy to even waste my gas visiting him.

She fussed, "Are you going to still be with him after he gets out? After all he put us through."

There was an unwritten rule that you don't leave your people when their down. Down meaning in the penitentiary. You were low. You'd be a deserter. People say, "She can't hang. She didn't have heart." The ones that stayed were put on a pedestal—never to have problems in their relationship again in life. I only know one relationship like that. But men never stayed, they never waited on a woman to get out the pen. It was alright for them to skip out, or break the rules. It's all bullshit!

That year when Mike went down, 1977, the same snitch wiped the streets clean. So many homey's went to the pen. Phyl's Keith, my younger brother, Roger, and Mike—just a few. They looked so good and wholesome in there, locked up. Mike was needy, he needed me to write the Governor. I didn't. He acted so good, respectful to me, loving me only. I didn't want him to get out. Oh, he loved me so much while he was locked up. I was his queen. He was proud of me. He had a lot of respect in there, too. Fellow inmates were getting out and offering me their services.

"If you need anything, just let me know. Me and Mike were best friends in the penitentiary," they'd say. "If anybody messes with you, let me know, I'll deal with them."

I told Mike he needs to stop showing my pictures in there. "You got people coming out with crushes on me, Mike. Stop talking about me to those criminals. No telling what they're in there for, not everybody was a drug dealer. Mike, I don't even know these guys and they know me, how I look, everything. You probably told them where I lived."

Mike just laugh.

"Okay, you're going to get me in trouble," I stated.

He promised he wouldn't show my pictures any more. He always wanted good pictures. I sent pictures in my dancing costumes. I got so embarrassed because some pictures were returned months later with a warning from the prison authorities. They sure kept them a long time.

Mike told me to go on and live my life. "I know you're going to be with someone else. Just remember when I get out, they'll have to go, you understand?"

"Yeah, Mike, I understand."

"So don't be getting too involved with those knuckleheads out there. Okay?"

"Yeah, Mike, I said. "I understand." I thought it was okay to have a boyfriend. After all, he gave me permission. So I considered myself a single woman. Available.

Mike's brother Dwight lived in California. He was his older brother and he loved Mike. They loved each other. Dwight was a very bright-skinned, green eyed, Louisiana creole black man. He would send for me and the baby to visit the in-laws from time to time. I think they wanted to half way keep an eye on me for Mike. One night we went out to a local club in California and I saw Huey Newton, the co-founder of the Black Panther Party. Well, in Oklahoma he was a hero and a celebrity. I was excited to see him. He saw me excited about him and invited us to his table. Dwight and his friend, Danny, were sneaking me out of the back door of the club. Dwight was mad at me.

"Do you know who you are messing with? That's Huey Newton. You don't mess with him." Dwight was furious. They sent me back home the next day.

My cousin, Tammy came over and wanted a ride to 30th Street off Jordan.

"Sharell, I met a whole bunch of fine men. Girl, go with me, you need to meet them. Wait till you see them. Come on girl, get out of the house and have some fun," Tammy said, trying to convince me to let up and meet some guys. I was hesitant, but I did need to have a little fun. I went with her and she was right. These guys were nice. They wore suits and apple hats. They spoke perfect English. Played with words. They all joked with intelligent humor, laughing loud. I missed this kind of fun, really never enjoyed humor to this degree. Their dad was in the midst of them, loud and kicking it, too. I liked them. They were gentlemen. Then I saw him. It was love at first sight. He circled around me, walking behind everybody. He was like a leopard, quietly stalking. He wasn't saying anything. Just looking at me. Then he smiled. Perfect teeth.

I remembered him growing up in the neighborhood, but it had been so many years since I'd seen him. Man has he changed. Look at him. His name is Richard. I later found out after he graduated from College, he interned at NASA Space Center in Houston. He was really smart. He talked about the east coast a lot. The people there, doing so much, moving so fast.

He followed me home that night. We stayed together mostly every night. We would put the baby in my waterbed and sleep in the baby's bed, it didn't move so much. He became a part of my life. He loved my son.

"Sharell, this should have been my son," Richard said. He was there when my baby took his first steps.

I hadn't told Richard what I did for a living. I knew he wouldn't go for that. It was getting hard to hide it. How could I tell him that. He didn't know I was married, either. Ah man, and my husband's in the penitentiary. When he asked me about my son's father, I would say he's not in the picture or I'd just change the subject.

C. Oakes

"Sharell, what's the secret? You know we are going to have to talk about it one day."

"Yeah, I know, but not today." I would play with him and never answer the questions. I didn't want anything to change. We stayed together everyday until I needed to make a little money, then I'd have to excuse myself. Deep inside, I was afraid to lose him. I knew Richard had high morals and values to go for a women like me. I need to keep quiet. Whenever I could, I'd break away, I would head for the club. I had to pay bills. Then the unthinkable happened. I was on stage, on my last song, nearly nude when Richard walked in the door with the gang, his home boys. I saw him first. I was stuck, I needed to run off the stage. There I was frozen with shame. Richard looked on stage and turned his head so fast. He kept his head down. He was hurt and embarrassed. His homies were embarrassed for him. The way he held his head down, he wouldn't look up. Damn, he's about to cry. I couldn't look. I just needed to get off the stage and run.

I knew it would never be the same between us again. I told Richard the whole terrible truth about me. What I did for a living. He was so angry. His Mom was mad at me, too. She wanted me out of her house.

"This girl is married, Richard. Anything could happen with you spending this much time with her. I know how much you love her, but she has a husband. Guys will kill you about their wives. Boy, that's nothing to play with, you have to end this thing you got between you and Sharell now. She's a lovely girl and I love her to death, but I don't want anything to happen to my son behind her." Richard's mother was adamant about ending things with me. I think she still liked me. She felt sorry for us, but also felt betrayed by my secrecy.

Richard tried not to see me again. All of a sudden, he hated my car.

"Don't park that car in front of my house. I'll come get you. Everybody in town knows that car and know you've been staying here."

Whenever we saw each other out, he couldn't keep his hands off me. I would end up at his house for the night or weekend, whichever. He'd go through the house singing, *She Use To Be My Girl.* I hated that song. I still wanted him. His smile was so beautiful.

"Babygirl, what have you done? What do you plan to do with your life? You're a good girl. How did you get messed up like this?

"Richard, I don't know what happened. I guess I was too quick to get out of my mother's house. I should have listened to my mother. She was so strict, I couldn't wait to get out. She was right, though. Mike was the first man that really took up any real time with me and I just thought . . . I don't know what I was thinking. I was foolish. It started out crazy and ended up crazy."

"Babygirl, you know I really like you—no, I love you, Sharell, but we have got to move on with our lives, I want a wife whose children all belong to me. I don't want no man coming around me and my wife, I can't have that. . . I'm not going to have that. I need someone I can start out fresh and with my children. Do you understand?"

I just nodded. I couldn't look up because I didn't want him to see me so crushed and wounded. I felt my life was totally screwed.

"You married a man, that's now in the penitentiary. Didn't you know what type of man you were getting involved with, Sharell? How did he support you?"

"He sold drugs," I replied.

"Sold drugs, Man!" Richard looked disgusted. "Babygirl, what do you plan to do with your life?"

To tell the truth, my hopes, dreams and plans were long gone by then and Richard let me know I could never be a decent wife for a righteous man. I was a nude dancer. I had depreciated my value as a worthy woman. I had messed up. Fallen from grace, and he sure let me know. I cried hard that night. What was I thinking, to fall like this. What was I thinking.

C. Oakes

Chapter 6

Rejection hurt so much. It made me disoriented. I didn't like it one bit. But it was time to get myself together—get back in gear and focus on what was important. I still had my little boy to look after. I loved him so much. He needed me to be a mommy. So I had to stop feeling sorry for myself and get it together. My baby was the only thing in my life that made me happy. It was never a question about me and my baby, he deserved a good mom and I wanted to give him a good home. I was going to take care of my baby. By this time he was a huge 18 months.

My hurt turned to anger. I was mad at Richard. My visits to Mike were getting scarce. He would write begging to see me and the baby. I wasn't ready for him. He was so horrible to me. I was so sweet and innocent and he didn't appreciate it. My innocence wasted on his ass. I finally started thinking about my marriage and all the craziness. Then I was mad at Mike. Somehow I still didn't hate him, but I didn't want to see him anymore. I needed a break. I wanted to leave Oklahoma.

I turned my attention back to the club and making money. I had a few regular customers that were pretty nice. I didn't have to talk too much. Once I got them hooked, I didn't have to beg for drinks or bottles of champagne. They were trained. Anyway the waitresses were good at hustling drinks for me. They were pros—smiling and finessing.

"Hello Sir, how are you today. May I bring a bottle of champagne for you and the lady," they'd say. Of course, they wanted to impress us and would agree to buy a bottle of champagne. So I made sure the waitresses were tipped.

"Oh honey, aren't you going to give her a tip. She's a good friend, she'll take good care of us. Give her five dollars." While customers wallets were still opened from paying for the champagne, I would politely take five dollars out and make a grand presentation to the waitress.

"This is for you. Thank you." I'd whisper, . . "Hurry back!" So I can get my next bottle while he was still buying. The champagne arrived already shaken up, then it would explode open with a big pop and champagne would spray everywhere. Half the bottles would be gone over the floor. I could never drink that much; anyway, the stuff was cheap, I didn't like it. My customers never complained. It was all fun and games. I received Christmas presents, holiday money, shopping money and bill money. Money just for me, that wasn't split with the club. My customers were so nice. I was still very innocent and they liked my innocence. I played by the rules and never met anyone outside the club. I never wanted to go outside the club, there was no reason. The club was my fortress. My protection.

There were a lot of new girls working in the club. I was glad for that, it made it easier for me. I wasn't on stage so much. I can dance, I have good shows, but sometimes I get shy. For no reason, I would have butterflies. One day while working, I saw this masculine hunk of a man, with long hair like SuperFly. He was in jeans and a t-shirt and he was bowlegged. He had a little five o'clock shadow. Rough, but really good looking.

"Who is that!" I asked if any body knew him, they didn't. He had a lot of girls around him—entertaining them. SuperFly came in everyday. I wouldn't talk to him. Not yet. I noticed he was buying drinks. I wasn't going to approach him to buy me a drink. I was shy. He didn't look like a regular customer, he was too good looking. Anyway, I was still wounded from Richard.

Eventually, I got enough nerves to ask his name. He narrowed his eyes and smiled, "My name is Lucky."

"Lucky," I smiled. "Are you Lucky?"

"It's just a nickname," He replied.

"Lucky, will you buy me a drink so I can join you?"

"Sure, get the waitress."

I motioned for the waitress to bring me a drink.

"You're not from here, are you?"

"Yeah, I grew up here in Oklahoma, but now I live in Seattle."

"Oh, how long are you visiting?"

"I don't know yet, I came to see my family. I might buy some property. I haven't decided. What's your name?"

I gave him my stage name.

"I'm Nikki."

"Is that your real name or is it your stage name?"

"Well, it's just Nikki, right now."

"Hi, Nikki. I'd like to see you outside here. Can I take you to breakfast after the club closes tonight?"

I was breaking the rules.

"Yes, that'll be nice. I'm out of here about 2:15 a.m. I'll just follow you, Okay?"

Lucky found a Denny's pretty close. We ordered breakfast and coffee and stayed out all night talking and getting to know each other. Daybreak was coming in and I needed some sleep. I had to pick up my baby from Momma's house sometime that morning.

"Let me have a telephone number, Sharell."

I told him my real name. He was so serious.

"I'll call you later today." Lucky had a way of telling you what he wanted and he expected you to do what he asked or said.

"Sure," I replied. I quickly wrote down my phone number. "Lucky, thanks for breakfast." I was smiling and I enjoyed just talking with him. Lucky had gone to Douglass High School. His parents were elementary school teachers. He seemed to have a real business sense. I trusted him.

"I'm going to call you later. Okay?" He said as we got in our cars.

I flew home to get some sleep before getting the baby.

After that evening, Lucky was on me like white on rice. Everyday he was right there picking me up and taking me to work or dinner. One day I was talking to an old friend when Lucky pulled up. If looks could kill, man, we both would've been dead. I knew then that I better not have any male friends over my house. It bothered me that I felt nervous about that guy visiting. The poor guy almost broke out running. I hadn't made any commitments to Lucky. We made love only once and it was just okay.

Lucky was possessive. Very possessive. He took possession of me right away. Kept me close. He knew I was use to being kept. He sensed it. I needed to be de-programmed but opted to leave Oklahoma with Lucky. He said we would do a lot of traveling. Just what I wanted. But, I had a baby. I didn't know how that was going to work. Lucky said we would take the baby with us. Momma said I wasn't taking her grand baby no where with no stranger I just met in a club. She wanted to keep him anyway. He kept her mind off losing Marzett. Momma was the only person that could have kept my baby. I couldn't leave him with anyone else. But, to tell the truth, I wanted a break from the responsibility of a baby. It was terrible, but true.

Lucky didn't waste anytime showing me his harem. I didn't know it, but I was working with his women. All those new girls came with him from Seattle. They all respected each other and called themselves "sisters-in-law" They had their own apartments or hotel rooms and were pretty friendly with each other. This was different. Lucky told everybody to meet him at his place. He lived on the eastside off 16th and Bryant. He had a nice home and lived with a white girl with two little boys. I was surprised at how nice and friendly she was to me, coming in her house with her man. I was never like that with Mike. She smiled a lot, she was pretty and looked like Goldie Hahn. He introduced me one by one to everybody.

"Hey everybody, this is your new sister, Sharell.

Sister! I thought.

"Sharell, this is Sandy."

She was the white girl with two boys.

"This is Yvette."

She was a black girl with one little boy. Those kids look just like him. I was thinking.

"Cute kids!" I nervously blurted out.

She was at the club and I recognized a couple of the white girls there, too. There was Renee, she was black and nicknamed, Flashy Lashy. Tonya, Frankie and Debbie were white girls. Alex was something else. She didn't have a accent. Alex may have been Italian—she was the prettiest. Everybody smiled and seemed happy for me to be there. I was told there were others that lived in Hawaii, Sue and GiGi. Sue was Japanese. GiGi was Filipino. Lucky was busy.

It was like a business meeting. Everybody there starting taking out money and giving it to Lucky. He would laugh at some because it wasn't that much.

"Where's the rest of it, Renee?" Lucky asked.

"Lucky, that's it," Renee replied.

"You wouldn't be holding out on me, would you?"

"Naw, Lucky," Renee said.

Then he would laugh, making fun with others that had more

C. Oakes

money.

"Ooooooo we, look at this. Come here baby, give me a kiss."

They talked about the difficulty of making money in Oklahoma.

"Lucky, they don't even table dance here. It's hard. They don't know nothing about table dancing," somebody complained. I couldn't keep up with everybody's name.

I was thinking, what's table dancing?

"We got to go around begging for drinks. It's hard getting them guys to buy us drinks. That's all they do is sell drinks. We get so drunk, I can't work drunk like that," she continued to complain.

Lucky was cracking up.

"Y'all might have to get some dates so we can leave here right," Lucky reasoned with everybody.

I was wondering what that meant, get a date. But I didn't say anything. Lucky told us all that we would be leaving Oklahoma and going to Hawaii.

"I want everybody to start packing and getting ready. We need some money, so we'll go through Nevada first. Yvette, you, Tonya and Sharell will ride with me. Renee, Franky and Alex will leave together first. Check out the Mustang Ranch, I want to see what that's about. I'll see you there. Debbie and Sandy I want you to go back to the house in Seattle. We've been gone a while— somebody has to check on it. Go back to work at the Flames or My Place for a while." Lucky was giving orders and instructions. Everybody had their assignments and was ready to go to their temporary homes.

Now that's what I'm talking about. I was excited. This guy was all business. Then he looked at me.

"But first we're going to Nevada and make some money. We're going to another ranch. I'll have to check it out," Lucky said.

The ranch, again, I had no idea what he was talking about.

I told my friend Jolynn about Lucky and that we were leaving Oklahoma, going to Hawaii and Vegas. She wanted to go. Jolynn was built like a brick house. She had a very, very small waistline and very, very big hips and thighs. Jolynn was an ebony colored sister that sported a beautiful set of teeth. One of her front teeth had a gold trim that made her smile sparkle. Jolynn always made money. She made lots of money. I wondered how she did it. Sometimes I would try to eavesdrop on her conversations to hear what she was saying to make guys spend so much. She had guys spending thousands on her. I was only getting a few hundreds from a regular here and there. What in the world was she saying.

My friend, Jolynn joined us. I was so glad she was going. I wasn't jealous about Lucky all of a sudden spending most of his time with her instead of me. She was my home girl. There wasn't any real love for Lucky, just respect. He seemed to know what he was doing. He had a plan and he wasn't wild. Mike was wild and violent. Me, Lucky and Jolynn had a sense of family 'cause we all were from Oklahoma, we related to each other. I felt safe with him. I knew he wouldn't let anything happen to me or Jolynn. He sent Jolynn to ride with Renee and Alex to Vegas. I thought she should ride with us.

When we arrived in Nevada, it was Carson City. I was disappointed. I thought we were going to a shining city. This was the country. It was dry and wide. Country looking. Yvette, Tonya and I were finally in a room to settle down for the evening. Lucky left. I guess he was checking out the town or finding the rest of the family. They should already be at Mustang Ranch.

Yvette started telling me all about Lucky and their family. The house in Seattle was gated and fabulous. There was a pass code to enter through the gates. The furniture was so wonderful. I was thinking . . . so what! She proceeded to tell me that I wasn't the prettiest girl Lucky has ever had. Damn, what was that about.

"Yvette, I'm not so pretty. I'm sure I'm not the prettiest girl he's had." I was getting sick of her picking at me.

"I just wanted to let you know you're not his best."

"Okay Yvette. I can live with that."

Tonya told Yvette to shut up.

"You know Frankie's his main girl. She makes so much money. Frankie has sugar daddys spending thousands every day on her. This one guy follows her around crying because she won't dance for him." Yvette continued to irritate me.

"Yvette, what's a table dance?" I asked.

"You don't know what table dancing is?"

"No, what is it?"

"Girl, that's dancing at the table for the guys. We get paid three dollars for one dance or five dollars for two songs. Frankie gets tens and twenties. We can make two hundred dollars a night table dancing."

"Every night?" I asked.

"Girl, yeah. They don't know what to do in Oklahoma," Tonya was agreeing.

"You got to table dance to make some real money. That's were the money is. Yeah, girl, table dancing. Lucky said never sleep with them customers because you'll lose them."

I learned that much in Oklahoma. She went on and on and I was getting sleepy.

The next day Lucky came in and had numbers for us to call to work at the ranch. He told us to get in at Moonlight Ranch. The others were working at Mustang Ranch. Jolynn was working at the Mustang Ranch.

I called Moonlight Ranch in Carson City and the lady said immediately that they don't hire black girls. She could tell by my voice that I was black.

"I'm not black," I insisted.

"You're not? You sure sound black."

"No, I'm not black," I assured her.

"What are you?"

"Well, I'm mixed and I don't look black."

Actually, I am black and look black, but I learned from working the clubs, I could be an "other." Whatever that was, just by being a light skinned sister wearing a straight haired wig. My wigs made me money. The longer the wig the more money. Guys would ask me what nationality I was.

"Well, what do you think I am" was always my reply.

"You look like you could be Polynesian, or something, they'd say."

"How did you guess? You are so good. Did you travel a lot?" I'd ask in my most shocked voice.

"I traveled while in the military years ago. I had a girlfriend that was Polynesian. You look just like her."

They would be proud that they could detect my ethnic background. I would be whatever they guessed. Sometimes I believed they just wanted to fantasize on some exotic women in their company or reflect on their past. Anyway it made my job easier.

Actually, I'm a black sister or . . . whatever they wanted.

Me and Tonya had an appointment to go to Moonlight Ranch. Lucky thought Yvette should wait and make sure we were there before she tried to work there. Tonya went first and she was hired immediately. I made an appointment for later that evening. When I arrived I made sure I was looking attractive and classy. The owner was there instead of the woman I had spoken with previously on the phone. He hired me immediately. He introduced me to this very beautiful red-haired woman and she took charge. She was gorgeous, elegant, graceful, she flowed when she walked. I thought she was such a lady, the southern belle type. She was the madam of the place. Her name was Vanessa.

Moonlight Ranch was four trailer houses attached together. There was a large kitchen with a dining table. A den-like area with a juke box and bar. Long hallways that led to individual rooms. Vanessa showed me my room, number 18. It looked like something from Miss Kitty's bar on Gunsmoke. The room had a bed, a small closet and only a basin to wash. The walls were red and gold velvet. There was a small chandelier that hung in the corner for lighting. We shared the showers that were down the hall. There was a fenced backyard with horses and a Great Dane dog. Vanessa said the dog thinks he's a horse. She introduced me to the maids.

"Now, Nikki," I gave her my stage name, "although the maids do the cooking and cleaning, they manage this place when I'm not available. You have to do what they ask. They can hire you or let you go. I trust their decisions completely. They will schedule your hours, you will work 12 hours on and 12 hours off. When you meet with a customer, take the money immediately to Ms. Jackson, the maid, so she can record it and set your time. Now we charge a dollar a minute and we split everything with you. Sometimes you'll get tips and they're for you to keep. Okay?" She was thorough.

The maids were all big dark skinned black women, dressed in uniforms. They seemed friendly enough. I must have spoken with one of them earlier. I saw Tonya. She smiled. Then Vanessa asked me to come to her room for a talk.

Just by spending that little time with me, Vanessa had me pegged.

"You never did this kind of work before have you, Nikki?"

I shook my head, no.

"Well, don't worry, I'll teach you everything you need to know. I'll teach you correctly so you won't hurt yourself. There are some things you just don't do in this business. You need to check your customers for infections, I'll show you how to do that. You can use rubbers if its okay with the customers. You know how to use them? Sometimes we can slip a rubber on without the customer knowing it. I'll teach you that, too."

I continued to nod "yes."

"Well, we have doctors that come every week to give everybody a check up. So don't worry."

I was very relieved. 'Cause I didn't have any idea what to do. I never even spoken to Lucky about it. Dating is what they called it.

"Now you go and make yourself comfortable. I'll see you in about an hour. We'll have dinner together in the kitchen." Vanessa was nice.

I had been at the ranch about a week. It wasn't too bad. I didn't have many customers. Hardly any customers. Vanessa showed me everything, every time she would think of something else, she would share it with me. I got really use to the maids cooking and cleaning. We left them tips in our rooms. Dinner was great, everyday. Ms. Jackson was okay but she let me know that if she had been on duty when I came for the interview, I wouldn't have gotten this job. She knew I was black. It wasn't a prejudice move or anything like that, it was just business.

There was a limousine to take us to town or to the casinos. We couldn't ride with anybody else. That was one of the rules. No boyfriends, sisters, brothers or anyone like that. We stayed in their protective care at all times until we checked out for home breaks. I liked riding in the limousines to go to the casinos or shopping. I felt rich and important. I played craps at the casinos. I'd look around to find the guy with the most chips, squeeze in next to him and copied his every move, I did whatever he did. Soon the guys would notice me, then they would tell me what and how to bet. It worked every time. I made much more money in the casinos than I did at the ranch. I cleaned up at the casinos. It was good 'cause I wasn't doing too much at the ranch.

It was my shift to work. It was early evening. The doorbell rang and customers walked in. The music would be playing when we walk out. We would line up, ready to please. Quincy Jones was playing. *"They were lining up back to back."* You think he was singing about us. *"What makes you feel like doing stuff like that, what makes you feel like doing stuff like that."* Then I saw them. They were mountain men, hadn't had a bath all year. They were dirty and ugly.

I'm praying, "please not me."

I hadn't been getting picked. I didn't feel too threatened about them picking me. I won't look. I held my head down, just in case. I didn't want anybody to get the wrong idea. I wasn't the one, please, not me. Damn, I was the first one chosen. I looked at Vanessa for help.

"Nikki, don't worry, I'll come get you in ten minutes." I was doomed. I walked the mountain man back to my room. He gave me the money and I took it to Ms. Jackson to record on my books. When I returned, the mountain man was out of his clothes lying in my bed. This wasn't going to work. I asked him to get up and come over to the basin. I started washing his dirty penis which was the regular thing we did with all the customers. I didn't want no parts of this money. They could have it. I wasn't going to do this. I'll just quit. Then I got the welcome knock on the door. Times up. Vanessa knocked on the door again. "Nikki, may I speak with you for a moment." She got me out the room. The mountain man was waiting for me to come back. I wasn't. He got mad.

"We didn't do nothing. We didn't do nothing."

He started tearing up my room. Vanessa asked all the women to come to the back of the ranch. She then asked the other men to talk to their friend and calm him down.

"Where is he?" They asked.

"He's back in room 18," Vanessa said, putting on the charm.

"We'll get'em." After talking with the mountain man, his friends came out ready to join him by tearing up the rest of the place.

Vanessa pulled out two Dobermans. She was fighting to keep control of the dogs. They were ready to attack the mountain men, those guys were making a mess up front. Vanessa was fiercely

C. Oakes

holding the dogs. The mountain men weren't coming back where we were all stashed to be eaten up. The dogs were going completely crazy. The mountain men acted like they didn't care, they were getting louder and worse by the minute.

"Where were the police," A girl asked.

It was time for them to make their daily stop at the ranch. Vanessa had Ms. Jackson call, but they didn't respond. I was scared. We were behind the doors with the dogs when the mountain men started heading toward us. We could hear them coming. Vanessa was getting ready to let the dogs go. She was making this attack sound to the dogs.

"Get em, Get em."

Then the police arrived. Just in time to save the day. We must have all lit into the police.

"Where were you. We needed you. It was bad."

We were all telling our versions at one time. There had been a terrible accident down the road. It took them off their normal beats. I was never so glad to see the police in my life. The mountain men left quietly. After a few weeks, I had enough, I was leaving the ranch.

When I contacted Lucky about the incident, we agreed that the ranch wasn't for us. However, I learned from Vanessa. She taught me everything about the business. Most importantly, this business is not about sex. The actual act of intercourse almost never happened, it was the last resort. Most customers at the ranch wanted to play games. Some wanted really strange games. There were more perverts than anything. We had toys for them. Others just wanted company. The company of beautiful women that they wouldn't normally get in a lifetime. Some wanted to feel important and fussed over with their big wallets. We just played the part. So now I had experience. I knew how to turn a date.

Mustang was a little better for everybody else. That's where Yvette and Jolynn ended up. It was a lot more friendly. Lucky would go there and party with everybody. Still, it wasn't what we expected as far as making money, so we left Nevada to go to Washington State.

I went to work at Charlie's in Woodenville, WA. That club was live. This was Renee's territory. She was giving me the ropes and a warning.

"Sharell, we can't turn any dates here in Washington."

I was curious. " Why not?"

"A lot of working girls are coming up missing."

"They are? Missing from where?" I asked.

"Everywhere, and it's only the working girls that are missing, too. Lucky don't want us doing anything but dancing here."

"Okay. They don't have any idea who's taking girls?"

"Naw, They don't even talk about it on the news at night. You know they don't care about us. They say the girls are running off from pimps and the life, but everybody on the street knows something is wrong. For all we know, it could be some crazy pimp kidnapping hos. Girls are just missing. Only ride with family, okay?"

You don't have to worry about me getting into a car with some stranger. I sure wasn't getting in a car with some pimp. There was no way I was doing anything other than dancing to make my money. This stuff was scary.

Only at times you'd hear about a girl that was missing was from the streets. We had to keep each other informed. We had to watch out for each other. We were invisible to mainline media. It was crazy, but nobody seemed to care. Police didn't care. It wasn't like a pimp was going to go to the police and tell them their prostitute was missing either. That was asking for trouble. Mostly the pimps just took the loss. Nobody knows what's going on. All we know is working girls were missing and for some reason, there wasn't any talk about it on the news and police weren't trying to find out. We all knew that and understood. The main thing was, just don't go with anybody outside the club and that was fine with me. I didn't have the hang of table dancing. One night Lucky embarrassed me.

"Sharell, you take that little money and give it to Renee. I can't do a damn thing with that. What are you doing with your time?" Lucky asked.

I hadn't made anything over fifty dollars since I arrived. I didn't know what to say. I just looked down, embarrassed. Renee came over with her hands out to get my money. It was only $30 dollars, so I gave it to her. Okay, I had to try harder. I wasn't use to hustling like this. Not this hard. They went from customer to customer, nonstop. They never sat down. Dancing every song.

You really had to hustle. Moving.

"You want a dance? You want a dance?" I finally started getting dances. It was a different style of stripping. There were two stages and the girls dance one song on each stage. They didn't have fabulous costumes or props. They looked more like swim-suits or lingerie. Sometimes guys would take tips to the stage, then the girls would give them a little extra flash. It was cool. They weren't playing country and western music either. They were playing Bad Company, getting down on The Stones and Bob Seiger. A lot of fast music, I couldn't lounge around anymore, waiting on someone to buy me a drink, or even have the waitress hustle drinks for me. That didn't happen. Shoot, all these girls were pretty. They had their stash of liquor in their bags, taking a swig every now and then, and heading back to the action. I liked it.

I was making every couple of days table dancing what I made weekly in Oklahoma. Finally, I had enough money saved for Hawaii. I needed a place to stay and I needed spending money. Lucky had the hook up for airline tickets. He promised I would go home every month to see my baby. I was missing him.

Chapter 7

When I got off the plane, I thought I was in paradise. This has to be the most beautiful place in the world. There were giant flowers everywhere, every color, every kind. The weather was perfect.

"Am I in heaven?"

It smelled fresh like water. Hawaiians were putting lais around our necks.

"Aloha, Aloha." They were welcoming everyone off the plane.

Tonya, Yvette, Renee and Lucky were already there. I came a couple of weeks later with Jolynn. I was glad to come with Jolynn. We needed to be together, to feel safe. I hadn't seen much of Jolynn since we left Oklahoma. We were so excited about this trip. Sandy, Debbie and Frankie stayed in Washington. I couldn't believe I was really in Hawaii.

We made our call to Lucky and he told us to check in at the Coral Reef. The Coral Reef was alright, it looked kind of dark. It had a boat theme, like we were on a ship.

"Jolynn, we need to get out and see what was going on."

After checking in we left to the streets to do some exploring. We were gone, walking down the streets of Waikiki. The streets were really clean to be so crowded. It was still early. Tourist were everywhere.

"Man, Jolynn, there's a whole bunch of gays here. Dang, they don't care who sees them. They really don't care do they?"

We were laughing. We had never seen such a openly gay population. Men were holding hands and kissing in public. We were just as wide eyed as anybody.

"Oh, Jolynn, it is so pretty here, I don't think I'll ever leave this place. Girl can you believe we're really here?"

I was 22 years old and doing it in Hawaii. We were walking down the main street when a guy asked us to get in his bike thing.

"You want a ride?"

"No, that's okay, we don't want a ride, what is that anyway?"

"It's a petty cab. I'll take you wherever you want to go. Get in."

"No, we better not. You make money riding people around like that?"

"Yeah, I do good. I do real good." We smiled at each other.

"Where are the best places to go around here?"

"Ah man, you got to wait till it gets dark, then the real fun begins. It's a party in the streets. You'll see. You guys just get here?"

"Yeah."

"You gonna do some business?"

"Maybe. Where's the strip clubs?"

"There's a few around, one is over there." He pointed to a building across the street. I took note. "Another one is at the end of this corner on the next block."

"Which one is the best?"

"I couldn't tell you, but everybody makes money in Hawaii. Hey, I got the kind." Jolynn and I looked at each other. We didn't know what he was talking about.

"You want the Maui whowi?"

"What's that?"

"The good stuff." He motioned like he was smoking weed.

"Well maybe later, I got to get some money first."

"Well, take this and be careful, this is the good stuff, when you want more, look me up, I'm Bear." He looked like a bear. "I'm around all the time, just ask for Bear." He gave us a joint. "I got to go. I'll see you around." He shook his hand at us, "Hang Loose," and was gone to the next group of tourists.

"Jolynn, look at that guy's body, his muscles are popping out, he's in good shape riding people around all day in those things." Petty cabs were all over the place, moving, parked. Cars were blowing with loud music rolling down the main street.

"Man, this is too much. I love this place."

"Me too," Jolynn agreed.

It was a world away from Oklahoma. I was sure moving fast, Carson City, Seattle, table dancing, now Hawaii. This was it. This was the life.

We stopped at this street buffet, looked around for something to eat.

"What's that?" Jolynn asked.

"I don't know." Nothing looked familiar. It smelled good, it looked good. There was a long line, so it must be good. Mc-Donald's was a couple blocks down, we ate McDonald's.

The sun was going down. I knew we had better check in, around the corner from McDonald's was a club. The band was setting up on the sidewalks.

"Jolynn, they're getting ready to play on the sidewalk in front of the club." Jolynn and I weren't going anywhere, we wanted to hear the band. I had never seen anyone setup a band on a busy sidewalk. It was going to be a party. The guys in the band were flirting with us and we were flirting back. They seemed like homies. The band started getting down.

"Jolynn, these guys can play." They were singing Marvin Gaye, Earth, Wind and Fire. They even sang some Maze.

"They sound so good Jolynn. Let's hang out for a little while before we check in—I really liked them."

"Girl, we better call Lucky."

"We will in a minute."

There weren't any front walls enclosing the club, it was all open. A crowd was standing around with us, there were a few tables and chairs to sit but we just stood, moving with the music. People were getting drinks and going inside to stay. We wanted to hang outside and enjoy the band. The Hawaiian men were good looking.

"Sharell, they are sure fine." Jolynn was laughing and sporting her gold trimmed teeth. I had a mental connection with the lead singer and was gonna have a little fun playing when I looked out the corner of my eye and Lucky was standing there, smiling, enjoying us being bad.

"Jolynn, there's Lucky."

"Where?"

I immediately headed toward him. "Come on, girl."

"I see y'all having fun. Y'all not having too much fun are you?" Lucky was joking with us. "Finding your way around?"

"Lucky this place is too cool. Look at this, the band's playing on the sidewalk."

"You get your room?"

"Yeah, we're all settled."

"Good." Lucky flagged a taxi down and we got in. "Take us to Hotel Street. Did you get something to eat?"

"Yeah, we ate around the corner at that McDonald's."

"That's what you wanted?"

"We didn't know what to order at that buffet place. Shoot, I didn't know what that food was. I didn't recognize anything. Did you?"

Jolynn shook her head, no.

"I'll have to take you to get something later. It's mostly Chinese and Filipino food at these street shops. It's good. You'll learn." He laughed. "You can't eat everything, but some is really good. I want you to meet some people."

We rode through Oahu. He showed us the club, Fast Eddie's. "That's where we party."

I didn't see any super markets. "Where do you buy groceries?"

"They're around." We finally arrived at Hotel street. I was totally missing something.

"Where is this place, Lucky?"

"This is Hotel street. This is where the girls work. They filmed Hawaii Five-O at that club across the street."

I looked and wasn't impressed. The street seemed to be a ghost town. We walked around the corner to King Street and there were a few bars, a restaurant, Bob's Soul Food. The entire area was seedy. Okay, this place has personality, it's called "the streets."

Hotel street was a dreary looking place. We walked completely around a couple of blocks to get a feel of the place with Lucky. He introduced us to the few people that were around at the time. I guess he wanted us to be seen with him, as belonging to him. Then he took us to this place called Sugar Shack. We climbed up a long flight of stairs, the door was already opened. The Hawaiians called themselves "locals." The manager was a husky looking local with a heavy accent. His name was Tony. He wasn't friendly as all. He took us through, to the back where the rooms were, showed us the set up. In his heavy accent he gave us the rules.

"The rooms cost twenty dollars."

I was thinking, this guy isn't serious. Pay twenty dollars for these rooms. They were just a little room, no doors, with a nasty little curtain that hung across the doorway on a string. The rooms were about the size of a dressing room in a department store. There's a wooden cot that was attached to the walls about three or four feet off the floor. It had a thin mat lying over the wooden cot. There were about twelve rooms. Six on each side. That was it. Nothing else. The only good thing, the most important thing, was Tony's keeping shop, nobody was going to act up in that place, if they were smart. We were extremely safe at the Sugar shack.

The next day we arrived on Hotel street. After the sun had settled down, one by one, ladies started coming out. They emerged like ghosts suddenly appearing from nowhere, spotting the sidewalks, ready to work. Some were very pretty, dressed very good. They looked like models. Others just were there. The hang out was a club called The Family on King Street. We gathered for drinks and music from the jukebox, we could chill for a minute, then go back to work, hitting the pavement. Walking around and around the block. The other spot was Bob's Soul Food Restaurant. There were several Chinese and Filipino places as well to eat and hang out. They opened up like garage doors and catered to the Hotel street, Players. I was disappointed to be there, walking on this street. I didn't know what I expected, but Hotel street wasn't my idea of making money. I expected more, something different, a prettier place. Shoot, I expected luxury. I was in Hawaii. What was this place. It had to be the bottom of the barrel.

A boat just came in. The news traveled fast. Military men were coming in groves. The service guys were young. They wanted to get some action. They seemed as innocent and naive as I was a few years ago.

"You want a date? You want a date?"

"How much?"

"Fifty!"

"Okay!" Soon as you ask, the guys would follow you, up the stairs to Sugars. Pulling out their wallets. Girls with their soldiers were waiting on the stairwell for a room. It was really easy getting dates on Hotel street. But we had to play the game, you didn't really want to have sex.

"Hey, give him twenty dollars for the room." The soldier didn't say a word, he handed over twenty dollars to Tony.

Tony looked on his pad. "Go the room five."

"Okay." We headed to number five. "How long have you been here?"

"We arrived about two hours ago."

"You come here often?"

"Naw, this is my first."

"Well, take off your pants." The soldier took off his pants and laid them on the floor. I started to work. I took out K-Y jelly and soon as I touched him, he exploded. That was easier than I expected. I washed my hands and headed back down the stairs.

"Honey let me know if you want to come back, okay." He nodded. I couldn't believe he was okay with that.

I was walking back on Hotel street and I could tell the real pro's were on the street. They had the gunslinger look in their eye's. This was all business. I saw Yvette and Jolynn. They were doing okay, too. We decided to stop for a drink at one of the clubs.

"Have you done anything yet?" I asked to see where I stood as far as getting some money.

Jolynn was her usual self. "Girl, I made over $200 dollars."

"Damn, Jolynn. Where?"

"Girl, the first guy I was with gave me $150 then I got another for $50." She was laughing. Yvette had $80. I had only $50.

"Well, I need to get out of here." I finished my drink and headed back to work. A soldier asked me if I wanted a date. "Sure."

"I only have $50." He said.

"You have to pay for the room, it's twenty."

"Can we just go around the corner."

"I don't know. Where?"

"Over there."

"Okay." He handed me $50 dollars and I followed the soldier to a dark corner. It was okay 'cause too many people were walking by. I started rubbing and jacking him off. He was finished. I was glad nothing was on me. I went to the club to washed my hands, then I headed to my next customer. I couldn't believe that was it. It was so easy.

Jolynn and I were circling the block when we saw the pros in action. They had this guy up against a building, feeling between his legs, asking for a date.

"Come on baby, you know you like it." Right on the street. They were bumping and grinding. All the time they had his wallet out, behind his head, taking his money out.

"Ahhhh baby, you like this." They were really laying it on him thick. He was on cloud nine. They put his wallet back in his pocket. He never knew what had happened. After taking most of his money, they let him up. "Ah, you don't want no date. You ain't got enough money." He had climaxed in his pants. He walked away, with a smile on his face without knowing he was broke. The pros never went up the stairs to Sugar Shack. They take the money right on the streets. One of the rules to beating a guy is never take all the money, that wouldn't be right. Bad karma. Most of the time, the girls worked in pairs. Especially when they creeped. They wouldn't let Tony know they were creeping, but one girl would drop the guys pants on the floor, another girl would be waiting outside the room, then when the time was right, she would crawl under the curtains and take most of his money. Never all of it. Girls were taking money right and left, making at least $1,000 per night each. Those were the real pros. We were really getting an education on Hotel street.

I worked with Jolynn every night. Yvette met some local girls and worked with them. The others in our group worked in Waikiki. Hotel street was fun and easy. We had a club, food, protection and fast money. I heard Sue had left Lucky for another guy. GiGi was still around but I hadn't met her yet.

Jolynn wasn't happy. She made the kind of money I wanted to make. Every night she had at least $500 or $600, lots of time she had over a grand. She has a deep sultry voice, tall, a beautiful sister. She must intimidate men. For some reason, Lucky and Jolynn didn't hit it off. They were friends, they liked each other alright, they just never really had that attraction for each other. He treated me good. We had an attraction for each other. Lucky would come get me and take me home for the evening, we would play, have fun and make real love or have real sex. Lucky and I were only friends, too. But for Jolynn, a lot was missing and she was ready to go home.

I need to go home, too. I needed to see my baby, check in with my probation officer. I really missed my baby. Lucky got Jolynn and me airline tickets and we went home to Oklahoma. I was so glad to see my baby and my family. I didn't visit Mike. He had sent threatening messages so I sure wasn't going to visit him. My little man was so big. I couldn't stop hugging and kissing him. How could I leave him again? I wasn't.

My sister, Carol, was pregnant, too. I wasn't going back with Lucky. I called Lucky and told him I was staying in Oklahoma, but he convinced me to come back and bring my son with me to Hawaii. After a couple of weeks, I was ready to leave. My sister Carol cried all the way to the airport. She cried so hard for me not to leave her again.

"Sharell, you're my older sister, I need you. Please don't go."

"I got to go, Carol. I don't like it here anymore. Why don't you come with me to Hawaii. It's so pretty there, you'll love it, Carol."

"I'm not going to no Hawaii. Just stay home, this is your home and family, we need you. Please Sharell," Carol cried and cried.

I got on the plane and left Oklahoma with my baby. I felt better having by baby with me. It wasn't so hard. I trusted the local Hawaiian women with my son. Somehow, they seem so much like Oklahoma women. I knew my son was in the best of care. I would take my son to the sitter just like home, pick him up at day break, just like at my mom's. The Hawaiian never looked down on working girls, or that fast life. It was a living, just as any other tourist attraction.

I was tired of Hotel street. I wondered why I hadn't seen any of Lucky's other girl's. Where were they? I even stopped seeing Yvette. Jolynn was gone, I was by myself. I was making good money, $300 and up a night. It was all honest money, I wasn't good at beating or robbing, but I could do a really good hand jobs. I learned lots of tricks from Vanessa in Carson City. I didn't have to steal, or any of that. I even had regular customers come to see me.

Sometimes there would be fights with guys and girls. Where the girls beat or stole money! If Tony had to get in the middle of any situation, he got paid. Other times girls would defend each other. I never got into any situation. With Jolynn gone, I wasn't getting into anything, anyway or for anybody.

One particular day, I learned a vital lesson. I was ready for

C. Oakes

work, walking down King street. This car pulled up. Usually, there are so many people watching you—the police, girls, or players checking on your every move—so there's a sense of protection. This guy asked if I wanted a date. I quoted my price and he agreed. He seemed safe. We were in the neighborhood. He wore really thick black framed glasses. He wasn't that big of a fellow. He was a brother. He was in a car, against my better judgement, I agreed and got in his car. Normally I went to Sugar's.

"Where are we going?" I asked.

"I thought we would ride a little farther down to this parking lot I know."

"Why?"

He just smiled. We went through a couple of lights. We were moving too fast. Then red flags started going through my mind. We were too far off the beat. Then he started.

"You don't even know me. You just got in my car. Why did you do that? You don't know me!" He took off his glasses. Then I saw his eyes. His eyes were scary. Then I knew. Damn, I'm in trouble. He had dangerous, crazed eyes. He made a point to take off the glasses so I could see them. The glasses were a camouflage for him to look helpless or a like cripple or something. I started assessing my situation. He was going on and on.

"Why did you come with me?"

"You seem to be a nice person to me. What's your name?" I was busy thinking, looking, and planning my escape. "How much farther?" I wanted to make sure we stayed in the city area. I sure didn't want to end up on the outskirts of town. This car is old. I was thinking. He didn't have electric door locks. He was talking crazier and crazier. I played like I didn't get it, like I didn't have a clue. We got to another red light. I opened and jumped out the car. He spun off. Burning rubber, getting away. I was cussing at myself, as I walked back to Hotel street.

Where's everybody? Seemed like I was the only one in the family on Hotel Street. Were they ducking me? Lucky was traveling so much between Seattle and Hawaii, I didn't see him. I didn't have any real friends. Yvette acted so jealous. Why was she bragging so much on Frankie anyway. Frankie was this and she was that. I was lonely. I continued to work Hotel street. I made money. I had my stash. It was okay.

I finally met a friend. Her name is Dana. She's a sister from St. Louis. She was cool. Young. They grow up faster in St. Louis than in Oklahoma. She was real young, but cool.

"Hey, how you doing?" For us, that meant, how's the money.

"It's okay. I do better in Waikiki."

"Really! What's it like in Waikiki?"

"You haven't worked in Waikiki?"

"No, not yet."

"Well, that's were the Japanese are. They're easier. That's the big money. They don't know the value of our money. We don't have all the zeros on our money that they have on their money. So, they're not sure how much they're giving us. You need to learn a few words and phrases in Japanese. I'll teach you. They're good dates. I come to Hotel street sometimes for a change."

"Where do people work in Waikiki?"

"In the hotels. Just get a room for the night and work there all night. We can share a room sometimes. I'll show you the hotels we can work in. It's cool."

We caught a cab and headed for Waikiki. Dana and I worked together on the streets in Waikiki. It was much more fun and action. I was getting bigger money dates. Dates started at $100. I was so happy cause it was less contact and more of a party, like a Hawaiian vacation. The girls were straight show girls. They were beautiful and classy. Nicer clubs, much more action. Fun.

Dana and I shared a hotel room every night that we used for our dates. We were becoming very good friends.

"Sharell, come with me to my apartment. I need to change my shoes. My feet hurt in these."

"Okay."

We walked to Dana's apartment, still asking for dates along the way.

"Come on in, I'll be out in a minute."

I heard a deep voice from a back room. "Baby, who's that?"

"It's a friend of mine, we work together," Dana responded to the questioning.

"She's a working girl?" The deep voice continued to question.

"Yeah baby, that's who I work with when I'm out there."

"What's her name?"

"Nikki." Dana came out where I was and we started heading toward the door to leave.

Her pimp walked in the living room and stood in front of the door to stop us from leaving.

"What are you doing coming into a pimp's house? Break yourself. I'll beat the shit out of you if you don't give me all your money right now." He was in my face. I couldn't believe I was in this situation. I looked at Dana. She was confused.

"Baby, we just came to change my shoes."

"Shut the fuck up, Dana. You brought this bitch here. I ought to kick your ass. If I tell you one more time to give me your money, I'll hurt you, do you understand?"

This ugly, bad breathe guy was in my face and going to beat me up, if I didn't give him my money. I handed him $200.00. He was right in my face, screaming.

"Who's your man? Who's your man?" He was walking around me. I was scared. "Who's your damn man, I said?" He was screaming at me just inches from my face.

"Lucky!"

"Lucky? So you're one of Lucky's bitches? Do Lucky know that you're at a real pimp's house?"

"I didn't know that I couldn't come over. Dana is a friend of mine. We work together. I came with her to change her shoes."

"This is a pimp's house and you're disrespecting it. Call your man."

"He's not in town."

"That's too bad bitch 'cause you're gonna have to stay here till he comes get you."

My heart was beating. I called Lucky in Seattle. The pimp snatched the phone from my hand.

"Yeah man, I got your bitch, she came over here disrespecting my house, up in a pimp's house. I'm a real pimp. Man, if you want this bitch, it'll cost you a G. Man, I need $1000.00. . . You want this bitch?" Then he hung up the phone. I didn't say a word. Dana was hurt and embarrassed. I was scared. I didn't know what was going to happen to me. This guy was real mean.

I slept on the floor. He was on the sofa too close. I was shaking, too scared to sleep or cry. I was thinking about my baby, I didn't know when or if I'll see him again. I didn't know if I was going to get hurt by this ugly, horrible man. I didn't say one word to Dana. She didn't know what kind of man she had? She had to know. Dana just looked at me, very sorrowful. The next evening Lucky was there, he handed the guy $1,000 to get me back. Before we left the pimp's house, Lucky jumped on me, he humiliated me, said it was all in the name of the game for me being out of pocket, in that fool's house. I never knew about that rule. He didn't do that shit in Oklahoma, how was I to know. Now, we can't have friends outside our family. He drove me to pick up my baby. I didn't work for a few days. I was too hurt and embarrassed, plus everybody had heard that Lucky had to buy me back from a pimp. Lucky later told me that guy would have killed me or I could have ended up in the hospital, anyway he would have hurt me real bad if Lucky hadn't given him the money. I never entered another working girls house and Dana ran away. I heard she went back to St. Louis. Good for her.

Chapter 8

There were lots of players in Hawaii. Everybody wasn't like that nut. The real pimps looked like movie stars. They drove Mercedes and Bentley's. Some were women. Man! There was this one player driving a gold Rolls Royce. The better the players looked, the more they seemed to care for their girls. I say that because the girls looked happy. Dressed good. Had nice cars. Hair and nails all together. Mike bought all my clothes so I dressed just as good as any of them. I think that's where I was having a problem with Yvette and the others with Lucky. They had nice things, but I don't think they put them together very well. I dressed good. Hey, that's one thing you can say about Oklahoma, they know how to dress.

This one guy likes me. I can tell he likes me. He follows me while I'm working, trying to make eye contact. I walk down the street, he would walk along with me, only across the street. Looking and smiling. Flirting. I can't look. That's being disrespectful. I could get charged like that. All he has to say is I was looking at him. Being disrespectful. Then it would be some mess. I would leave Lucky, but shoot, I'll end up with somebody that might beat on me, like Mike. At least Lucky didn't make any habit of kicking ass just to be kicking ass. He wasn't going to let anything happen to me or my baby. He sends me home when I need to go. I got to check with my probation officer every now and then. I'm still mad about being held hostage and charged by that fool. Lucky really hurt me. Why didn't he just kick that punk's ass and get me out of there! Damn the game. It ain't shit. He's making an example of me. I'm his damn home girl from his hometown. Nobody ever told me anythng about this life or game. He bought me a diamond and gold pinkie fingernail; I wear it to snort coke. Everybody snorted coke. He was trying to make up to me. I don't have anybody here—no friends, no family. The life ain't shit. At least before, I could have friends.

I continued to work Waikiki. I met some locals. I met a good, local Japanese woman that owned the store where I brought my supplies, my rubbers and KY jelly. She taught me Japanese phrases so I could communicate with the Japanese tourist. They seemed to trust you more when you could talk and communicate with them.

"Hi there."

"Hi." I pulled out a couple of dollars to pay for some zig zags and mints.

"No no no, never keep money like that."

"What?"

"You have your money all messed up, it's folded. In Japan, folds will depreciate the money. Make it no good."

"Yeah?"

"Keep it straight."

"Well, I have to hide it . . . so it gets folded." I hid my money all over myself. I learned to never keep it all in the same place. So money would be under my wig, in my shoes, a little in my pockets. I kept a few dollars for spending in my purse. Most of it would be under my wig or in the bottom of my shoes.

I was doing good in Waikiki. The tourist didn't experience the vacation without a date from one of the working girls.

"You want a date? Hi, you want a date?"

"Yeah!" It was a Hollie, a white guy, I sized him up, he seemed okay. No mental red flags. We really learn to trust our feelings and intuitions in this business. He followed me to the room. All the rooms in Hawaii are kitchenettes. The rooms that the girls use didn't have the cooking utensils, the pots and pans, stuff like that, the regular rooms had everything. But all the rooms are kitchenettes.

The date didn't go well. He wasn't happy cause he came too fast. Just the way I liked it, a hand job. He wanted his money back.

"Well, give me some of it back. That wasn't worth a hundred bucks."

"I can't help it if you came too fast. That's it." He snatched my purse looking for my money. My money wasn't in my purse, but I had twenty dollars in it. I'm not gonna fight. I had enough fighting in my life. I can't believe how some girls go toe-to-toe and fight these guys. I'm getting the police. I ran out of the room right to a cop.

"He took my money. He took my money."

"Who?"

"That guy there. He's coming out my room." The guy was following me with my purse in his hand.

"Officer! Officer this girl is a hooker, she's a hooker, sir. She working the streets."

"How much did he take?" The officer asked me, looking real concerned for me.

"He took two hundred dollars from me. He snatched my purse. It was in my purse." I cried to the cop.

"She's a lie. She's a damn lie." The hollie tried to persuade the police. But the police didn't want to hear it. All he knew was this guy was running after me with my purse in his hands.

"Give it back to her. Give it back to her right now." The officer screamed in his face.

"I didn't take two hundred dollars from her." The hollie tried to defend himself.

"Give it back right now." The officer repeated.

"She's lying."

"You got my purse and I had two hundred dollars in it."

"Give her the money and sit your ass down on the ground." The officer was big, bad and buffed. He was in the guy's face. The guy opened his wallet and handed me two crisp $100 bills.

"I want your name and badge number. I'm reporting you. What's your name, I'm reporting you."

"My name is King Kong. Now sit your ass down till a car comes to get you. You don't mess with these girls." The officer was now looking at me. "Where are you working?"

"I'm working over there. Well, you stay close so I can keep an eye on you." He was looking at the guy when he said that. "I don't want nobody taking advantage of you. You understand?"

"Yes Sir," I replied.

"Stay close around here so I can watch you. Don't you work anywhere else."

"Okay! Okay." I was glad that he wanted to watch out for me. I see that officer every night. The police in Waikiki knew I wasn't a thief.

I stayed on that block in plain view of the officer every night. Every now and then I could see him looking out the corner of his eyes. He was a good guy. Protective of me. I appreciated him, I was so tiny and he didn't trust these guys out here.

Cars were driving by playing music so loud. *Bad Girl, talking about the bad bad girl. Toot toot, beep beep.* The cars just blowing, *toot toot, beep beep. Bad girl bad girl, you're such a dirty bad girl, toot toot . . .* on down the road. I wonder what made Donna Summers sing that. All the cars were playing that song, blowing at girls. It was a party out there.

"Hey, what's your name?"

"I'm Sharell."

"I'm Coco. This corner okay?"

"It works for me." The girl's here didn't trip over territory. We were here one night, somewhere else the next, constantly moving.

"Where you from?"

"Oklahoma." I said with pride.

She laughed, "Oklahoma, what's in Oklahoma? I didn't know there were any black folk in Oklahoma." Coco is a amazon. She's got to be 6 ft. or more with those high, high heels. All dark skinned legs.

"Where you from?" I was curious about her now.

"I'm from Vegas. You ever go there?"

"I was in Carson City, but not Las Vegas. I worked the ranch there," I said. She smiled, but not at me. She was asking for dates with her eyes, a smile and a nod. There was something special about Coco. She wasn't the average girl out here. Guys were stopping and backing up when they saw her. She was so tall. She had a lot of class about herself. A pro.

"Hi, can I come with you?" Coco asked a tourist. I watched her and observed her style as she worked. Customers were at awe with her and so was I.

"Yeah, how much for the both of you?"

"That's a hundred a piece."

"Okay," the customer said with no problem. I just followed the lead.

"Where are you staying?" Coco asked the customer.

"I'm over at the Golden Palace in room 262."

"See you in a few. Okay?" Coco assured our date. The taxi drove off. It was a ten-minute walk to the Palace. I could tell we were going to be friends.

Coco and I worked that same block everyday. One day I saw this very tall handsome, fine, classy man strolling down the street. He was elegant. He was a player, but looked like one of those movie stars. I told Coco, "Look at him." I was stealing peeks. I wouldn't just look at the man. I was glancing. Coco was cheesing. She was really putting on the charm. She had a little naughty smile that she would do for some extra special customers that she thought might spend a lot of money, but there she was putting on the charm for this guy walking down the street. I would never cheese like that at a player. He smiled back at Coco, flirted back with her. After he passed by, Coco smiled at me, "Sharell, that's my man."

"What!" I could see them together. They fit.

Tourist couldn't pass us by. We were a good team, anyway she knew a lot more than me. She had charisma. If we were out together, on the same corner, most customers wanted us both. We rarely had separate dates, she would ask for the big money, too. She got us $500 a piece to go to Hilo for an evening. We were back the same day. Some times the customers like me, then sometimes they liked her, but they always took us both. It was good chemistry. What I really liked about working with Coco is she didn't try to bring me into her family, or do any lesbian business and there was a lot of girls hitting on me. Coco never said anything about the game or the life or any of that bull. She was just trying to make some money. I bet she invited her friends over.

Coco would beat customers, too. She knew lots of tricks. She took over the dates, which I didn't mind. Once she asked the guy to get in the shower to freshen up, then she stole his money, his clothes, and some jewelry. She gave me $300. I don't know what she got. I know it was more than $300. I left Waikiki and went to Hotel street the rest of that evening.

We were working our regular corner and this guy made a sudden stop. Coco could smell big money. He wanted us both.

"Hi, can I come with you?" Coco asked.

"Yeah, how much for the both of you for the evening?" We were looking at each other. Smiling, trying to get a sense of each others feelings.

"What do you think?" I asked Coco.

"Well, you probably can't afford what we make an evening. How long are you talking about?" Coco asked the date.

He assured us that he could afford it. "Let me take you girls with me to party tonight."

"How much can you spend?" Coco was persistent.

"Will you make $1,000 a piece tonight?" We didn't say another word. We got in the taxi. "You got to spend the night with me."

Now we knew damn well that wasn't going to happen. That was really against the rules. We said okay. He stayed at the Pagoda. Once we arrived in the room, he gave us the money. I wanted to leave then, but Coco was whispering for me to wait. We partied with this guy, bar hopped, danced, smoked some Maui whowi weed, everything. We both got into the bed with him, he was too tired and drunk to even try anything with us. He passed smooth out.

"Sharell, let's go." Coco whispered. I was more than ready. We were leaving and Coca looked back at me.

"Sharell, get his key," She continued to whisper. I grabbed his room key and we both left. I didn't see Coco again after that night, but I heard about her. A tall black girl beat for big money. Coco made a sting. A big sting. She beat for over fifty grand. Damn, Coco was gone. Lucky asked me if I knew about the sting. I told him I had heard about it. It was big talk. Stings go down in history. I couldn't tell anybody that I gave her the room key to the big money, the sting, and didn't get any of the cash.

I was working by myself again. Yvette was working Waikiki, I'd see her occasionally. We were kind of close. Getting to be friends. We watched each other's back. Sometimes we watched each other's kids. They were the same age. Renee, Flashy Lashy, had run off. Lucky found her stash and he took it. She was mad and went back to Seattle. She wasn't going anywhere, just trying to make a statement.

I finally met GiGi on Hotel Street. GiGi was fat. She said she was Filipino. She was thick and buffed and liked to fight. Anyway, I think she was mad at Lucky and wanted to start something with me.

"So, you're Sharell?"

"Yeah, and you're GiGi?"

"I heard a lot about you, Sharell."

"I hope it's all good."

"Yeah, it's good. That's a nice ring."

"Thanks."

"Lucky give it to you?"

"Naw, I had it a while."

"Let me see it?" Red Flags were going off everywhere.

"Girl, I don't take off my jewelry." Um! GiGi was going to try to take my jewelry. She must really be mad at Lucky.

"When was the last time you saw Lucky?"

"It's been a couple of days."

"Well, if you see him before I do, let him know I'm looking for him."

"Okay, if I see him." What was that about? Lucky was busy. GiGi hadn't seen Lucky since we got in town. He's gotten three new girls. All were Hawaiians. Damn, I need to go back to Waikiki away from Hotel street. These girls liked to fight.

I went back to work on my block in Waikiki. My police officer acknowledged me with a smile and a be careful flash with his lips. "Okay, Okay." I was wording back to him. I sure liked that cop. King Kong. That's what I called him. I missed my corner. I don't know why I left here and went to Hotel street anyway. People were roller skating down the main drag. Petty carts were out. Girls were everywhere. It was busy and I was ready for work. "Hi, can I come with you?" I got that from Coco. It worked. "Hi, can I come with you?" He was a local Japanese. He stopped immediately and nodded. He followed me to the hotel. This was my first date, so it paid for my room for the night. After paying for the room, we entered the elevator which was outside by the entrance door. On the fourth floor, room 410. As soon as we entered the room, the local Japanese checked out the closet, started looking through the drawers and cabinets. I didn't know what he was doing, I guessed he was checking the room out. Trying to be careful. "What are you looking for?" He didn't answer. "What are you looking for?" I started taking off my shoes. Then the voice came. It had been a while since I heard the voice. The voice was calm, right in my ear, as if someone was standing next to me.

"He's looking for a knife!" He continued to open drawers, close drawers, looking. . . My mind repeated the statement. Looking for a knife! Panic . . .panic. Looking for a knife. Fear swept through my body, from the top of my head to the bottom of my feet . . . Fear.

The voice still talking to me calmly. "Be aggressive! Be aggressive."

I started going for him. "Oh baby, you are so fine, I want you so bad. Ummmm, Ummmmm," I was going for his shirt. Unbuttoning it. I was doing what the voice told me to do.

He started pushing me away. "Don't do that. Stop! Not like this, not like this."

"Baby, I want you, I want you so much." I sat down on the bed. "Honey, I know what. Let's order some drinks." I called down to the front desk. "I want to order two drinks for room 410. Baby what do you want?" He didn't answer. "Let's just get two Hennessy." He nodded Okay. The front desk hung up on me. I thought they would get the hint that I was in trouble. This was a hotel for working girls and they didn't have drinks and they sure as hell didn't have room service. I played it off. "Honey, they said you have to come down and get the drinks." He said Okay.

As soon as he walked out the door, he snapped. He recognized that I played him out the room. I slammed the door behind him. I started calling down to the desk again. They wouldn't answer my rings. I guess they thought I was crazy, asking for drinks and room service. I kept ringing and ringing. The local Japanese was outside my door, trying to pick the lock. I looked out my sliding glass doors to the lanai and it was too far to jump. I kept trying to call down stairs. Finally, they answered. I was hysterical. I couldn't get it out fast enough. The manager came up. I was so hysterical. Shaking. I knew this guy was big trouble. The voice told me so.

The manager walked around the building, the guy was gone. After about an hour, I finally got myself together to leave the hotel and get back to work. As I was leaving the room, outside, going to the elevator, the voice came back.

"Don't shut the door." I didn't shut the door because once the door is shut, it's locked. I pulled the door together but not enough for it to click. I was about to push the down button on the elevator, to go down to the lobby, when the local Japanese came

C. Oakes

from behind the elevator. He was after me. A lump was in my throat. I couldn't scream. I made strange gurgling sounds that weren't even loud. I could feel his fingernail on my back, trying to get a grip on my blouse. I ran for my life. Hit that door open and slammed it shut. I flew to the phone. Hysterical again. I'm crying like crazy.

"He's up here, he's up here. He was behind the elevator." I was crying and sobbing. The manager called the police. They came to get me from the room. "Officer, I want you to know this guy is very dangerous. He dangerous. He's dangerous."

"We haven't found anybody around here fitting his description." A police said over the walkie talkie.

Then I heard it. "We got him."

King Kong was there. "Where was he when he came after you?"

"Behind the elevator."

I heard the officer on his walkie talkie. "We found him, we found him."

King Kong looked at me, hold on a minute. I listened to the walkie talkie. "Where did you find him?"

"He was on the roof."

"What?"

"On the roof?"

"I told you, this guy is dangerous. Look officer, this guy is the type that will chew titty's off. You understand what I'm saying. He's the kind that will cut up girls, officer. You need to put him away." I pleaded with King Kong because I knew this guy was a maniac.

"We can't arrest him, he hadn't done anything."

I went home the rest of the night. Too shaken to work.

Man, I couldn't stop thinking about what happened. Somebody told me what to do. . . step by step. . . Something told me, he's looking for a knife. . . and not to close the door when I left the room. Was that an angel, was it Jesus looking out for me, was it a past relative. How can Jesus love me? After everything I've done. I remembered when Marzett died, a voice told me to thank him. Who was that, was it the same person? That happened. I heard it, that voice clearly spoke to me. He was there for me, talking in my ear, telling me what to do. . . in my ear. I finally fell

asleep, still wondering. For the first time in my life, I acknowledged him, he's real, whoever he is, he's real, watching me.

Chapter 9

I decided I would try the dance clubs in Waikiki. There was one right on the strip. When I walked to the club, it seemed okay. It's huge inside, it has a nice stage, good lights, smoke and bubble machines. That's cool. All the chairs were stationed in the middle of the room, in front of the stage. No tables, just the chairs. In the back, against the walls were booths. The booths were secluded, in the dark. They were positioned to look like a maze. Total privacy.

There was a good mixture of girls, Asians, Hawaiians, Caucasians and Blacks. The manager, Noel, welcomed me wholeheartedly. She was Hawaiian, very pretty, very nice and overly generous. I liked her. In fact, she invited me to her house. I declined for the time being. I just didn't know her that well, and I surely don't do a lot of visiting any more. Not in this environment. She said the girls rented rooms from her during their stay in Hawaii. I'll keep that offer open, just in case.

There wasn't any real schedule at the club, The Tiki Room. It stayed open 24 hours every day. Just come to work when you want to make money. I had plenty of costumes and I was ready for the change.

That night I arrived for work. Noel gave me the once around. Their system was different. They had table dancing, drinks and bottles of champagne. Oklahoma didn't have the table dancing and Washington didn't have the drinks. Hawaii had both. They had the booths, too, for total privacy. But once you get up from a customer, he is open game. So even if you have to dance on stage and there's a drink setting in your spot, you could, I mean, you will lose the customer and his money. That's vicious. It was a straight cut-throat game. Well, I'll just see how it goes.

I watched for a while and these girls made money, they were straight hustlers. "Oh Lord, what's that?" I thought. She was doing a floor show. Opening her legs. Dancing, stretching her legs wide open. Showing everything, but nothing was between her legs. It was only skin. No split, no vagina, no penis, nothing between the legs, just smooth skin. I was in shock. I continued to watch. She was turning over and over, stretching wide so you can see, everything, which was nothing. I was speechless. She was a man. She didn't have a penis but she didn't have a split either. The customers didn't care. How many worked here? Hawaiians called them Maihoo (sic). Well I'll just go with the flow.

It was my turn to dance. I'm on stage. The new girl on the block. I took the show. Guys were waiting on me, mesmerized. I sat down with my first customer. The waitress came right over and he wanted to buy me a drink. I told him I wanted a bottle of champagne. Might as well start right. I didn't know the routine. Exactly what were they doing? Were they turning tricks in the club? Surely not!

One Asian girl was bragging that the customer won't ever get sex from her. "I make two to three thousands every day, every day, I don't care what you spend, you'll never get this. Never!"

Do they make that much? So, they're not turning dates in the club. I got a few drinks and dances from the customer. I made about a hundred from him, that's good, for my first customer. He was good for a few more dollars. It was my turn to dance again. The black girl, Bobbie, a maihoo came over.

"Hey girl, I'll take him over to the booth so no one can get him while you're on stage. Tell him to go with me, then you can come back and get him when you finish your set," Bobbie explained.

Sounds good to me. "Okay Bobbie, I'll tell him to go with you."

"Honey, go to the booth with Bobbie until I get off stage. I'll meet you back there." He agreed. I went on stage, danced my set, went to the booth to get my customer. Honey's head was laid back, eyes rolled back into his head, only showing the white. Honey was in La La land. I tried to wiggle my way back with the party, but he didn't want me to interrupt them. Bobbie was working him good. Bobbie ignored me, too. She took my customer and I told him to go with her ass. I was pissed. She took all his money and I got a measly hundred bucks.

The first night at The Tiki club was pretty good. I made about the same as I did on the streets, but, shoot, I couldn't compete with the maihoo's or the other dancers. They were ruthless. They just ran over me. I wasn't ready to go back to the streets either, so I stayed. It was different working with transsexuals, sharing the dressing room, listening to their conversations and lango, it was all new and a world away from Oklahoma. I'll learn. I'll get down and dirty, too. They were bad at The Tiki club.

Meanwhile, Lucky opened an after hours club named Lucky's. It was downtown in Honolulu. All the players went there after the girls finished working. Players packed the joint, showed off their women. They were smooth and classy and spent plenty money on cocaine and Cognac. The girls all had a drink called Beautiful, it was Amaretto and Cognac, straight over ice. It was really good. Lucky's was a classy set. Everybody had a plate of cocaine, too. Music, snorting, no dancing, just talking the game, gossiping about who took whose woman, how fine she is, how much money she gave when she wanted to be with them, 'cause the girls had to come with money to get with another player.

"I told that bitch, she got to come better than that if she want to be with a player like me." On and on. The real players didn't talk like that, they didn't tell their business. Their women sure weren't called bitches. Shoot, if Lucky had come to me that way, I wouldn't have been here. He played me just right.

The girls stayed quiet. They didn't talk with the players. That was disrespectful, except for the women pimps. There were two of them. They looked like men, carried themselves like men, and dressed like men. They rubbed themselves between their legs like they had something big there like a man, talking slick. . . with the rest of the men, gossiping.

So every night we met Lucky at his after hours club. It was getting pretty popular. He didn't talk much with the other players. Lucky just listened to everybody and laughed at the jokes. Girls were throwing themselves at him. The club looked good inside. That's what I liked about Lucky, he did things, not just talked about them. When I first met him, he said we would travel, go to Hawaii, here we are in Hawaii. Lucky had about ten or twelve women that met him every night, dropping their loads on him. He had caught one of the club owners' daughter. Her mother owned the club off Hotel street, where we hung out. Her name was Eva. Lucky was on top. He loved it.

I don't know why, but his local women thought I was something special to Lucky. I wasn't. We enjoyed each other. We laughed at the same things. Lucky had a good sense of humor. It was he and Yvette that had the strong relationship. Lucky mostly stayed at her house when he was here in Hawaii. They had a little boy. Yvette had been with Lucky about four years. She always had an excuse not to work, so she watched my kid most nights. Which I didn't mind, she took care of him, treated my baby good. He was going on three. I had been with Lucky about a year. Yvette and I learned to lean on each other cause we were the only ones there that were from the mainland and we were his only black women that lived in Hawaii.

Renee had gone home. She went back to work in Woodenville. Tonya and Frankie choose other pimps. Frankie said we were stupid to stay with Lucky. She thought Lucky was hooked on cocaine. She said he wasn't the same, didn't have anything to show for the money he was getting every night.

"Well what is he doing with the money?" She asked.

I tried not to think about it.

"In Seattle we had things, Sharell, buying new cars. Going places. Showing off. What's he doing. All I see him buying is cocaine. You guys better get out now while you can. You're stupid if you stay." I was inclined to believe her, but I wasn't getting with another pimp. Anyway, I think Frankie was jealous of Lucky's new girl, Star. She was pretty and drove a Porsche. She left one of the singers of the Malibu's to be with Lucky. The Malibu's had several number one hits. When Star chose Lucky, it was big talk. Frankie was supposed to be Lucky's number one girl, but she couldn't handle Star.

Her questions kept resurfacing in my mind. Where did all his money go? The other players were driving new cars, the women dressed well. What was up with Lucky? I thought Lucky was going to beat Frankie and that pimp's ass when she left him. GiGi chose another player, too. I hear she did that a lot. (Switched men). The pimps didn't care as long as they got paid. Some of the other girls just ran off, too. There were so many women that it was hard to keep up with all of them. Alex got with a woman pimp. I was surprised by that. She didn't look the type. But Lucky picked up other women. The local Hawaiian women loved him. Star said she remembered him from a few years back. She

C. Oakes

said she always had a crush on him.

Lucky stopped sending me home to see my probation officer. I hadn't been home in six months. I was worried about that. I violated my probation, damnit. I tried not to think about it. If I go home now, I'm looking at real time. How did I get myself in this predicament? I know how I got myself in this mess. I wanted to get away from Oklahoma at the time.

Phyllis called me and told me she saw all my furniture at the flea market, even the pictures of me and Mike.

"Girl, all y'alls furniture is here at the Flea Market. They got it set up like y'all's living room use to look, down to the recliner and the chair. They're selling everything."

We had 3' x 4' poster size portraits of us in beautiful gold frames.

"Girl they're selling you and Mike's pictures that were hanging on the walls." Those pictures were stunning.

"All my stuff was in storage, Phyl."

"Not anymore. You want me to do something? I can call the police."

"Somebody broke the lock to the storage. I think the people that managed the storage did it. I might have been late on the payments, Phyl. Mike had a big album collection. All his clothes were in there."

"You got some money? I'll get some of your stuff for you."

"Shoot, that stuff will be out of style pretty soon. Can't worry about it now, Phyl. I want to leave all those memories of Mike and my marriage."

There was nothing I wanted to hold on to.

"No Phyl, just let it go."

"All your stuff, girl, you sure?"

"Yeah. Anyway, I'm gone. Take care, baby, I'll check with you later."

I had a great condo in Aeia, near Pearl Harbor. It was in a high rise building on the tenth floor. I loved my apartment. People in Hawaii were so much fun. Most apartments were in high rise buildings. Nearly everybody in Waikiki had a telescope positioned on their balcony or lanai, peeping in bedrooms. Bedroom drapes were conveniently left opened to give a good sex show. They knew they were giving a good show, too. It was like they were making a porno movie. They made sure the bedroom lights were on, so you can see real good and see everything. It was all fun.

This guy I met in Honolulu, Ron, gave me his condo or apartment to live in. He was one of my regular customers from Hotel street. He looked more like the Waikiki type, but he came to see me often, circling the block, over and over, off Hotel street until he found me. That was before I started working Waikiki. We never went to Sugar Shack. We would always go to his place. I just gave his information to Yvette or somebody, then I'd go to his place. I finally gave him my telephone number so he could call me whenever he was in town. Sometimes he would pick me up from the club. He was a perfect gentleman. I didn't have to work hard. He paid me good. Basically, he was cool. He said he worked in the movie industry. He always asked me why was I hooking.

"You are so beautiful. You're smart. You have so much potential. How did you get in this kind of work?" I hated that question more than anything, cause I hated to think about the mistakes I'd made. I hated to be reminded that I didn't come from this. I was raised good. My parents taught me better. I was raised in the church. Shoot, my real daddy's a preacher. Well, maybe they're right about PK's.

Ron promised me he could get me a job, making good money if I wanted to do something different. I could work in the movie industry, he would help me get out of this, if I wanted to. I was scared that my probation violation would show up somewhere. Then I'll go to jail. I was safe for now. So I can't leave Hawaii or Lucky. I should have left him earlier, before it got out of hand. I should have left with Jolynn. I didn't have to pay anything to stay in his condo. I was basically apartment sitting while he traveled. That guy really liked me, wanted something better for me. My place was totally nice. In Oklahoma, it was just average, but here, it was great. I told Lucky about Ron and his offer for me. I told him he worked in the movie industry and offered me a job. Lucky started staying at the apartment with me more often. He had some of his Hawaiian women living with me, too. It was two bedrooms, so there was room for one more, but he had another sleeping on the sofa.

At first, Lucky was doing good, his club and his women were

all good. Then jealousy set in, some of the pimps and players started bad mouthing him. Then this group of business owners, Lucky said it was the Hawaiian mafia, told him he had to pay them a percentage to keep his business opened. He couldn't run a place like that without paying the piper. Lucky didn't blink, he stayed opened, only he hired some Moniques loaded with machine guns for protection. They were at the front door, walking around the parking lot. They were big and bad and weren't scared of anybody. All the players congratulated Lucky on his smooth move, but eventually they stopped coming around. I couldn't blame them. What if there had been a real fight? What if there had been a shooting or a killing? There wasn't that much love for Lucky. These guys didn't want no trouble, they were too smooth and pretty to get down and dirty. If any real shit came down, it would have been crazy. Just wasn't that much love for Lucky. The money stopped flowing, bills weren't paid, so he had no choice but to close shop.

Lucky was going down fast. Frankie was right. Cocaine was the real pimp, too much for his pockets. Plus he had so many women to sport and snort with, and extra for whichever girl he was taking home for the night. His game was getting old.

While I was at the club working, Lucky started staying at my apartment. He was using the walls for target practice. He was an expert at throwing Asian weapons. Holes were all over the walls.

"Lucky, why are you doing this? You're tearing up this man's place. Please stop."

He didn't care. Lucky didn't say a word, he just continued to throw those damn weapons. I was pissed and sad that he was tearing up the apartment that was left in my care. I lived there free. It cost close to $700 per month to live in something like that in Hawaii. How was I going to explain this. Lucky didn't give a shit. He was going to make sure my thing was messed up, too. He didn't want me to have anything better. Ron offered me a better life. At least, he cared. During this time, I was happy that somebody cared about me, wanted something better for me.

Yvette was keeping my baby again. Lucky had gone to Seattle to visit Sandy, Debbie and Renee. I hadn't worked the streets since my bad experience. I was still at The Tiki club. For some reason, the local girls still thought I had something special with

Lucky. Maybe because I wasn't working the streets. I don't know. Two of the girls were still staying at the condo with me. One day they showed up at the club with Star and Eva, saying they were just coming to share a cab home with me.

"Sharell, I didn't do good tonight, I need a ride home."

I was ready to leave anyway. I got off work, jumped in the cab with them. They sure looked rough.

"Where have y'all been looking like that?" They were all in cut-off jeans and t-shirts. Star was really looking rough. She was supposed to be so fly. I never saw Star looking like that. "Girl what have you been doing? Look at your hair." It was all over her head. She looked wild, she was talking so fast, like she was on speed. "What have y'all been doing?" Something wasn't right.

"We just come to ride home with you." We rode from Waikiki to the condo in silence. Every now and then Star would say something and everybody would break out laughing like it was so hilarious. I didn't get it. I tuned them out. I had things on my mind—what I needed to do about everything. I wasn't paying any attention but, soon as I got out the cab and the driver left, they started jumping on me.

"What's going on? What's going on?" I was yelling, trying to get some kind of answer. "Why are y'all doing this?" I was completely perplexed. They were calling me everything but a child of God. All four were hitting me, pulling me, tearing my clothes. I couldn't believe what was happening. Just at that time a security officer came by. He saw them jumping on me.

"Hey! What are y'all doing?" He was Hawaiian too. Kin to somebody there, they just played it off.

"Hey bro . . This bitch needs to be taught a lesson."

"Just don't hurt her too bad. You hear me?'

"Yeah, we gonna teach her a lesson is all."

"Yeah!" Star was saying so only I could hear. "This Black bitch need someone to teach her some rules. The way we do it here."

They were cursing and fighting. They dragged me to the elevator. I was fighting back all the way to the apartment. It was four girls and me. A couple of them was too flimsy to mess with me, they didn't count. I'm a country girl. They opened the apartment and dragged me in. Star went for my closets. She took out all my clothes, tearing them up while the others were keeping me busy. She put them in a bag, took them somewhere. Star was the biggest of them all. She was about 5'10". Thick boned. I'm just 5'2". I was so hurt that they wanted to beat me up. Why? I continued to fight back. The two that couldn't fight, gave up. So it was me and Eva. I was whipping her ass. Then Star took over. I was too tired and she was too big. I gave up fighting. I took my whipping and my bleeding like a prize fighter. I still couldn't figure out why Star wanted to do me in. But why? She was the main one, the rest followed her lead. I was blacking out. I know I was getting hit, but I couldn't feel the licks anymore. Just at that time, the security guard came up to my apartment. He was knocking on the door, but they wouldn't answer. He came in with his key. I knew what was going on, but I didn't feel it.

"Hey that's enough, that's enough. Y'all stop now."

He had this smirk on his face. My feelings were so hurt but I couldn't cry, I was too beat up to cry. They took their ghetto asses out the apartment and left the building. I couldn't believe what had happened. It was almost like I was watching it from a distance, in a movie. Then the truth set in. They were going to try to do me in. I couldn't believe it. I couldn't believe Star. I looked up to that bitch. I thought she was it. I wanted to be like her. Not now. Why was she was worried about me? I'm nothing. How could she resort to these extremes? She drove that Porsche. She had a home in Hawaii. She was jealous of little me. Why? I'm nobody. They would have killed me if they could have gotten away with it. I thought about how little they appreciated life. The guard came back. He stopped it. He shouldn't have let it happen.

I called Yvette. "Yvette, Yvette, girl they jumped on me."

"Who, Sharell, who?"

"Star, Eva, Traci and that punk ass Joanie. Yvette, I'm hurt. They were trying to really hurt me."

"Sharell, they came over to get your baby."

"What?" I screamed.

"Girl, yeah. They came over to get your baby. I asked them why they wanted your baby and where was you? They couldn't tell me anything."

"Why were they coming to get him?"

"They were saying some old shit. I told them he was sleep and you would be over to get him in the morning, then I shut the door.

I wasn't giving them bitches your baby. They didn't look right."

"Girl, thank you, thank you, Yvette. They were going to take me out if they could have gotten away with it."

"I guess they were. Why else did they want your baby?"

"To take him out, too? Girl, I'm hurt, my feelings are hurt. I looked up to Star. I need to go to the emergency. . . Why Vette? Why they wanted to do this to me?"

"Sharell, I don't know. I'm so sorry this happened to you."

"The security guard stopped it. He knew they were jumping on me and he let it happen, he let it happen, Vette. He told them not to hurt me too bad."

"They probably were gonna tell Lucky you ran off. Sharell, girl, what kind of bitches are they?" "I don't know, Vette. They're some treacherous bitches."

I called Lucky and told him what happened. I got a few stitches. He came the next day. Only he didn't do a damn thing to them bitches. He barely said anything to them. He acted like it wasn't shit. He was more worried about losing them bitches than he was about them wanting to take me and my baby out. I was dumbfounded, I was finished with him. I didn't want anything else to do with his ass again. He treated the game and those bitches better than me. Star and them bitches just looked at me like it was okay what they had done to me. Sneering at me. I'll get them bitches. If it's okay what they did to me, then I'll have to get them bitches myself. I never hated anyone, but I hated them bitches.

Lucky got them to move out of my apartment. He knew I would probably hurt somebody. He was trying to mend the fences with those whores, not with me. He's weak. Somehow I started seeing Lucky. I really saw him and his values and principals. All that player shit, rules, game wasn't nothing. Oh, it went for me, cause I was innocent, I was dependent, I needed someone that cared about me. I care about me. Hey, I'm by myself on these streets. I have no protection. That bullshit game is a lie. I planned on getting them back. I didn't want to be with Lucky anymore. I just wanted to get them more. I'll just wait.

C. Oakes

Chapter 10

My friend that owned the condo came back in town. I wanted to dodge him, but he saw the mess and came to the club for answers.

"Sharell, what happened to my condo? It looks like a war zone in there."

"Ron, I'm sorry about the place."

"Just tell me what happened, please."

I couldn't explain.

"Sharell, I never asked you for anything. I thought you were responsible enough to stay there."

I couldn't tell him the truth, that I had absolutely no control and my pimp used his walls for target practice.

"What happened to you? Look at you. Who did this to your face?"

There was sorrow in his eyes. I know I looked bad. I couldn't tell him my pimp's other women came up and beat the shit out of me. I didn't say anything. I just closed my eyes, waiting for the interrogation to be over.

"Look Sharell, I don't know what you're involved in, but it's best that you find another place to live."

He felt sorry for me, but as soon as he started talking again about the condo, he was mad all over. I really didn't feel like being chastised about it.

"Okay Ron, I'll be out by the end of the week. Ron, I'm so sorry, I really am, I hope you can forgive me someday."

He was a gentleman. "Sharell, leave the key in the office." He looked at me, scanning my face for the last time. I looked worst than I felt and I felt so, so bad.

He was short with me. "Take care."

Ron was gone. I never saw him again. I was sick, nauseated, I felt bad and terribly sorry for the condo. He entrusted me with his place. It was demolished. I packed what little I had left and moved to Waikiki into a weekly kitchenette that I had to rent. It was the same hotel where Yvette was staying. Joanie's punk ass was staying there, too. Traci stayed at Star's place.

Joanie was scared of me. She would see me coming out of my room going to work. She couldn't look at me. I stared at her but wouldn't say anything. I was disgusted with her. She knows she was wrong. Joanie was a pruney white girl with dentures. She made money and all, but she wasn't a fighter. She was homely. How did Star get this poor girl in this mess? I felt sorry for her, which was nuts.

I thought Traci was my friend. Traci was gorgeous. She was nice and I liked her. She acted as though she liked me too. She hurt my feelings. I watched her, I couldn't believe it. She was hitting me and pulling my hair, just like the rest of them. Star dragged her in this mess, too. How could she do that to me? We were friends. How could Star talk them into doing such an ugly thing. Somehow, I wasn't mad at Joanie and Traci. They were followers, they just wanted to fit in with Miss Star. To tell the truth, I looked up to Star, too. Star fell off the pedestal hard and took a few down with her.

Joanie and Traci both left Hawaii soon afterwards. They didn't say anything. There were no goodbyes, see ya laters or anything. Lucky tried to find them but there wasn't any word about them, not even a clue as to where they had gone. We didn't know what happened to them. I hoped that they were okay. They ran. They probably felt bad. Shoot, they were just following Star's treacherous ass.

Now Eva thought she was bad. Her momma was a queen, owned the club we hung out in. She was eyeing me wrong, talking to me wrong. Eva was evil. She wanted to be something special, but she wasn't. She didn't have enough guts to stop the bullshit. She missed her opportunity to be somebody and stop living off her momma's name. She should have stood up to Star. Now she's acting tough. Okay, she knows I was whipping that ass. I'll get her sooner or later.

To deal with Star was going to take some planning. Her turn will come. I'll stay around just to get her. Hate was growing in my core existence like an ugly weed. I was feeding on the hate that had blossomed inside me. I was playing in my mind, daydreaming about what I was going to do to Miss Star. I would get her back one day. I could see it. I was possessed with this hatred in my guts. All my clothes were gone. My jaw was messed up, still swollen. I had to get stitches in my head. My back had scars too from whatever they were hitting me with. I was pissed. I often daydreamed of really hurting Star. I was seeing it. I was feeling it. I was planning all kinds of scenarios. I was consumed by what I would do to Star. I'll wait. I'll just have to be patient for her slick ass.

It had been about a couple of weeks since the incident. Lucky ran around with Eva. He played her close. I guess he didn't worry too much about me and Yvette. We weren't going anywhere. I wasn't going anywhere cause my probation was violated and he knew it. Eva was with him more than Star. I couldn't understand that, I really didn't care. But I know Lucky had a thing for Star. Didn't she know that? He really liked her. Why was she worried about me? She wanted me out the picture. Lucky didn't show anything special for me. Well, as long as he didn't mess with me now, I was fine. Eva thought she was some bad shit now. Lucky spending all his time with her. She wasn't it. She was stupid.

Meanwhile, there was a huge wedge between me and Lucky. We didn't talk. He couldn't even look at me. He had nothing to say. Why not? How could he let this go. He's not a homey. This is not Oklahoma's style, and he's surely not a friend of mine.

Lucky came to my kitchenette with Eva. He was making his usual rounds. Eva was acting hostile as always, in my room, in my space.

He started walking toward the door. I was thinking, he's leaving her here? Is he crazy? "Sharell, I'm going to check on Yvette. I'll be back in a minute."

I just looked at him. He whispered the same to Eva. She was acting so in love. Like they're so tight. Lucky went upstairs to Yvette's room. Is he crazy leaving her here with me? I was watching Eva. She's walking around my room and talking shit like she's bad.

"Yeah, you got your ass kicked, didn't you?" In her heavy Hawaiian accent. "We fucked your black ass up."

I wasn't saying anything back to her, I was shrugging my shoulders and smiling. I was edging her on. She continued to talk bolder shit. I was hoping she do something stupid. I was thinking . . . Please give me a reason to kick your ass. Eva walked to the kitchen, then I got up from the sofa. That's right, Eva, come over here. I know she's not doing what I think. She's crazy. Eva was getting a knife from my sink. This is my chance. I'm going to whip her ass. I was thrilled. I started whipping Eva's ass. I beat her down. I held both her arms up so she couldn't move and just beat her in her face. I beat her nose. I beat both eyes closed. It felt so good. I was sitting on her chest, she couldn't move or do anything, I kept hitting her and hitting her with my closed fist. I didn't want to stop, but I knew I had better stop before I really hurt her.

"Now bitch. Now bitch. What you gonna do now? Do something now!"

I kept my hands around her wrist and dragged her to the phone so I could call Lucky.

"Lucky you better come down here, I done whipped this bitch's ass."

Lucky flew down the stairs.

"Lucky, she went and got the knife from my sink, I wasn't doing nothing, I wasn't saying anything to her. She just started talking shit, saying she was going to fuck me up. Then she got the knife from my sink."

He looked at Eva, then at me, then at Eva. Lucky couldn't believe it. I was thinking . . . Hey, I'm a dancer. I have dancer's muscles.

Lucky said in disbelief, "Sharell, I was just gone a few minutes."

Lucky picked Eva up and took her to the hospital.

Lucky had to inform the Hawaiians that Eva was hurt and had to be taken to the hospital. They weren't happy. He later called us at Yvette's place.

"It's bad news. Eva's nose is broken. Her eyes are bad, too."

He acted sad. He never acted sad or anything about me, when I got hurt by all four of those bitches. She lied and told her family that all of Lucky's women jumped on her.

I heard Yvette saying, "That's a lie. It was only Sharell."

"I know, I know." As he laughed, "Hell, that's what they did to Sharell."

"I know it is." Yvette agreed.

"I guess Eva was too embarrassed to say Sharell did all that to her," Lucky explained.

C. Oakes

"Did Eva say anything to you?" Yvette asked

"No, she's not talking to me. She wants me to do something to Sharell. That's not my style. Now, her folks are in it, keeping her away from me."

Yvette was looking at me, making concerned faces while she was on the phone still talking to Lucky. I kept quiet because I didn't have anything else to say about the bullshit. I felt the pleasure of sweet revenge. It soothed the hate in my heart for that girl. I didn't want it to come out that it was hard for me to stop hitting her. But it felt too good. She had done so much dirt to me, I was glad she was hurt.

"Well, I got some more bad news." Lucky said, still talking with Yvette, "We all had to leave Hawaii."

That wasn't bad news to me.

"We have five days to get out before anything happened to any of us," He said.

I was alright with that. Eva's mother had the connections to the Hawaiian mafia. I didn't care. It was time to leave. I was ready to leave. I had some bad things happen to me in this place. Hawaii's a nice place and all, but we stayed too long. We wore our welcome out. Guys started talking about Lucky. Causing conflicts. Bad things were happening to me. Don't get me wrong, I had a great time, I had fun. We just stayed too long. We were there a little over two years.

Lucky was making arrangements for us to leave. He got a hold of his flight contacts and we were getting tickets. He should have had enough money for everybody's ticket, but he didn't. One by one he was getting us out. Then it happened. Yvette got caught. She was working in Waikiki, trying to stay on the main drag, when Eva's brother, Larry, and some other family members, snatched her off the streets. They beat Yvette horribly. Yvette stayed in the hospital a week. She suffered temporary memory loss. She looked so helpless in there. I felt sorry for her. It was a trip, cause I did it. I'm the only one that whipped Eva's ass. Nobody else was around. She lied on them.

What really is a trip is Eva's brother that beat innocent Yvette, saw me and did nothing. He liked me. He's had a crush on me from the first day he'd laid eyes on me and I knew it. I was walking in Waikiki, he came upon me and didn't do a damn thing. He was startled. I believed he hoped he wouldn't see me. I don't think he truly believed I could have been involved in the first place. I was more quiet, introverted and had the most class. I was smaller. I didn't look the type. Now Yvette was loud and obnoxious. They thought for sure she was part of it. I always knew Larry liked me. I always liked him, too.

Just like Lucky never said anything to them bitches for jumping on me, he never said a word to me about beating Eva's ass. He acted like it didn't happen. But I was last on the totem pole. He got everybody out of Hawaii before me. I did tell him that I saw Eva's brother walking down the street. He saw me too and didn't do anything. Lucky probably knew all the time that Eva's brother, Larry, had a crush on me. Why else could I stay in Hawaii. Maybe Lucky just didn't give a damn about what happened to me. I continued to work at the club. I took a cab everywhere I needed to go. It was so ironic. Here I am, in Hawaii, working every day.

Lucky was like a distant associate. I didn't have anything to say to him, just what was needed to get by. This whole relationship was getting old. We never had a real passion in the first place. I just looked at him as a friend. I wanted to learn how to make money. Real money. He was a business man and I wanted him to teach me things. He never went over the top. He was too involved in the pimp game. Anyway, I was asking for it, wanting to learn worldly things, money, travel. He taught me alright. He taught me that I didn't want this life. I felt trapped. I'm scared to go home. I don't know what I'm facing there. I don't want to go to jail. I'm not a criminal, I did some juvenile stuff when I was a little too old. I was already 18 when I stole expensive perfume in the department store, it was over $25, in Oklahoma, that's grand larceny, plus all Mike's stuff ended up on my record, like I did some of that shit. Oklahoma is so unforgiving. You will go to the penitentiary in that state.

Now, there was something else that was on the back of my mind, really worrying me to death. I couldn't shake it. I was still getting nauseated. It was a little over a month since I was jumped. I'm still getting sick. I thought I was hurt why I was so sick. Don't let it be what I'm thinking. Now my breast is looking perky. Really perky. I'm afraid it might be something else. Please tell me it's not so. I couldn't be pregnant, not right now. Lucky is not

C. Oakes

the parental type. He's not even close to his kids he has now.

Lucky wasn't looking like himself. He looked like a street bum. He hadn't brushed his teeth. His hair was uncombed. He looked bad. He stayed at the room with me most nights, sleeping on the sofa. We still had nothing to talk about.

Local women kept my son, I was ready to leave. Lucky wanted to take care of some things first. He walked into Eva's momma's club on Hotel street loaded with Asian stars, knives and pure insanity. Lucky held up the club and started whipping Eva's brother, Larry. He wasn't leaving Oahu until he set everything straight. Plus his name was on the line. They jumping on Yvette like that, really hurting her. He is suppose to be protection. I didn't see it but I heard about it. Lucky told everybody not to move and went after Larry. Whenever someone tried to jump in he'd throw a star or knife, barely missing them, then gave a warning. "Next one's gonna get you. Nobody else moved." Then he continued to beat Larry. I asked Lucky about what happened, he told me God told him to go in there and get Larry. He said he had to do it. He was serious. He's crazy!

There I was still working at the club in Waikiki. After Lucky whipped Larry, I was feeling a little more at ease about being there. I stopped taking the taxi everywhere. Then one day I was walking down the street and a taxi pulled up, stopped in front of me and Eva jumped out. I know she's not coming by herself, without some help. Eva knows she can't whip me, what is she doing? I stopped in my steps and watched her. She went to the police car parked behind the cab and the officer gave her something, it looked like a gun. She put it in her pocket and started walking toward me.

"Well Lord, I guess it's my time to go. What about my kid? What is going to happen to him?

She continued to walk toward me. I was ready for whatever was going to happen to me. She was going to shoot me. This day, I was going to die. She came closer and pulled it out. It was a billy club. It had a black leather handle with a strap that was wrapped around her wrist. She still looked bad. Her nose was wrapped up and she still had two black eyes. Eva raised her hand to hit me with the solid lead, I caught her arm so she couldn't come down hard on me. She nicked my eyebrow. It bled bad. Blood was streaming down my face. She was happy with that. The cop came and took the billy club from her.

"That's enough, that's enough."

She got back in the cab and left. I thought I had a bad wound. Blood was flowing everywhere. I jumped in the first cab I could see and went to my room. Lucky was there, bruting.

"What happened to you?"

"A policeman gave Eva a billy club and she hit me with it."

Lucky came over to look at it. He washed my face, studying the area.

"Sharell, it's not bad, it's just a nick."

I looked and couldn't believe a nick bled like that. It was just a scratch, I was so relieved. I thought I would need more stitches. At the least, I would have a bad scar. But it's a nick.

"Sharell, get packed. I'll get the baby. Let's go."

Chapter 11

When I arrived in Anchorage, AK, it was daylight. Yvette and the others were already there. Anchorage was alright, I guess. It looked dry and brown. The weather was cool. Traffic was minimum. It was a brown country town. The streets, roadways and neighborhoods were all brown. A straight contrast from beautiful Hawaii, with the flowers and all. It seemed as though the town was asleep. It was quiet. We passed by some restaurants. They had deer burgers signs, elk burgers; man, they even had bear burgers listed on the building. This is going to be a trip living here. I sure need to buy some warmer clothes for me and Matt.

We arrived at this gray, block looking building and got out.

"Where's everybody?"

"They all stay here, let's see. Yvette's on the third floor. Renee's here, she's right down the hall from your room."

"She is, man it's been a while since I saw her."

"Eva and Star are staying in Hawaii."

I just looked at him. Like I really cared about what they're doing.

"I have a reservation for you. Go ahead and check in. Get some rest. You'll see everybody soon enough."

I unpacked and got comfortable in my little hotel apartment. This was an apartment building that rented by the week. It was an okay spot. Mostly working girls and construction workers stayed at the hotel. I was excited about being there.

I played with my son, Matt. He's so big now. He's almost 4 years old.

"How would you like a little sister or brother. Would you like that, baby." I whispered and I kissed and hugged him over and over. I was excited about having a baby. I started singing. . ."Momma's gonna have a baby. Momma's gonna have a baby." I always wanted two children before I turn 25 years old. I was getting close. By the time I have this baby, I'll be 25, lets see. . .in six months. I hadn't told anybody about my pregnancy. It was our little secret. I know Lucky isn't going to be happy. He's not the parental type. In fact, I don't think he likes kids. But he's a smart man. His family are all educators. My baby would have good genes and I can raise my own baby.

There was a knock on my door. "Who is it?"

"Girl open this door." There was Yvette and Leon, her son. We hugged. "Lucky finally got you out of that place. I know you're glad."

"Yeah, it was good for a minute. How's the money here?"

"It's good. I work at the Great Alaskan Bush Company."

"What? What they mean by Bush company? I was laughing. "What kind of place is that?"

"It's a club. Sharell, you're gonna love it. You gonna love Alaska. It's so much money here. There's the fishermen's money, the oil fields money, and the guys that just live here, they all got money. If you live here you make money. You get money every year from taxes for just living in Alaska."

"What?"

"Yeah, money from oil taxes."

"For real?"

"Girlfriend, this place is rich. Just wait till you see what I'm talking about."

"Are there a lot of girls working here?"

"Not like it is in Seattle. Come on, put some clothes on and I'll take you out to eat."

"Okay." I grabbed something for me and Matt to put on and we were out the door. I know Matt was glad to see his buddy, Leon. They were in their own little world, Leon showing his new car. We were out the apartment to the front desk, there was a cab phone that we just picked up to call a taxi, which one was already waiting out front.

We arrived at this soul food restaurant. It was down home food. There was some characters in there, too. This one guy was a numbers runner. They asked us for our birthdays so they could play our numbers. We played our birthdays, too. They said we should play since we never played before, said it was beginners luck and we would probably win. I was looking at the menu, cabbage, corn, greens, meatloaf, mashed potatoes, roast, fried chicken, fried catfish, macaroni and cheese, neckbones, everything. Gosh, it's been a while since I've eaten like that. I was hungry, too.

"Yvette, where do the babies stay?"

"I take Leon to this old lady. Miss Frances. What time is it?"

"About 7 p.m."

"We need to take the kids to her and then we'll go to the club." We ate, sat around a while, talked to the old school guys. I was amazed that blacks were there and had been there so long. These people reminded me of the people in Seattle. They're not prejudice. They're like real folks.

Ms. Frances was a dark skinned, older lady with lots of kids at her place. She kept mostly dancers or working girls' kids. They didn't mind going there. Toys were everywhere. Ms. Frances was an old player and understood somebody responsible had to take care of the kids. She didn't asked questions or give any accusing looks, never was she condemning. She knew she had an important job, and she wasn't going to get any praise, just pay. Shoot, some of the kids had been there for weeks at a time. But, the kids were alright, they ate, diapers were changed, they were loved. If any got sick, she would nurse them or get word to the mommas. The mommies would guiltily compensate her righteously. The kids were alright at Ms. Frances house.

Soon, we were finally at the Bush Company. It seemed a lot bigger inside than it did on the outside. It was sectioned off in layers. The stage was it. It had the biggest and longest runway I've ever worked. It was classy. Big lights lined the whole stage. There were colored ceiling lights, smoke machines, bubbles and a DJ. The DJ was cool. He was charismatic, fun and sexy. He had as much fun as the customers. Girls danced two songs. They would give their song list to the DJ before their set, or let the DJ do his thang. He made money, too. Oh, he made big time money for that extra push he gave for the dancers that were good tippers.

The chairs were all covered in animal skinned print. Tables seated four and the layers gave you a little privacy at the top section. Big Tony was the waitress. She was the most smooth, sophisticated waitress I'd ever seen in my life. Big Tony was really slick. Big Tony was too slick. She could do some tricks with changing out money.

They hired me right away. Miss Cox was the owner. She gave me the rules, which were so cool. They only wanted half on the drinks, we were expected to get drinks or champagne. These drinks had real alcohol. Other places had only sodas, except for the champagne. The champagne was half gone when it arrived at the tables, because it had to spray everywhere, to make the presentation. We would scream with excitement, you know, to make it a celebration. When we had enough to drink, we just informed the bar to cut us off, give us water, juice or soda. Shoot, you can't make any money passed out.

There was a tiny kitchen that was leased to an Asian couple. They cooked some really good stuff. I never knew what to order. I'd just say, "Hook me up." They fixed me up good, too.

Downstairs was the dressing room. It was huge. There were showers and makeup mirrors that were lit up like the stage—lockers for all the dancers—just get one and lock up your things. Take your stuff home every night. Man, this was great. We got dressed and went to the floor. Yvette introduced me to the DJ. He asked for a list of songs that I liked, just in case I couldn't make it to the DJ booth before my set.

"Girl, my customer just walked in the door. I got to go. When do you dance?"

"I'm way down on the list."

"Well, get you a drink, they'll give you two drinks to loosen up."

"What?"

"Yeah, that's David, he's Miss Cox's son. Tell him you want a drink and introduce yourself." I went to the bar and sat, waiting on David, but I didn't have a chance to introduce myself. This guy came over and offered to buy me a drink and asked if I table danced. He asked me to join him at his table. Now, this was too easy. That night I made over $300—well, close to $400. I was impressed.

"Hey, Yvette, when does this place close?"

"It doesn't."

"Danggggg."

"Just leave when you want. Girl, we can go on dates and come back to work."

"What? You got to be kidding."

"No, I'm serious, we can do what we want here. It's wide open. You ready to go?"

"Yeah, I'm tired. Okay, let's get dressed." We got dressed,

talked about our customers—how much they spent—then headed out the door.

"Girl what time is it?"

"It's four in the morning."

"Yvette, it's still daylight." Yvette started laughing.

"Ain't this a trip. This is Alaska. Some people put aluminum foil on their windows to keep the daylight out."

"How long is it like this, I mean, how long do daylight last?"

"All summer."

I had heard about Alaska, but never gave it any real credibility, as far as six months of daylight in the summer, but it's true. You would never know it was still daylight outside because it was so dark in the club. I think the windows were painted black. We walked across the street while talking with other dancers about the night, how much money we made, who were the really big spenders. The dancers were so nice and ready to help me by giving me their advice—the do's and don'ts of Anchorage, Alaska. These were the classiest dancers I've ever met. We got us some food to go, then grabbed a cab. We picked up our babies and went home. I was tired.

The next day, I couldn't wait to get back to the Bush Company. I liked that place. I was going to work that stage. The stage had built-in tables, looked like a shelf, that was big enough for drinks, and big enough for me to sit on, just under the lights. Some customers wanted to sit at the stage and tip the girls that gave them an extra peek or special show. They stick money in their g-strings or just threw it on stage. I was sitting on the stage talking to a group of guys. They were taking turns buying me $25 drinks. I hadn't had a chance to pull one from the stage, yet. I needed to see who I wanted. Who would spend the most on me. So, I was there just entertaining the group, my drink was a pretty flaming drink. I was there blowing out the fire, doing my drink presentation thing, when one of the guys in the group went barreling through the crowd. People were tumbling like bowling pens. Before I could react in any fashion, he had run from the stage, toward the door. He had knocked down everybody in his path, just like he was the bowling ball. I was sitting on the table, with my back to the stage. Everybody was moving by then, getting out of the way or up from the floor. Then I looked behind me, a dancer was there with two gigantic boa constrictor snakes rapped around her from head to toe. You couldn't see her, you only saw the snakes. In two steps, I was out of there, stepping on heads and shoulders. I don't know how I got there, but I ended up in the top section of the Bush Company, jumping up and down.

I have a natural fear of snakes. I was so worked up that I couldn't dance the rest of the night. I had the jitters. After that day, I stayed off the tables at the stage. In the dark, the animal skinned chairs looked like snakes. On top of that, customers started bringing their pet snakes. I would dance for a guy, then a snake would crawl out of his pocket, or I'd walk up to a customer and a damn snake would be wrapped around his neck. I was a nervous wreck. It got out of control. That dancer with the snakes had snake feeding parties. People went to her house when it was time to feed the snakes, so they could watch the snakes swallow poor little mice. She laughingly said, "mice scream like a woman." Sick! Miss Cox finally had to ban all pet snakes from the Bush Company. They were out of control.

I sure liked the Bush Company, though. Miss Cox had another son, Jack. He was my favorite. Jack was so cool, sweet, charming and fine. He was dating one of the dancers. She was an airline stewardess. In fact, most of the girls working at the Bush, had other professions. They were students and teachers that worked only in the summer, from every where, or military mommies that needed extra money and, of course, us working girls. What impressed me about the club was there were so many regular professionals—an attorney, dancing on the side. There were a couple of girls whose parents were managing their careers. I thought about my mom, she would have managed my career really good if she was in this type of business. But, naw. . .that's really daydreaming. These ladies were older, too. They didn't look it but many were in there forties. I found out right then and there, that you can look good as long as you exercise and don't gain weight. These ladies were beautiful, classy, professional, and skinny.

There was so much cocaine, we never had to buy it. Customers would bring it to us. It was the good, pure stuff. Customers would bring us king crab, salmon, coke, smoke, everything. I had gotten so spoiled at the Bush company, I stopped dancing on stage. The girls would pay me $50 for my turn. Sometimes we only

C. Oakes

danced a couple of times a night, cause everybody had to have a turn. Plus, these girls had real shows—Las Vegas style shows. I sold my turn. Sometimes I wouldn't dance on stage for weeks at a time. I was getting big. I was showing. Shoot, I made my money on the floor. Anyway, I was feeling a little self-conscious because my stomach was getting pudgy. Miss Cox would look at me smiling.

"Sharell, I hadn't seen you on stage in a while. You need to get on stage tonight." I turned that stage out. I knew how to get the place going. The DJ was behind the DJ booth, throwing his clothes off, too. He's so crazy.

I was at the Bush company only about four months. I couldn't hide my stomach anymore. It was obvious. I think Lucky knew for a while, but we never discussed it. We had really lost our friendship in Hawaii. I didn't talk to him much anymore, just to say what I needed to say when I needed to say it. He would come over and try to be friendly, but I didn't know how to be friends with him—a traitor. That's one thing about me, I'm loyal to a fault. You can't buy trust. I was his homey. I guess everybody isn't like me.

I didn't know how I was going to get out of this life. . .so I just continued doing what I was doing—in the fast life. I didn't want to think about important stuff, like my future. But, I would find myself walking down the street and wondering how in the world did I end up here, at the bottom like this. I was suppose to be better. I was raised good. I was popular, smart. What happened to me. It happened so fast, my life was wasted. Now I was lost... out of touch with reality, myself, my family. . .I never looked at myself. I didn't know how to get back . .to the real world. My values were gone. I didn't think twice about turning a trick. That was nothing to me now. What was I doing? Anyway, nobody would want a woman like me. After everything I've done, who would want me? Sometimes I would think about God. I believed He still cared about me. I believed he loved me. I was told that all my life, but I never prayed. What was I suppose to say?

"Sharell, I'm sending you to Seattle till after the baby."

"Umh . . . Okay. When do I leave?"

"When do you want to leave? You need to get out of here. Come back after the baby." I knew it was best. I wanted a healthy baby, plus it didn't look good dancing with a big stomach.

Sandy picked me up at the airport. She was so nice. We got along good. She worked when she wanted something for herself or the kids. Sandy had a sugar daddy that gave her money, real money. He paid all her bills and sent her and her kids on a vacation every year. Plus, he paid her way in a poker tournament every year. It cost ten grand to buy in. I thought that was crazy, no way in the world would I put ten grand in a pot on a poker tournament. Well, she had a shot at winning just like anybody else. But, Sandy was too damn animated. She would get mad when somebody played stupid, then win. Ahhhh man, that would just get her cussing, throwing cards. She'd leave the poker room. But she would go every year to the Texas Hold'em tournament in Las Vegas, faithfully.

I couldn't get a job in Seattle because of my pregnancy. I wasn't going to any of the shady places around either, plus, Sandy wasn't going to take me to any and there were a few in the Seattle area.

Sandy said this Highway 99 killer was still making his mark in the Seattle metro-plex area. It's been a few years now. I guess it's starting to get some news coverage. It was like a sad shadow over the city. Everybody was paying close attention. They found another body lying near Sea-Tac, close to some river. Most of the girls that were killed worked on Highway 99. They say it must be a cop because the girls were going with the killer. So it must be a cop. . .why else would so many girls go with this guy and nobody sees anything. That is so strange, because everybody was watching each other's back, taking down license plate numbers, keeping drivers license until the girl comes back, but still another girl was found dead.

"Sharell, you need to do something to make you some money. I'm going to show you how to play poker." I was excited then. "I'm taking you with me to the Roadhouse tonight. It's down the street, in Puyallup."

"Okay." I wanted to learn poker. I'm always ready to learn something new. We went to the Roadhouse and everybody was really nice. They were all Sandy's friends, she would have kicked ass if they hadn't been nice to me and they knew it. Sandy wasn't a little girl, she was big. She wasn't fat or anything, she was a good

5 ft. 10 or 11 inches. Thick bone. Sandy was really good looking, blond and didn't take any mess from anybody, with a heart good as gold.

They started me off at the quarter table. I was given a cheat sheet that showed all the different hands in poker, what won. I'd look and play. One thing about it, they didn't show me any mercy in the quarter game. That game was vicious. With the cheat sheet, win or lose. I learned very fast. I really liked that Texas hold'em game. We played other games, too. Let's see, omaha, kick, five and seven card stud. I found a new love. Sometimes I'd come out of there with fifty or sixty dollars. That wasn't bad for a beginner with a five dollar buy in.

Everybody knew Sandy's lifestyle. They knew she was with Lucky and he's a pimp. They put it together that I was having Lucky's baby. They were cool. I don't believe there are many places like this around anywhere. The ladies were bringing me gifts and hand-me-downs for my baby. I got all kind of furniture and accessories. I got everything for a baby. They were great. They were so excited about my baby. I was amazed by their generosity. It was 1980, I think I was the only black person in Puyallup, WA. (Well, not really, there were a few of us around). But, I loved Puyallup. It was great.

Chapter 12

Lucky was there when I had my new son. I called him my blue bird because he was born with purple lips. He was beautiful. I named him Ronnie. Matt and Ronnie were my reasons. I knew deep in my heart, things had to change. I couldn't see a future down the road. Nothing. I needed a home for my children. I wanted a normal home, with friends and a neighborhood. Shoot, I wanted to go to PTA meetings.

Sometimes you just have to wait for the right circumstances. Thankfully, I still had my family, especially my mom who loved me. There's something about mothers, they get those knowing feelings—always know things at the right time. If they don't know, then, they'll find out. My mom sent my sister Carol to see about me. I was so happy to see her. She was having a baby herself. Way too far along to be riding on the greyhound bus for 48 hours. But, there she was, in Pullayup to see about me and our new baby. I didn't know it then, but she was the flashlight to my escape route.

"Hey Sis, let me see my little nephew. Girl he's so pretty."

"Thanks. Girl, Momma is something else sending you to see about me."

"Yeah, you know Momma ain't feeling it, you way up here having a baby by yourself."

"Carol, I really appreciate you coming like this. Why don't you stay here with me. Live out here, I'm telling you girl, it's nice in Washington. It's green year round. People here are cool. Not like Oklahoma, white folks here are real."

"Naw girl, I can't leave my momma. Sharell, Momma told me to bring Matt back with me."

"She what?"

"Uh . . she told me, to bring Matt home with me, and that's what I'm going to do. You know Momma ain't well worrying about you and Matt, way up here. So, I'll take Matt back to Oklahoma with me, okay. Now, all Momma has to worry about is you and little Ronnie." She was kissing him and hugging him carefully.

"Carol, you are so crazy."

"I know."

"What are you having?"

"I'm having a girl."

"You got a name for her yet?"

"Erica."

"You're just naming her after Erica Kann on the soaps."

"I know. She is bad, isn't she. That's the way my baby is going to be. Just like Erica."

"Be careful, you might get it."

"Honey, this is my Erica. She's going to be bad, too."

Carol had a son, Quincy, when Matt was two years old. This was her second child, too.

"You look so pretty, Carol, pregnant. How long are you staying?"

"Girl, I got to get back, I wasn't suppose to leave town, pregnant like this. My doctor will have a cow if he knew I was in Washington State. So, I'll stay a few days, but I got to get back."

"Well, let me enjoy you while you're here." I did appreciate my sister coming to see about me. I was glad to send Matt home to Momma, too. He'll be better off there. Now, it's just me and Ronnie for a while.

I couldn't go home broke. I was stashing money here and there. I started sending my money to my momma, just in case Lucky started snooping around and found my stash. He was always finding somebody's stash. My jewelry came up missing. Things Mike had given me were gone. I put it in a safe place, so I thought. I hate to think Lucky took my jewelry. But my pieces were gone. Would he really steal from me? He's the only one that's coming to my mind, and in my business, you trust your gut. Anyway, Lucky started looking bad, not taking care of himself—he looked rough.

Lucky came with a new trick called freebasing. He was smoking cocaine now, cooking it with ether then scraping it off a mirror to smoke. The first time I smoked it, it was such a rush. Man, that first hit was something else, then I wanted sex. That was the only time I wanted Lucky. Every night we would get high on freebasing or I would get high with Lucky then go to work. I think Lucky was trying to string everybody out. That's all we did. He started selling his guns, paintings, and little by little things were gone or missing.

C. Oakes

Star's coming to Seattle.

"Lucky, why is she coming here. I hate her."

"Star's not doing well. I have to bring her here."

I just walked off. All the bullshit I went through in Hawaii was resurfacing. I wanted her to pay for my clothes, that I never got back. No way was Lucky going to spend the kind of money I had on clothes. Now, this is my chance to get this bitch. I was getting her and she didn't have anybody to help her do her evil shit here. All I could think about was how venomous she was. Hateful! I use to think Star was it, I looked up to that girl and she did me like that, I was consumed with revenge.

The day Star arrived, I had played it all out in my mind— exactly what, how, when, everything. I was going to get her. I was at the house in the garage, doing laundry, when they pulled up from the airport. Lucky got out of the car first. Slowly the other side opened and Star got out. She looked different. I went to the window to get a better look. Daaaamn, she looked bad. Her hair was in two braided ponytails. She didn't have that Star attitude. I just watched for a while. They were coming in the house. I continued to wash clothes.

Oh, I hate Star. I never knew hate like this before. It had festered and had grown worst. I was feeding it with my mind, body, and soul. I imagined beating her down, stomping her face in the ground. They call that premeditated, cause I was meditating on getting her and it felt good just thinking about it. I was nervous to get too close to her. I might attack. She was getting closer. Then I got a real good look. What happened to Star. Daaaamn, Star's front teeth were gone. Daaaamn, she looked like shit, sad, pitiful all in one. That hate that consumed me, disappeared. I felt sorry for Star. She looked completely horrible.

I was always told, "Revenge is mine, saith the Lord." I never knew what that meant before this day. Every bit of hate I had for that girl flew out the window, it was gone. There was nothing I could do to Star worse than this, with her conniving ass. Star had a beautiful smile, now it's gone. I guess I would eventually get more clothes but losing your original, just for you, teeth. Man! Star had a beautiful set of pearly whites.

"Girl, what happened to you? What happened to your teeth?"

"Oh, I got in a fight with a trick."

"Damn, Star he knocked your teeth out?"

I was thinking to myself, "That's why I don't fight those tricks." That wasn't the only thing wrong, she had track marks on her arms. I guess the grass wasn't green at Star's house after all. Who would have thought, she was a junkie. Damn. I felt sorry for Star. I felt genuinely bad for her. In a blink of an eye, it was gone. That ugly dreary hate for Star was gone. Amazing, I thought, this is truly amazing. I can't describe the depth of hate I had inside me, growing every day. I didn't realize how much I lost despising Star until I truly forgave her. I mean I was losing myself in this darkness. I was thriving on it. Role playing different scenarios in my mind, different tactics of vengeance. I never want to feel like that again. Poor Star. Man, He got her back.

It was time to go back to the Bush company. I was ready. Me and my little man were leaving for the Alaskan wilderness. Lucky and Star were leaving later.

"Sharell girl, I'm so glad you are back. I've been getting this money by myself. Let me see your little man. You named him Ronnie. Why you name him Ronnie?" Yvette had my baby, dancing around, kissing him. She was glad to see us.

"I don't know."

"He's gorgeous."

"Thanks."

"What does Lucky think?"

"I don't know. Girl, this is my baby."

"Lucky isn't the same is he."

"Nooo. He's gone down."

"Sharell, I met somebody else."

"You are lying."

"No I'm not. Lucky don't have anything. I'm tired of working and not getting anything for it. I got to look out for me and Leon. He use to be doing things all the time, buying stuff, now I don't know what he's doing."

"Freebasing. That's all he wants to do. Have you tried it yet?"

"Girl, yeah. Lucky was here two weeks ago. I got so high."

"You like it?"

"Yeah. Up here, they're not using that ether anymore to cook it."

"What do they use?"

"Soda."

"What? Regular baking soda?"

"They cook it to a rock and smoke it like that. It's better, I'll show you."

"Wait till you see these apartments. Yours is in the next building from mine." Yvette had found some beautiful apartments. She was already settled and had my apartment waiting for me. Yvette found the hookup for used furniture. She had my phone installed.

"Yvette, girl, you did good."

"Ain't these nice. I love it."

"What are those things in front of the driveway?"

"That's to plug up your car in the winter."

"Really!"

"In Alaska you have to keep your car plugged up so it won't freeze in the winter. You hook it to the battery."

"Oh! Okay. I guess I'll hook up my car when I get one." We laughed because a car wasn't feasible for us in Anchorage.

There were four apartments to an building. The complex was a huge stone rock design. There were about six complexes in our area. They had full length mirror walls on one side in the front room and a mirrored wall in the bedroom. The closets were mirrored. It made the apartments really look big. A huge gas fire place, huge rooms, nice. There was a little club across the street, Scotty's Place. It stayed opened all night. Scotty owned the apartments, too.

Everybody at the Bush company seemed happy to see me. I was glad to be back. I needed to work to get rid of my baby fat, and all. These ladies were my friends.

"Girl, it's about time you come back."

"Hi, Fantasy." She was the prettiest girl in the club. She was one of the dancers whose parents managed her career. Fantasy and I went to open other clubs from time to time.

"We missed you." She gave me a big hug. "What did you have?"

" A boy, I brought pictures. Seeeeeeee."

"That's nice. He's pretty. Hey girl, you want to come to

Fairbanks with me. We're opening a club up there. The Lonely Lady. Me, Fat Tony and Vicki are going, they're flying us out on a private plane. Cool uh."

"The Lonely Lady. What kind of name is that?" Fantasy just laughed.

"You can make lots of money. There's not a club in Fairbanks at all. We'll make all the money. Well, let me know."

"Okay, thanks for the invite, I'll let you know."

My cousin, Diana moved to Alaska. Boy was I happy to see her. Now, this was starting to feel like a real home. Someone that really knew me was here, living in my city. My family knew I was a dancer. There was this underlying disappointment, but nobody ever talked about it. I guess they had confidence that sooner or later, I'll get my damn senses. Diana was absolutely beautiful. She had the kind of beauty that stopped traffic. Everybody thought she was my mother's daughter. With Diana in Anchorage, I felt better. We were really close, like sisters. Just to have her here, in Anchorage meant everything to me. Finally, my family was closer. Diana was a military wife. She would invite me to her house for perfect dinners. I never had anybody to bring with me except Ronnie, of course.

"Diana, would you help me take this weave out?"

Diana has long beautiful hair. "Take your weave out? Yeah, I guess. What do you want me to do?"

"Just cut the string where it's sewn in."

"Okay. Girl, why do you put this stuff in your head?"

"I want some hair. Diana, I feel so cheated, everybody in our family has long pretty hair but me."

"Ah, Sharell, but you got the looks and you're smart, look how pretty you are. You don't need hair."

"Girl, yes I do. All men care about is hair, they don't care about what you look like, just as long as you got a body and hair. I'm not lying, girl, it's a shame. Your face, your brains, that doesn't matter. All you need is hair and a body."

"Sharell, now."

" That's right, the longer the hair the more money. You got to know how to throw it around. You know. You got to slang it right."

"So, you're just going to sew you some hair on."

C. Oakes

"Yep."

"Honey, it's so tangled. How is this stuff in here?"

"Just cut the string."

"I'm trying, I can't see the string. Sharell, what is this stuff in your head. It's too messy. I can't see how to take it out."

"Girl, why are you crying?"

"I can't take this stuff out. It's a mess." Diana was laughing and crying at the same time. I cracked up at her crying about it.

"Diana, that's alright. I'll get it out, girl, don't worry about it. It's okay. I do this all the time. Give me a hug. I got to take Ronnie to the sitter before it gets too late. Cuz, you are something else. Love ya." Diana is something else. She loves me. Crying like that cause she couldn't take my weave out. Man, she's funny. I left with half my weave hanging from my head.

Star was Lucky's project. He truly cared for her and wanted to see her better. I think he felt guilty about her. I heard she lost her Porsche and house in Hawaii. He never felt guilty about me. He always seemed mad at me. I had nothing. Trusted his ass across country to get some business started, make some money. It wasn't Lucky's fault Star was a junkie. She was insecure. I don't know why she was so damn insecure. Star was beautiful, had a good conversation. She had an excellent conversation. She talked really fast and she's a good hustler. Star had good game. She liked the needle was all. Lucky was just an excuse for her to be a junkie. At the club, Star would be in the corner, passed out. Miss Cox would ask me to call Lucky to get her. Lucky finally sent Star back to Hawaii. I hope she's alright.

I was smoking rock cocaine left and right. Every night I smoked cocaine. This was the new high. I started leaving my baby at Miss Frances 2 or 3 days at a time. He was growing so fast. Ronnie was about six months old. He was so quick that I had to buy a baby leash to tie his leg to the coffee table. That way he'd have a smaller perimeter to travel. Then, I could do some cleaning. I put all his toys close to him, in reach. He would climb out of a play pin. He was fast. I told Miss Frances about the leash. Boy was she glad. I brought a baby leash for her house.

The more I smoked cocaine, the more I didn't want to be in the club. I started turning more tricks. Quicker money. The customers offered so much money to leave with them, they wanted to take the party outside for more privacy. They'd give you what you made in a night to leave with them. Plus, everybody, I mean, all the customers were smoking coke. Cocaine was the culture. We would get their money, their coke and go back to work. It started to be so expected, they knew what to bring, plenty money and have plenty of cocaine. I never smoked it with the customers. That wasn't slick. It made you look bad to the other players. They'd talk about you. Call you a strawberry. That was the nickname for girls that got paid with drugs. Plus, you never wanted to get too high with them. You have to keep your guards up, no matter what precautions you made, keep your guards up. Couldn't get too relaxed, anything could happen. So you had to keep it business. It's all business. So, I would just take some coke home with me. Shoot, they had bags of the stuff.

"Sharell, I got this fisherman, girl, with thousands on him. He wants a date. You want to go with me?

"Hell yeah, how much is he paying?"

"He said two hundred a piece."

"I hope he don't think we're staying all night for that."

"No girl, you know I got that covered. Okay. Let me tell Yvette.

"Yvette, I'm going with Shelia on this date."

"Wait, let me see who you're leaving with."

"That guy by the bar."

"I'm going to say hi real fast, so I can get a good look, before you leave."

"Okay."

Shelia and I were in a cab with the fisherman. He had plenty of money on him. His wallet was about three inches thick of hundreds with a rubber band around it. We took the fisherman to the hotel that we used for dates. He was a nice, easy trick. Shelia wanted to take his money. I knew I wasn't any good at stealing. I can usually ask for more money than I could steal, but I was game. I wanted to be slick and beat the trick for a few grand. I guess about five or six grand was in his wallet. For some reason, people think I'm really slick, but I'm not. I'm just a country girl, far away from home.

His wallet was in his pants, on the floor, by his head. There I was sitting on his face. Blocking his vision. He couldn't see a

C. Oakes

thing. I was reaching for the wallet. Slowly, reaching, quietly, taking my time not to disturb him. I had the wallet. I had the wallet. Now get the money. Quietly, get it out and put the wallet back in the pocket. Shelia was working his bottom half. He was totally distracted. I had his face covered up. He couldn't see what I was doing. I had it. I had the money. Now slowly put the wallet back in the pocket. I raised the money up so Shelia could see I had it. I looked at her. I motioned my lips, "I got the money." The role was thick. Before I could take another breath, before I could blink my eyes, Shelia snatched the bank roll out my hand and ran out the door. I was stuck. I couldn't believe this bitch. She took the money and ran out the door. The trick was drunk with sex, he didn't know what was happening.

"What's going on?"

"I don't know. She just ran out the door." We got up, he started checking everything. My money is gone.

"What?"

"My money is gone from my wallet." He grabbed his things and ran after her, but she was long gone.

"How well do you know her?"

"Hey, I just met you both. She asked me to join you and her. She took your money and I'm not getting anything. I was counting on that—I left work." He walked around, looking on the floor, in case some fell from her grasp.

"Well, don't worry about it. It's more where that came from." These tricks, he'll tell that story over and over again to his buddies. Then the trick took off his belt and paid me two hundred dollars, plus cab to get back to the club.

Yvette thought that it was funny. "Girl, she just snatched it out your hands and ran out the door like that. That's why I don't do anything with anybody, except with you or somebody I really have to know good, cause these bitches will get you killed."

I never saw that snake, Shelia again. She was long gone. That ate me up for weeks. After that, I made sure I knew who I was working with, I mean, the kind of person I was working with, and I never tried to steal from another trick. He could have turned on me. What if he thought I was in on it and took that mess out on me, I could have been in trouble—deep shit. She ran out and left me like that. That was dangerous.

Yvette, really was gone. She choose another guy, broke Lucky's heart. I found out she was legally married to Lucky. That was a shocker. I would have thought he'd be married to Sandy before Yvette, he was so crazy about white girls, you'd think he'd be married to one of them, but Yvette, man. Yvette had enough of Lucky. I think he was spread too thin for her anyway. I was scared to leave. I had a case in Oklahoma to deal with, man, what if I got with somebody that beat me like Mike did, I wasn't going anywhere, not for a while.

Lucky opened another after hours club. It was in an old house. It didn't have the class that was in Hawaii. The place in Hawaii looked like a club. This was just an old house. Lucky wasn't the same. He use to have a quiet mystique about him, now he looked like a "has been" pimp. Old. You know, the type that talked about the old glory days. Lived on his reputation. He tried hard though. There were a few women still left around that remembered him, but his attraction was dwindling. He wasn't catching the girls anymore. Shoot, girls were trying to get with me more than him. That really tripped me out. I would just shoot them on toward Lucky. I wasn't gay, that didn't stop them from liking me.

I had been getting high every night, going to the after hours, then going back to work. Not enough sleep. Poor Ronnie was low on the totem pole. I finally grabbed my baby and was going to the apartment for sleep. In Alaska, a lot of times, we slept with the doors unlocked. It was still a trustworthy environment. Lucky was in and out, sometimes we'd find one of our friends sleep on the couch or making breakfast. This time, I hadn't slept and I wanted my sleep, when Cook, a friend, came over and put some cocaine in my nose while I was asleep. My eyes popped wide open. I couldn't believe it.

"Man, Cook, what are you doing, I just went to sleep. Dang Cook." I wanted to cry. "I'm tired." After that, I got up and snorted coke with him.

The next day, I eventually went to sleep at the after hours club. I hadn't slept in days. That's when I was slapped with a reality check. I didn't have to wake up every morning, alive and well.

I was lying on the couch, finally asleep, when the top of my head felt like it opened up. I was spinning. There was some loud

C. Oakes

noise. It sounded like the ocean and birds. It was really loud. It felt like a vacuum was sucking me away through the top of my head. I fought hard to stay. I mean, I fought hard to stay in my body. Lucky came in the room, I tried to say something but nothing came out. He thinks I'm sleep. I could see everything going on in that room. I tried to scream. Nothing. I tried to move. I couldn't. I continued to fight to stay in my body. It was a battle. I was squinting hard with my whole being. Literally, fighting for dear life. If I can just move. I was trying and trying to move. I couldn't get up. I tried and tried to move just a little. I remembered saying to myself. Move a little. Then with all my might, I rolled off the couch. Bam! I hit the floor. The impact snapped me out of it. "What just happened to me?" I was scared. I was truly scared out of my whits.

"Lucky, I couldn't move. I saw you come in the room, but I couldn't move. I couldn't say anything." He just looked, not really interested. They had given me a nickname, 1-2-3 knockout, cause I started hitting the cocaine pipe and falling out. Lucky said I would shake. Then I would get back up and take another hit. Fall out again. Crazy. But now, this was it. Things had to change.

I was afraid to sleep. When I dozed off, I would wake up immediately and shake it off. I was scared that I wouldn't wake up. I didn't know if God would take me away next time I was sleep. I realized that He let me wake up every morning. I didn't deserve that much. What if He just took me right now. I couldn't die now. I needed to get right. "Lord Jesus, not now. I would surely go to hell." I was a mess. Nobody took me seriously. What was I to do? I knew I needed to pray. I need Jesus in my life. I wanted to find God. I was desperate. I needed prayer. I hadn't prayed in years. But I was willing to do anything to be safe. I just didn't think I was good enough for Jesus. How could I ask for anything. I've done so much wrong.

I wasn't raised that way. I use to be good, sweet, and innocent. I sang in the youth choir. All of us in the choir hung out together. I traveled with the church, on the church bus. Those days were fun. Clean fun. Man, what made me go so far. How did I get this far gone. I just turned from God. Now, I'm truly scared. I can't sleep. I might not wake up.

"Dear Heavenly Father. Help me. What ever it takes, Lord.

I'm ready. Whatever it takes to turn my life around, Lord, I'm willing." I was on the floor, face down, begging for forgiveness, begging for my life. Begging for Him to save me. "Lord I need you. Help me Father. Let me live." Oh, I was crying and crying, yet, feeling so relieved. "Thank you, Father. Thank you, Lord Jesus." I knew, deep down inside, it's going to be alright. "Dear Father in Heaven. Lord, thank you, thank you." I knew I was close to death then and I was willing to do anything to live.

I slept peacefully.

Chapter 13

I had my things packed, waiting for a taxi. I hadn't seen Lucky in a few days. That's the way he does when he's found a new fool to pay him. He sticks with them for a while. I was there with my suitcases anxiously waiting for the taxi, pacing, looking out the window. "Good. Here it comes."

I sat Ronnie down so I could take my bags to the curb. I was glad that Carol had already taken Matt. That was a real blessing. It would have been difficult with two babies, trying to escape. I'm ready to go. I was headed back home, to Oklahoma. Boy that sounded good. I had to hurry before Lucky popped up. I went back inside to get more suitcases when the taxi stopped in front of me. I grabbed two suitcases, stepped toward the back to put my suitcases in the trunk. "Damn!," Lucky got out the cab. "Damn. I got to have the worst buzzard luck in the world."

"What are you doing?" I was stuck. I couldn't say a word. The cab didn't want to leave me. He kept looking at me with I'm sorry in his eyes. Lucky just picked up the suitcases and took them back inside. He beat me up. I hated him. If I had had another man with me, it wouldn't be an issue, but to leave without any protection, well, you'll get hurt.

Lucky hung around me for weeks feeding me plenty of cocaine. But I was determined to leave. Then he surprised me with a party. We celebrated the same birth date. He's about eight years older than me. Lucky had the bathtubs full of expensive champagne, the Don stuff. He was meeting and greeting everybody at the door with a bottle of champagne and a plate of cocaine. It was classy. Lucky seemed to be his old self. The big time pimp. Splurging and entertaining. My cousin, Diana, was there with her husband. It was fun. Me and Lucky were the first to leave the party. Diana said they left the next day. It was a nice jester, but I was leaving his ass. I had to get my life back on track. I didn't have time to waste anymore. I didn't pack, I didn't look back. I just grabbed my baby and jumped on the plane.

When I arrived home, my friend Phyllis came to the rescue. Still boosting. She had boxes of clothes for me and Ronnie. Keith poked fun at me about coming home pitiful, making his wife feel sorry for me. Keith and Phyllis, still the same. I was glad to see them. Keith only been out of prison a few weeks. In fact, after serving five years on a twenty-year sentence, my husband, Mike, was out, too. He was in California. Momma said he brought some girl over and introduced her as his wife.

"Honey, you and Mike got married?"

"Yes ma'am." She said.

" Well, honey it ain't legal cause he's still married to my daughter. That nigga's lying to you." Momma was giving it to her straight

"Let's go. Tell Sharell she can come home. It's alright. I'm over her." Mike was hurrying his illegal wife out the door.

I was so glad to see Matt. My twin brothers were about fifteen, Matt was five. Their friends all had little brothers or nephews around Matt's age. They had wrestling and boxing tournaments. So all the little kids in the neighborhood were in fight tournaments, for the bragging rights of the older boys. They said Matt could beat everybody on the block. Twins would crack up telling me stories about how they made Matt wrestle and box. Their friends were all mad because Matt was the neighborhood champion. They were proud of Matt. Their nephew was like a little brother to them. Matt was my little man. He seemed so big and stocky. I was hugging and kissing my big boy. He had so much to tell me, he couldn't get it out fast enough. Twins turned my baby into a prizefighter. They loves Matt and I love them all.

This legal case was my major problem. I left Oklahoma, while on probation. Shoot, they may make me do the entire five years. Well, as long as it will be cleared up, I was ready. I had strength. I was willing to do anything to put my life back on track. But first I needed to make more money. I had to pay the attorney, give my mom money for my kids. Mom put me in touch with a good lawyer. He got me one year in a minimum security prison. So I worked at one of the clubs a few months. I was able to save a couple more dollars for my mom and my kids before I left for my incarceration.

"Mom, please don't come down here with me."

"Sharell, just hush." Momma didn't want to hear it.

"Mom, please don't come. I don't want you to see me going to prison, Mom. Momma! Momma, why you got to come? It's

C. Oakes

going to make me weak seeing you in there."

Momma was constantly walking in step with me.

"Please Momma, don't come inside the courtroom. I'll go by myself. Just leave here." I turned to give her a hug. "I'll go inside by myself, Mom."

I listened to the charges and sentencing, the jailers were hand-cuffing me, leading me away to jail. I looked back at my mother and she had broken down. She was crying, wiping her eyes. She looked swollen, her face looked dark and red. Her daughter was going to prison. I couldn't take it. Seeing her hurt like that. I started crying. I motioned my lips. "Go home, I'll call you."

When I arrived at my temporary residence, I was met by a welcome party, ready to kick my ass.

"Yeah, that's the bitch that left Mike while he was down."

"What is this?" I couldn't believe it. These girls, are they crazy? They were Mike's friends. They heard about me. But did they hear about him kicking my ass damn near everyday. I bet they didn't hear about that. I was bracing myself in case I was getting it. Then I saw a friendly face.

"I know one thang, yall ain't fenna do a damn thang to her."

"Neecie, that's the bitch that left Mike when he was down."

"I don't give a damn, this is that man's wife and yall ain't fenna put y'all's hands on her. I mean that shit. Who wants to touch her? You bitches got to come through me and I'm not playing. Just somebody touch her."

Oh, I remembered her. It was Neecie Sanders. I met her one day on the streets when I was looking for Mike, I hadn't seen him in a few days. She was with her husband. They were both talking with Mike. He was so glad to see me, he grabbed me and was kissing and hugging me. I was pregnant with Matt. He intro-duced me as his wife to them both. All day we set around and talked as two normal couples. They were telling their street sto-ries. Mike was always proud to have me. He kept me close that whole day.

The lynch mob reluctantly broke up. I couldn't believe that Mike still had so many loyal fans.

"Hey, thanks. And thanks for remembering me. I can't be-lieve they were going to jump on me about my own husband."

"Man, they're so damn ignorant. They don't know a damn

thang about you and that man. All I know is he told me that you were his wife. I know that man loves you and they ain't going to lay one finger on you."

Women were coming out of their rooms to get a good look at Mike's wife. They were whispering and moving on. You could tell the ones that wanted to do their time and mind their own business, because they didn't want to hear it and didn't care about it. But, there were a few that liked drama. They wanted crap. I learned real fast I had enemies here.

"How long do you have?'

"I got a year."

"Well, you'll probably be out in about nine months."

"Oh yeah?"

"Uh uh. You just do nine months on a year."

"That's good."

"When was the last time you seen Mike?"

" It's been a few years."

"We use to see him all the time when he was locked up. This use to be a coed facility."

"What?"

"Yeah, it used to be coed. Mike stayed here before he was released."

"Damn, that's why they all know him." I wonder what he said about me. I bet he told them all kinds of lies on me.

Neecie was a good friend while I was locked up. She was real pretty. She had a wholesome, clean look. Neecie demanded a lot of respect and got it. She was in for drugs. While I was there, her friendship was invaluable, she showed me the ropes.

I got settled in and was able to keep my babies on weekends. They stayed in my room with me. It was a regular picnic with so many kids around. Clearwaters use to be a motel. There were two, sometimes three, people to a room. It was clean. The guards were straight butts. Like it was part of the job. There was no reason to be so mean and abusive. So spiteful. Just didn't make sense. I learned to stay out of their faces. I didn't ask questions or invite any attention towards me. I didn't have long to stay so I needed to be cool. Neecie told me not to tell anybody about my time. She said they didn't like short timers and people will try to get your release date screwed up. She didn't have to tell me twice.

I know my momma was tired of prisoners. My brother and Mike were at the same facility for a few years. She used to see them both while they were locked up. Although, Momma didn't like Mike, she was nice to him. He didn't have any family here in Oklahoma, so she would visit with him when she visited Roger. Now it's been only a few months since their release and she's here again, visiting a prisoner. This time, it's me.

There was something peculiar that I noticed. It was strange to me because these were straight criminals. This facility ranged from light weight shoplifters to killers that were here on good behavior, but still, killers were here, in this facility. There were even one or two child abusers. . . they didn't get treated well by the other inmates. Child abusers stayed to themselves. They got heckled a lot. . . they got pushed around. They were treated real bad. There were a few embezzlers and con-artists around, too. But, basically drugs was the main reason most were locked up.

What caught my attention is everybody faithfully read their Bibles. This was different. I hadn't seen this since I've been deep in the world. I mean in the fast lane. I hadn't seen a dependency on reading the Bible like this. I liked it. Maybe I should try reading it.

"Neecie, everybody in this place has a Bible."

"I know, and I got mine. Sharell, when you're down like this, you need the Lord to get you through each day. It really helps. They all know it. That's the way we do when we're in trouble. We call on the Lord when we need him. And when we get out, we forget. There's extra Bibles around. You want one. I'll find you one. A church comes to get us for prayer service once a week. It'll get you out of this place for a while, if you want to go."

I got me a Bible. It was a King James version. Probably from an old hotel room. I looked at it for a few days before I opened it. I remembered at my church in Oklahoma, I was never truly in touch with the message.

My dad is a preacher in Alabama. Everybody loves my dad. I would get so jealous because I only had a short time with him and I had to share him with all the kids that saw him everyday. But I found myself checking out his mannerism instead of his message. And man, could he sing. I loved hearing my dad sing and preach. He was so good. They would shout. Church would last a long time. It was good. But the message went over my head. The singing was good. I love the singing. I even felt the vibes from the music. But I could read the Bible and never understood anything. I wasn't tuned in, I needed to concentrate. Since I had the time, I decided that I'll just start reading it from the beginning.

Lucky came to Oklahoma. I wasn't ever going back to him. There wasn't any love and our friendship got ruined. What was he thinking? He visited me once or twice. I just told him, I'm not going back. He left. But, others from Alaska and Hawaii came to see me. "What was that about?" I wasn't going to get with any of them pimps. I never want to get in that life again. I was getting so many visitors. Men were coming to see me left and right. My brothers came, I got four brothers, they all are good looking guys. My cousins and uncles came. They are good looking, too. Then Dwight came, Mike's brother. Girls started hanging around to check out my visitors. Mike, finally came. I was glad because that put an end to the bull about me leaving his ass, "while he was down" shit.

I was so scared to see him. I had another baby. I didn't know what or how he would take it.

"So, where's my new son?"

"What?"

"Where's my new son? You know I'm legally his father, cause you're still my wife."

"Mike, Momma told me you brought your new wife over to meet her."

"I just did that so she could tell you to come home. She tell you I said it's okay for you to come home?"

"Yeah, she told me, and she told me about your new wife. Where is she now?"

"Oh, she left. I wrecked her mother's car."

"You're still messing with those insurance companies?"

"Hey, I'm starting over, I need some money."

"Mike and his brother, Dwight, came to visit every week for a while. This was Dwight's first visit to Oklahoma. He liked it. Mike eventually went back to California but Dwight stayed, he said he would stay till I got out. That was nice. Mike said he would be back before I got out. I still loved him. Momma was so mad at me.

"Sharell, after everything we went through behind that sorry ass nigga, you're going back to him?" I know I looked stupid. I wouldn't argue, I just left. She couldn't believe me.

I was reading my Bible regularly. I started really getting into it. The way I started, from the beginning, was good. I began to understand The Father, at least that's what I thought. Then I jumped to the New Testament. It was really getting good. Then it hit me.

"If he has ears, let him hear." As I was reading, Jesus was saying a little prayer for me. Hoping that I would understand.

"This was too much." Then just like that, like a light switch came on, I had understanding. Just like that, it was like something turned on in my brain. I understood. I started reading things that I had only heard secondhand.

"Oh, that's where that saying came from? I never knew that was in the Bible." I started taking mental notes of the saying that I always heard. This is it. It was like I found some money or something. It was good.

My time was getting real short. Dwight continued to visit and check me out of the facility on weekends. I had to get a job. That was one of my conditions of getting released. I had to have a job and a place to live. Mike had to learn to read and write before he was released. That was good.

The only place that would hire me was a nursing home. I was so happy to finally get a job because I didn't want to stay any longer than was necessary. But, I couldn't handle working there. Those poor patients. They were old and sick. They had open sores that were saturated in urine. It smelled bad. I was in tears everyday. It was too much. I couldn't handle it, I couldn't help them. I couldn't feed them or clean them. Man, I would cry. Although we used gloves, I couldn't eat or get my hands clean enough after working. I had a weak stomach. What was I going to do? Then I remembered my new friend, Jesus. I had gotten close to him while I was locked up. I asked him to help me. I needed fixing.

"Lord, I can't do this. Whatever I need in me, Lord, please fix me so I can help these poor people." After my prayer, I was able to work at the nursing home. I was able to turn the patients, clean them, feed them. I wasn't crying everyday. I could wash my hands and they were clean. It was like magic.

The day I got out, I'll never forget this as long as I live. Vee Ervin and some other inmates ran to my room.

"Girl, your brother-in-law is crazy."

"Why, what happened?"

"Girl, they just made him leave the premises. They told his crazy ass to get off the premises and don't bring his crazy ass back."

"Why?"

"He came in here and told the guards that you were getting out today and he was coming to get you."

"You are lying."

"Girl, he's crazy isn't he?" They were cracking up.

"Your crazy ass brother-in-law. They told him to get his ass off the premises." Laughing.

I knew my time was short, but I didn't have any idea exactly when I would be released. I decided to get dressed and walk toward the office to see what was going on. Everybody was still laughing, even the guards were laughing telling me about my crazy ass brother-in-law.

It hadn't been a good hour, all the excitement was over, and I was back in my room when I got a knock on the door, it was the guards.

"Pack your things. You've been released."

"Whaaat?"

I was walking toward the office with a couple boxes, things I hadn't given away and there was a crowd standing around looking in disbelief. I opened the door and there sit Dwight with this big grin. Dwight was very handsome. He was a light skinned, Louisiana creole, with pretty green eyes and nappy reddish blond hair. He was so funny. We walked down the hill, outside the gates to his car, cracking up.

"Dwight, how did you know?"

"I met the Governor's secretary. We went out for lunch a few times. I had her put your paperwork on top. When they told me to get off the premises, I just called her. Then I had her tell them . . . Sharell Lartigue is being released today. Yeah! And tell them her brother-in-law, Dwight Lartigue, is coming to get her." We laughed for days. It's still hard to believe.

Mike moved back to Oklahoma after I was released. I still would never move out of state with him.

"Sharell, how could you travel all over the country with this man and won't move anywhere with me?"

I never answered that question. I had a way of just looking at him. But the truth is, I was still scared of Mike, I needed my family's protection while I was with him. Anyway, freebasing wasn't out when Mike went down. I've already gone down that road with Lucky and I wasn't ready to go through it with Mike. Smoking Coke or freebasing. Everybody's going through it. I don't know how Mike's going to handle it. I know he was going to smoke cocaine sooner or later. He may have already smoked it.

Mike was good with Ronnie. He was his dad. Mike seemed to love Ronnie just like he loved Matt. He made no differences between my children. Mike had some good points but his bad points, man. I was worried about making love again with my husband. I didn't know if I would feel the same to him. I didn't understand how he could possibly still love me after I've been with so many men, but my past five years was the last thing he seemed to care about. He took his time getting to know me again. He seemed more patient and secure. He was literate now. It was cool. The fact that he could read, was a big deal.

He explained to me, "Sharell, while you're in prison, you take a lot of shit off guards and you can't do a damn thing about it. I couldn't kick their asses so I had to learn to control my temper. Why get mad, I couldn't do a thing about it. Out here is a breeze. After five straight years of taking bullshit off guards and other inmates, I know I can take your bullshit." He was smiling.

I was truly happy for a while. We were happy, but this blissfulness didn't last cause smoking coke was the "in" thing. Mike went crazy. We both smoked. I was back in the clubs dancing. I was bringing home drugs from customers, just like up north. But Mike was way more crazier and dangerous than Lucky. Shoot, Lucky didn't care about us getting high by ourselves, but Mike jumped on me.

"Where's mine? I know you got some for me."

"What? Mike it was just a little bit."

"Get your ass back to that trick and get some more. You're not going to be getting high and not bring me any. Who do you think I am, get your ass out now."

"Mike, I've been home a couple of hours now, he may not be there." Then he hit me hard. I was on the floor.

"I said get me some coke." I started getting dressed, crying, stumbling, trying to hurry before he hit me again.

Another year wasted with Mike. He's no husband. How could he love me the way he fights me like that. I'm not raising my kids around him beating on me. I'll end up dead. The cocaine. . .the women. He's worse.

In fact, Dwight and Mike got into a fight about me. "Man, I'm tired of seeing you mistreat her like that. Man, I ought to just shoot you . . . I ought to just shoot you now. Mike, man I've done so much wrong—I've killed, I've stolen and robbed. I've done too much wrong and I know I don't have long to live, but you and Sharell can make it work." Dwight was crying. "Y'all can make it. You got a chance. . If not, man . ."

Mike was crying too because Dwight had a gun, pointing at him and on the verge of shooting him.

It was a crossroads for me, too. I knew right then, I had to do something. Me. I had to stand up. I know I couldn't live like this any longer. It was out of control. After everything I've gone through, I didn't want this life. I wanted more.. I asked for a divorce. I wasn't sneaking away. I wasn't running away. I was walking out, on my own, standing in his face. I just told him, Mike, I don't want to be married to you anymore. He hung his head. He didn't believe me at first. Maybe because I wasn't running or acting scared, or bringing my family into the mess. Maybe we both had grown up some, while we were apart. But he couldn't blame me, he wasn't ready to do better. It was too much madness around the kids. He didn't argue or get mad. I didn't have to fight. I just walked away. It was over.

C. Oakes

Chapter 14

It was 1983 when I moved to Dallas. I always thought I would end up in Dallas because it wasn't too far from home, but it was far enough to meet new people and start all over, have a brand new life. I knew how to make money, so I wasn't worried at all.

Me and my kids lived with my cousin Christy for a while, just to get started. She was very kind and accommodating, letting me and my kids move in with her. Christy didn't have kids, I'm sure we were a bother. Matter of fact, everybody was good to me, helping me with my move. Christy's parents, my uncle Skip and Aunt Jeanette were wonderful—made themselves available if I needed anything. I sure love my family and they love me. I lived with Christy about two months before I had my own place.

But man was I wrong about Dallas. I've never been to a place that was this hard to make money. The clubs weren't table dancing yet. They didn't know exactly how to table dance. I guess they heard about it. But they didn't know too much because I mentioned it to this dancer at this place, Geno's, that had little bitty round tables. Before I knew it, this girl climbed on top of the little table and started dancing on top of the table. The guys were holding the table steady and making a human barrier with their arms incase she hit the floor. I couldn't believe it. She could have broken her neck. I didn't say a word. I had to get my feel of the place before I started giving free information to everybody.

In Dallas, the clubs were huge. They had anywhere from two to five stages positioned around the club. Girls would start at the first stage and dance through the last stage. When the girls got to the stage closest to where the guys were seated, the guys were expected to get up and put money in the dancers' G-strings. If you were cute and white, by the time you got to the last stage, your G-string looked like a green tu-tu made of money. Just dancing one set, white girls came off stage with good money, close to a hundred or two hundred dollars, maybe more each set. I have to give it to them, they did good dancing all those stages. But on the other hand, if you were a gorgeous sister, those white guys weren't getting up, in front of God and everybody in Texas, putting money in no sister's G-string.   I don't care how fine you are, if you're black, they barely looked at you. Shoot, somebody might see them looking. That's just Texas. Well, I really didn't want to be up there, dancing on five different stages no way, hoping somebody might put a dollar in my bottoms. That wasn't going to work. Beside, I had to do better. I have two little boys depending on me.

I went to several different clubs in Dallas, the Million Dollar Club, Culeculars, Showtime. . . Showtime had the five different stages. Those white girls were cleaning up dancing all those stages. My legs were jello when I finished one set. I couldn't walk, didn't have control over my legs, and I barely had forty or fifty dollars after a night. Shoot, after the babysitter and cab, nothing was left. I didn't know what to do. I was too embarrassed to apply for a real job because they might see that I was locked up, in prison. Welfare wasn't an option either, not for me. Nothing against welfare and all but, I couldn't live off it. I need too much. My hair cost too much, my clothes, my kids. I don't see how they made it. I can't blame women, staying home, raising their kids, plus everybody's not willing to go to my extremes to make a living. I can't say whether or not my way is better. In fact, I know its not the right road to go, but I'm used to having money. Doing what I want when I want. I went from club to club looking for my spot. The Million Dollar Club was close but I wasn't making enough. I needed something else. I needed some help.

I was working, some of us were table dancing, but it wasn't quite there yet. I pulled a customer in a corner, trying to hustle a couple of dollars, talking him into a private dance.

"Hi, can I join you?"

"Sure." He was an older gentleman.

"My name is Nikki."

"Hi, I'm Steve."

"Nice meeting you Steve. You come here often?"

"No, but I like it alright." The way he was looking at me, I knew he liked it alright.

"Let's go somewhere private. I want to give you a private dance."

"Oh yeah? What's a private dance? Where'd you like to go?"

"Over there is good. Can I dance for you?"

"Sure. Is this going to cost me anything?"

C. Oakes

"It's five dollars."

"Five dollars!"

"Yeah, I give real good private dances."

"Okay." He handed me twenty. "I'll just work this off for you. Is that okay?" I started dancing, not waiting for an answer, giving him a good workout. I made a few bucks with him and had ordered a drink. Now, this is what I'm talking about. It was getting better.

This guy was watching me from the top balcony. I could feel his look. He was grinning so hard, going crazy, motioning for me to join him upstairs. He was black. I really wasn't ready to have a close friend. So I ignored him a while and continued to dance for my customer. Other girls were catching on fast. That made it better when I asked for a table dance. It was okay because there were only two stages. I wasn't too tired to do the extras here and there.

This guy was still trying to get me to join him. I finally climbed the stairs to join him, I could tell he wasn't a regular customer.

"Girl, bring your pretty ass up here and talk to me. Ooooowe, look at your booty. Turn around so I can see." I did a quick whirl. "You got a pretty booty. Can I touch it?'

"Nooo! I'll dance for you."

"Okay. How much?"

"Five dollars."

"Can I put it in your panties?" I stuck my hand out so he could give me the money in my hand. He gave me five dollars and I started dancing.

"Turn around for me so I can look at that booty." I laughed, he was funny. "Damn girl, what's your name."

"Nikki. What's yours?"

"Jerry. I got to have a number or something. Can I have your number?"

I didn't answer. I continued with my dance.

"Where are you from?"

"I'm from Oklahoma City."

"They grow'em like that in Oklahoma? Are there more like you in Oklahoma?" I just smiled. "I got to go there." He couldn't stop grinning. I noticed he was sharply dressed. I liked it. He had white cotton, heavy starched designer shirt. No jacket.

Creased jeans. Loafers. He was preppy. He looked businesslike. I liked it a lot.

I was curious now. "Where you from?"

"Seattle." I rolled my eyes. "I just came from there not too long ago."

"Yeah, where'd you live?"

"Mostly in Puyallup. My son was born in Tacoma."

"Really!"

"Uh uh."

"How long have you been here?"

"I just got here. I don't know how long I'll be here, I'm not doing too good."

"Girl, this place is going to be popping pretty soon. The Republican convention is going to be here. Money's going to be everywhere. Those Republicans are the rich ones. You better stay a while. Anyway, I got to see you more. You got a man?"

"No. I got two men."

"Really?"

"Yeah, one's five years old and the other one's two. That's enough for me."

"Naw girl, you need me. Can I see you again? How are you getting home?"

"I usually call a taxi.

"I can take you home."

"I don't think so. I just met you."

"Girl, what do you think I'm going to do to you. You better save your little money and ride with me, let me take you home."

I laughed, "Well, I get off at two in the morning."

"I'll be back to get you."

Jerry was waiting for me in a two tone chocolate, brand new, Cadillac Sedan Deville. It was pretty. It looked like him. Conservative. He didn't get out. I put my costume bag in the back seat and slid in the cushy front.

"How did you do?"

"Not that good. I got a few dollars. Nothing to brag about at all."

"Where do you need to go?"

"Well, my kids are at my house with my cousin."

"Oh yeah? So you don't have to hurry home?"

"Well, I don't want to take advantage of a good thing. I usually go straight home."

"Can you call your cousin and tell her you're going to be late."

"I could, but I won't." Jerry started pouting.

"Will you stay with me for a while, they're sleep aren't they?"

Jerry was a very clean, good looking, dark skinned black man. He spoke good English and smelled so good. I missed a good, mature conversation and he had one. I didn't know much about this man but no internal flags were waving. My intuition was very keen now. He was harmless. He seemed just as lonely as me.

"Nikki, I got some wine at the house. Have you had anything to eat, yet?"

"No. I can cook a good steak. Can I fix you dinner. Girl, wait till you taste my cooking." He was wearing me down. "You want a nice bubble bath and dinner." He was grinning again, ear to ear. It sounded so good and I wanted it so much. I didn't say a word. My eyes and silence spoke volumes. I went home with Jerry.

Jerry's place was much more than I expected. It was spotless. He had delicate, cherry wood furniture. Everything so perfect. I couldn't bring my kids over here, they might dirty something. He lived in an exclusive, singles only condo. Airplanes flew so close to his balcony, you can reach out and touch one. You would think the planes would be very loud, but they weren't.

Jerry was so meticulous, everything perfect. My bubble bath was wonderful. I drank cognac. He brought Johnson's baby oil for my skin.

"Nikki, Johnson's baby oil is the best if you want nice skin." I let him rub my back while I was still wet, then he gave me a terrycloth house coat. "Here, put this on." I was getting the treatment. I could smell food on the grill, it smelled great. I decided I would enjoy the morning, indulge myself with this good food, the luxury of quiet time and brandy, but most of all I wanted to enjoy Jerry's sweet company.

It was easier with Jerry. He helped me in so many ways, turned me on to a better way of doing things. He was more luxurious, he was smooth, but still a pimp. He had one other girl. She lived in Seattle and had family money. I didn't ask too much about her. Wasn't my business.

I had been in Dallas a few months but I never noticed the

A Long Way Home   131 obvious. The working girls. They were there every night. Driving around town. The girls in Dallas drove cars asking for dates. Up and down Harry Hines Blvd., driving Cadillacs and everything else. Being cool. Going to exclusive hotels and clubs, tipping bartenders big so they could sit and be propositioned by the guest in the hotels. You didn't say too much, just sit pretty. The managers could tell who they wanted to work in their hotels. It couldn't be too obvious; but they wanted the amenities of pretty, available women for their customers.

I drove around Dallas, honking at cars, going to the airport and metro hotels, waiting for the Republican convention, so I could make this grand theft money that the entire city of Dallas was rearing up to make. In fact, the city of Dallas went through a major makeover getting ready for the Republicans to spend the cash.

This was the first President to formally visit Dallas since the Kennedy assassination and they wanted to make a good impression on the nation.

Party girls were flying in town, setting up shop to make the grand theft cash, but the Republicans had a different plan. They stayed at the Wyndham Anatole and didn't come out. They brought their own food with them, didn't even eat at the local restaurants. Dallas businesses were in shock. The Republicans were very frugal. It wasn't a party no where in sight. The convention was such a terrible disappointment. It was the talk for a while, all the sacrifices that were made for the convention went down the drain.

We cut our losses. It was time to turn the page. Jerry wanted to go to Florida. The Hurricanes would play in the Orange Bowl this New Year's Eve. Matt was in school now, he couldn't travel with me anymore. I sent Matt back to Oklahoma to stay with Mom, and Ronnie stayed with me.

Florida was so much fun. I enjoyed the people, they were all senior citizens and man were they fun. I've never seen such young, hip senior citizens in one place. I was in Ft Lauderdale, sitting in the bar, watching people moon us while they were swimming. The back of the bar was a glass wall of the swimming pool. Girls and guys, getting in the water, giving us a show. Sugar Ray Leonard was in the lobby taking pictures with fans and handing out autographs. It was so much fun. To top it off, while I was there,

C. Oakes

talking with the people at the bar, this 70 year old looking guy slid me a vial of coke. I took my hit and passed it on to the next guy. I was invited to dinners and clubing. We went to the Banana Boat and went to some Cuban places. We were shaking maracas made of pebbles in soda cans. We were singing. I had fun. It was way past two in the morning, and the streets were still packed with pedestrians. I wasn't making any money, though. Man, they partied with me the entire trip . . . hated to see me go.

"Nikki, why don't you stay here. We'll help you find a place. Florida is a nice place."

"Oh, I'm sorry, I can't stay. I wish I could. I got to get home and take care of my kids."

"Raise your kids here. Florida's a great place to raise your kids." I sure wanted to stay, but I couldn't. Jerry was disappointed that I didn't do good in Florida. I made alright in Dallas after I learned the game. So, I had a plane ticket waiting for me to get back to Dallas. We traveled around Texas for a while, but the police were so, so bad. Too much trouble. Harassing girls. Having sting operations, picking up everybody on the streets in these petty wagons. Giving tickets like crazy. I exchanged rental cars a lot so the police wouldn't know my car and target me, but they stilled messed with the working girls. I tried to stay toward the airport hotels and work in that area.

I had gone home to Oklahoma to get Matt and bring him to Dallas with me and Ronnie. I enrolled him in a local school. We were staying with Jerry. I was working the streets and clubs. Not doing too bad, but I was a nervous wreck. Paranoid, that everybody was a undercover cop. All us girls looked out for each other. Giving each other "the look" if things didn't seem right. In fact, we had prayer each day before we began work. Funny uh!

I found a babysitter. She was alright. Not as clean as I would like, but she was available as long as I needed her. That gave me and Jerry room to move around different parts of Texas.

We decided to try Odessa a couple of days, just for the weekend. Odessa was a little town, not much there. Where did Jerry get this place, I don't know. It was morning, Odessa looked dreary. Me and Jerry left the night before. The babysitter didn't answer when I called. All night she didn't answer. I thought maybe she was asleep. That morning we called again. Again, no answer.

"Sharell, she's not answering."

"I wonder what she's doing?"

"I don't know, but we're leaving. Call a cab." We were on the next flight out of Odessa. When I arrived at the apartment, there was a card from child protective services attached to the door. They had the kids. I went through the apartment, looking, scared to death. My clothes and shoes were missing. What did this girl do? I called the number on the card.

"Hello, may I speak with officer Daniels?"

"This is she speaking."

"My name is Sharell Lartigue, and I believe my kids are there."

"What are the children's names?"

"Matthew and Ronald Lartigue."

"What is your address."

"6713 Sherry Ln., Dallas."

"Yes, we have the children here. When will you be able to come for your children?"

"I can come now."

"Just ask for me, Camile Daniels. When you come to the facility, the receptionist will direct you to my desk. Do you know where we're located?"

"I have your card, is it the same address?"

"Yes, just come to the address on my card."

"Thank you, I'm on my way."

"Can you believe that bitch?" That bitch left my kids. Jerry, where did you get her." I was so upset. My neighbor was knocking on the door.

"Come in."

"Hi, your kids were walking around by themselves late last night. They said they were hungry. I fixed them a sandwich and asked where you were and they didn't know. I didn't know what to do so I called the police. Where's that girl that watches them for you?"

"I don't know. The bitch left my kids and stole my clothes."

Jerry was pacing around. "I didn't want to say anything to you last night but I was worried when she didn't answer the phone."

"You think she left last night?"

My neighbor spoke up. "Well the kids were outside early yesterday, sitting by themselves.   She was gone early."

"Man, I can't let this happen again. I can't. I got to do better than this." We rushed to child protective services.

Camile Daniels was in a small cubicle, she was reading something, looking real official. Jerry and I walked in, she just looked up without much of a hello.

"Ms. Lartigue?"

"Yes."

"Please have a seat." I knew right then she was going to be problems.

"Your children were picked up last night by Dallas police department and brought to the children protective services department because of abandonment and neglect."

Well, I surely don't neglect my kids. I had to defend myself. "I didn't leave my kids by themselves. They were with a babysitter."

Ms. Daniel interrupted, "Ms. Lartigue, your children were found by themselves, hungry. We were told they were wandering the streets in the middle of the night."

"The babysitter left them and stole my clothes."

"Well, because of the threatening circumstance, we decided to put you and the children under child protective supervision due to neglect until further notice."

"Look, Ms Daniels, I'm a good mother, I take good care of my children. We don't need any supervision because I don't neglect them. The babysitter had been taking care of my kids for three or four months now. I left town for the weekend, the reason I came back is because I didn't get answer when I called the house. I'm a good mother."

"Ms. Lartigue, can you tell me your sons, Matt's teacher's name?" I didn't know. She looked me in my eyes with a, "I made my point look."

"Where are my children now?"

"First, Ms. Lartigue, we need to make an appointment for a home visit. Let's see, I can come in two weeks. Is that good for you?"

Jerry and I looked at each other. "What day?"

"I can come on April 24, at 6 p.m., I need to come when the children are home. Okay?" I nodded in agreement. "Now, take this paper to the in-house facility, that's the building behind us. The officer will release your children into your custody. I'll see you in two weeks."

"Thank you." I waited to get her response, but she never looked up.

My kids were so glad to see me. Matt was giving me the full blown story. "And Momma, she put your clothes in a garbage bag. . . and I said, hey those are my mommas clothes. . . Then she made us go outside, Momma." I had to slow Matt down while he was telling me what happened, because he'll start to stutter. "We were outside all day till night time. We were huuuungry. She left us outside, so me and Ronnie went to my friend's house but they weren't home. She took your stuff and left us outside, Momma. What kind of babysitter was that, Momma? She was suppose to be watching us."

'We're not going to worry about her anymore. I got my babies with me now." I smiled to reassure my kids. I'll never let something like this happen again.

Jerry walked around, I know he felt bad. "If I see that girl, I'm going to kick her ass."

"She can't fit my stuff. . .and I know those big feet can't fit my shoes. Why did she do this?"

Jerry's always laughing and making jokes. He couldn't figure this one out. Shaking his head in disbelief. "I bet not see her again." He found that sorry ass babysitter in the first place.

Matt wasn't finished. "And momma, the police came. They took us in the police car. . . I'm glad you finally came to get us."

All I could do was thank God that my kids were safe. Anyway, I had enough. I was leaving Texas.

Chapter 15

I'm back in Seattle, I can't believe it. After everything I've gone through. I'm back. I'm kind of glad to be back here. Oklahoma didn't feel like home anymore. Texas sure wasn't it. The great northwest is probably my destiny. I need to focus on making a good home for my boys.

Jerry found us a place in Magnolia. It's a little suburb of Seattle. The neighborhood was cool. We lived in a duplex. A military base was walking distance, right by a park. There's lots of parks here, and plenty of water. In fact, Magnolia's a gorgeous place. It has its own little seductive personality. The neighbors came over and introduced themselves. People were friendly. They had become attached to the boys. The bus stop was right in front of our duplex and Ronnie had an audience. He would draw pictures, then sell them for a quarter to the people at the bus stop. Matt told me about Ronnie's entrepreneur adventure. I made him stop, but the neighbors got a big kick out of it. You need to be careful with your children and they sure don't need to be hustling quarters at a bus stop.

Everybody loved my boys. They were excited about Ronnie learning to ride a bike. Everybody watched his every attempt, and was ready and willing to prevent any scrap, scab or fall. He was so determined to ride, and man, was he fun to watch. Ronnie was about three and Matt was seven.

The neighbors always had something to tell me or offer me information about what was happening in Seattle. Everything was going on. The Bumpershoot, Seafair, take the boys to watch the Blue Angels. The Bite of Seattle's this week, the hydroplane races going on, eat at Ivar's. Thirteen Coins, so much to do.

Yeah, Magnolia's a real nice place to live. But there wasn't any black folks around. I want my kids to grow up around some black folk, somewhere, sometime. So they can have a good rounded environment and know how to interact with everybody. Well, I decided that Sundays would be the day we visit the black community. Go to church in the hood. Eat at Helen's Soul food restaurants. Jerry was totally against that. He said he didn't deal with any mud ducks.

"What are you saying?"

"I don't want the kids around those mud ducks."

"Jerry, what's a mud duck?"

"Those ghetto queens and hood rats." I couldn't believe what I was hearing.

"Where in the world have you been. That's exactly what I'm talking about. I don't want my kids growing up like you, Jerry... ashame of black people. My goodness, calling us mud ducks. That was the ugliest thing I'd ever heard in my life. Where's your pride?" I was thinking to myself, ..."Be careful, Negro, that's Strike One!"

The kids were enrolled in school, I was determined to be a better parent, I was going to know the teachers' names, the principals, everybody and they were going to know me. We had a community baseball team, the little league, and I thought it would be good if Matt played ball. He was so big for his age, they thought he would hit the ball out the park. They started moving everybody waaaaay back, but he couldn't hit the ball. I was embarrassed. I told him he had to learn to hit the ball because he was the biggest kid out there. And obvious to me and everybody else, he was, also, the only black kid on the team. Everybody expected him to knock the ball out of the park. He'd walk up to bat, the other team's coaches looked at Matt and wave the players to move back, move back to the outfield. The parents and I were speechless when we saw Matt wildly swing at the ball. No coordination, none. You'd think playing ball comes naturally.

"Well, we're going to do better." We practiced, him hitting the ball, everyday till he was slugging. I would be yelling at my baby, "Keep your eyes on the ball Matt, just watch the ball." He'd swing, he'd swing, Finally he got the hang of it. Soon, my boy was the team slugger. Man, that big black kid could hit that ball. I was proud of my baby.

Ballard is a suburb of Seattle, too. It was just down the street from Magnolia. Mostly Norwegians lived there. I found a club in Ballard called The Sands. It only had one stage. This Greek guy, Gus, owned it. He was so cool. He acted like Italian mafia—his personality and the way he carried himself. Super cool. He didn't let the girls take anything off in his club. Now that was different. But he was right. Gus would say all the time, the less you give the

C. Oakes

more you get. I understood Gus, he was a hustler. No free shows at the Sands.

Gus said. "Stripping isn't necessary, you can make money without all that." We had to wear thigh high socking with our costumes and we never took anything off while on stage. We had a private lounge where we danced with the customers. We'd put on a sexy dress or gown, order a drink, which was pop or juice, customers paid $50 to go in the lounge. The lounge was just the other side of the room, nothing secluded or anything. Nope, we didn't take anything off at the Sands. On the other hand, it wasn't so innocent either, because by it not being a topless or nude club, it was easier to make money on the floor. Guys were more willing to spend cash for a peek show. We would get ten and twenty dollar each song for a little peek of something. I made good money at the Sands. I felt better dancing for a living, too. The Sands stayed open as long as we wanted it. They didn't sell any booze so we could stay open till 4 or 5 in the mornings. And it stayed packed with customers. I made two to four hundred every night I worked. I only worked three or four nights a week. I was able to spend more time with my children. It was cool. A hundred bucks was a slow night. It was so perfect.

I would leave going to work about 9 pm. The kids were ready for bed by then. My next door neighbor's daughter, Lana, babysat. She's about thirteen. I was usually home at 2:30 in the morning. Jerry was always there to pick me up after work It was easy.

I decided I needed to continue my education. Computers was the new thing now. Today, you need to know how to use a word processor. I took classes while the kids were in school. I learned on the Wang computer. It was 1984 and the new technology was exciting. I was home about 2 pm, before the kids came home from school and preschool. I'd have dinner ready for my babies. We'd do homework, bathe, then turn on the tube in their bedrooms. They would be sleep before I left going to work. Lana had it easy. If there were any problems, her mom, Teri, was just next door. There were never any problems, plus I was only five minutes away.

Red flags were coming up with Jerry though. Every blue moon, he'd take us to visit his folks in the hood. They looked so poor. I didn't understand that. These black guys around here, looking so good, driving these great cars, and their mothers and sisters looked like . . .I don't know, neglected. It wasn't like that in Oklahoma. Sisters were stepping. It didn't seem like Jerry came from this neighborhood. He, being such a conservative, clean fellow. Driving this new cat, living in several different places. His nieces and nephews looked homeless.

They all lined up to give Jerry a kiss. He'd scream and give them a hug and a dollar. They all loved their uncle Jerry. But red flags were coming up with him. I didn't like the way he was coming between me and Ronnie. Ronnie would cry about something and want to come to me, but Jerry would grab him and wouldn't give him to me. He'd laugh and pick him up.

"Boy what's da matter with you?" He'd whirl him around. "Why you got that ugly face. Look at you. Look at you." Ronnie would still be reaching for me, but Jerry would wear him down, till he stop crying.

"Jerry, let my child come to me when he wants me. I don't like you coming between us like that."

"Ah girl, you gonna make the boy into a momma's boy."

"That's okay. He's my momma's boy. Let him come to me. I mean it, Jerry." Then Jerry made a big difference between Matt and Ronnie. He was always playing and wrestling with Ronnie and was totally ignoring Matt. If Matt made Ronnie cry, he was ready to tear into Matt. My big boy could tell Ronnie was Jerry's favorite. I didn't like that one bit, showing favoritism with my boys. I didn't like it one bit.

Since I've been in this life, I've had to learn to listen to my inter feelings. My intuitions were telling me something wasn't right with Jerry. I'd put if off a little, not wanting to face what my mind was telling me. I didn't want to think it, but I was feeling like Jerry was some kind of pedophile. In fact, I was getting warning signals left and right. I learned that I get those feelings for a reason. The reason was Jerry. He was putting them in my head. He put them there. I wouldn't get those feeling out the clear blue sky. So why was I feeling like this. I'd watch Jerry close. He would want to dry Ronnie off when he came out the tub. Grabbing him from me. Like it was alright. I was raised around a bunch of men, my uncles never did that. My daddy has five brothers and my mother has three, they never came around at bath

C. Oakes

time, dinner time, or anytime taking over, not when the momma had it covered. Marzett didn't act like that with my little brothers either. I started getting panicky about Ronnie.

"Jerry, I got him. You don't have to do anything with my kids. I think something is weird about that anyway."

"Weird, what are you talking about?"

"I'm talking about all this attention you keep showing Ronnie. I don't think its normal. It's weird. You act like a pedophile."

"What! Girl, you're crazy." He was leaving. He's laughing. I was thinking to myself, he's trying to laugh it off. He knows what I'm talking about. Look at him, always laughing.

Man, I was kind of proud of myself, the way I told Jerry just how I felt. Now I got to figure out how I'm going to get rid of his ass. If my mind tells me something is wrong and I don't listen, then it's my fault. Nobody to blame but me and I sure am getting red flags. My intuition was telling me, Jerry has to go.

Since I left Oklahoma, I hadn't smoked any cocaine, but me and Jerry snorted plenty. I decided I wouldn't smoke anymore and I hadn't. But I notice Jerry was getting skinnier and skinnier. I'm thinking he's been smoking coke. I didn't bring it to his attention. I decided that I would wait and let that be the reason to fire his ass.

Jerry let all the furniture go back to the dealer. But I hadn't gotten much of anything since moving to Seattle. We had a dinette set and a bedroom suit, a few tv's and that's it. So I brought it to his attention.

"Jerry, I got a problem."

"What now, Sharell?"

"I think you're smoking coke." He stopped and looked at me but didn't say anything. "We're not moving ahead. We've been here six months and I don't see us moving ahead. We should have more than this little stuff here and there. I think I need to be by myself for a while. I need to take care of my kids and get our lives together."

"Sharell, you're right. You are right."

I was thinking, "damn that was easy."

"Before you go, we're going to get you some furniture and a car. You're not going to leave me like that. I know I'm a better man than that." Jerry took me to a couple of his friends in the car business. I got a new 1984 red alliance. My first brand new car. I was excited. I got a king size bedroom set, a living room set, a kiss on the cheek, then he was gone.

Wow, this is great. I loved it. I'm single. For the first time in my life, I appreciated being single. I'm doing things different this time. No more men around my boys. None. You think somebody's digging on you and all the time, they're wanting your kids. The next time I move in with a man, my kids are going to be old enough that nobody can influence them in any way. They're going to be too big for anybody to hurt them, and I'm the only parent here. "Don't be trying to raise my kids." I can't stand it when somebody is putting their little two cents in on raising my boys. My boys are off limits. I'm a single parent and never again will I bring a man in their lives. Not while they're babies. Maybe when they're grown. That a big "Maybe."

Gus, the owner of the Sands club, was curious about me.

"Nikki, who's your man?"

"I don't have a man."

"Come on now, all you girls got a man."

"Not me. All I'm doing is taking care of my kids, that's all."

Gus was very generous to me. He wanted me close to him, in his inner circle. "Nikki, I got an empty unit next door. If you need somewhere to stay, you and your boys can stay there. You'll be close to work. It'll be easy to check on your boys at night. It won't cost you much."

"Naw, that's okay Gus. We're fine. Thanks for the offer." Gus has a nice place next door to the club, in fact, it's really nice. But, I'm not moving. My babysitter lives right next door. She's pretty good, I don't want to lose her. Our neighbors looked out for each other. School was close. Plus I wasn't moving my boys next door to a club like that. Anything could happen.

My life was great, then I started getting these strange feelings, I started feeling like somebody was following me. When I got off work, I could sense it. I was being followed. So, I started driving around town before I'd go to my house, where my children were sleeping. I had to be careful. You never know what could be going on, working in a dance club. Girls were still coming up missing.

That Highway 99 killer has a name now, he's called the Green River killer and he's still going strong. He's been killing since

C. Oakes

before I left a few years ago. I'm glad somebody's paying attention now. There's about twenty victims that they know about. Nobody knows anything about this nut. They got a Green River task force that's been working on the case. And nothing yet. I'm scared. It could be that Green River nut following me. There were so many stories about this freak. Some claim they know who it is, he's in prison now, or he's dead. All I know is he hung around working girls. Most of the girls worked Highway 99, and 99 isn't that far from here. There were all kinds of girls gone now, White, Black, Asian, he was doing them all. You had to be careful.

Somebody's following me again. I need to tell Gus. I got to let somebody know that I was being followed when I got off work at night. Lord, who is this . . . following me like this. I'm scared.

The next night after work Gus was at the bar and I sat next to him. "Gus, somebody is following me home every night." Gus stopped and turned around to give me his full attention. We were both quietly looking at each other, sitting on the barstool.

"Somebody's following you?"

"Yes, Gus. I know it sounds crazy, but it's true."

"Nikki, how do you know?"

"I don't know, I can just tell, I get feelings about things." Gus was laughing at me. "Gus, I'm serious, somebody's following me every night when I get off work. Then one time, I speeded up and they speeded up too, I drove around till I lost them."

"Nikki, Nikki it's me."

"What?"

"It's me. I hired somebody to follow you. I wanted to know what you were doing."

"You're lying!"

"No I'm not. It's me. I didn't believe you didn't have a man. I figured you had somebody, but you don't. You're not doing a damn thing are you?" He was laughing loud. He was making fun of me then. "You're a trip. I didn't believe it. You just go to school and work. You don't have a man or nothing. What's wrong with you, girl. . . you don't have anybody."

"Ain't nothing wrong with me." I was pissed off now. "I just raise my boys."

"You sure do. You have a boring life, don't you. He was

getting a big laugh about my boring life. What do you do for fun?" I just rolled my eyes at him. "Hey, I need somebody to help me manage the club at night. I'll pay you five hundred a month, you don't do too much, just help change the music on the jukebox, seat customers, check on the girls when they need to be on stage. Tell me what's going on. You'll still work, make your money. It's just a few extra bucks. Not much to it." That meant I would have to work more often. I still agreed to join Gus's inner circle.

One of the girls at the Sands was named Ruby. She was cool. She wasn't 5 ft tall. She was Italian and Black, mixed. She had long black hair and she could do a split. Man, that girl would jump up then land straight into the split. I would tear something important if I tried that. Ruby's very pretty and has a lots of customers. But she's hard core, too, she's younger than me, but she's cool. All the girls I worked with were cool. They knew I didn't have many friends in town and one night after work, they took me to this after hours club to party with them.

The guys at this club were different from the pimps and things I'd been around. They were all businessmen and they were gangster hustlers, the old school type. They were old gentlemen. They sure weren't the pimp type. They all seem to have money, big money. They were all good friends too. They didn't know about me and didn't appreciate me being there. They were giving Ruby "the look" about bringing me around them.

Ruby just laughed loud, "Nikki, what do you want to drink? This is Nikki, y'all. Then she whispered to me, "Is Nikki your real name?"

"No, it's Sharell."

"Oh well. This is Sharell y'all." They just nodded. I got a glass of Hennessey. Then the biggest plate of cocaine that I'd ever seen, passed in front of me. Everybody turned to see what I was going to do. I just did what everybody else did. They didn't make lines to snort with a rolled up twenty, they just took a scoop with a match book to their noses. Emptied part of a cigarette, filled it with powder, then passed the plate.

They were playing poker with real money. It must have been anywhere from 20 to 50 thousand dollars in front of each person, maybe more. They were laughing, making jokes about each other.

Johnny was the main guy. He really intimidated me. Johnny looked mean. They were talking about Johnny bad.

"Yeah, Johnny always taking these welfare women, trying to make queens out of them."

"You just fuck yourself man. That's what you do."

Meanwhile, they were cracking up at this guy named Bobo. He had a hat and was passing it around for them to contribute money and he stood in front of each one till they put money in it.

"Look at that nigga over there, passing the hat. Man you ain't in church. Look at him."

"Y'all better come on and put some money in here. You know we got to get our woman out of jail." Bobo's girl had been with all of them at one time or another. They laughed hard. "Our woman got to get out of jail. Y'all fuck her just like I do. Why should I be the only one paying. Put some damn money in here so I can get our woman out of jail." He was laughing hard, too. Bobo didn't care, he wanted everybody to pay, and they did.

Let's see, I met MC, Man, Joe, Percy, Deano, a few women, I can't remember everybody. I just had fun with them all. I was up all night. I come dragging in the house, early in the morning. It was the weekend, so I gave Lana an extra twenty for staying with the boys all night.

My nose was so caked with white powder, I had to let water drip in my nostrils with a wet paper towels. I wasn't any good for my boys. I had to recover, come down, then get some sleep so I could function later today. But I enjoyed my new friends.

I went to the after hours club every night after work. It was like happy hour for us. We got a real drink. I was able to talk to regular guys. They weren't tricks. Tricks are a totally different animal. They don't want a relationship. All they want is their little freakish desires met with no strings attached and a trick can be way out there.

These guys spent big dough, they definitely want a relationship, they're gonna mark your ass with their diamonds, furs and cars. They were gentlemen. Their girls had huge rocks on their fingers. I'm talking three karats or more. Their women wore long minks. Kathy had every color mink, fox, and sable. Johnny had brought Kathy a white Mercedes, she had a Cadillac, and he built her a house.

They pride themselves on how their women looked, they spoiled them rotten. I never seen black men like these. To me, most black men with money like that wanted white girls. They thought like Jerry. Only messed with high yellow sisters. Most of the ball players only let the white girls dance for them at the club. Didn't make me any difference cause I made my money.

I stayed quiet around everybody. Mostly all these women were really loud. In Oklahoma, we weren't loud like that. These girls cussed like soldiers. Kathy didn't talk loud like the rest of them. Kathy wasn't a dancer either but she went to high school with Ruby and the rest of them. They were all good friends. Kathy was cool. I was glad to see her at the club when I got off cause she had more class. I didn't feel as comfortable with the girls I worked with, nothing wrong with them, it's just that I didn't feel as comfortable hanging out with them. There were a few dancers that were okay, but they didn't come to the after hours club.

Everything seemed to be working out. I met some new friends that were cool, and good people. These guys took me in like family. They knew I was a single parent with two boys and they were looking out for me. In a way, they felt obligated to help me. Making sure I was alright.

During the Christmas season, they brought my kids all kinds of toys. This environment was different. They still had a problem trusting me. Just like Gus, they couldn't believe me. They thought I might be the police. I didn't talk like everybody else. I wasn't slick.

"Why don't you have a man? You're good looking. Are you a lesbian or something?" Johnny was always questioning my sexuality.

Me and Kathy became good friends and Johnny didn't know what to think.

"Sharell, are you sure you don't like women?"

"No, Johnny. Why you think I'm gay. You keep asking me stuff like that. I just haven't met anybody. I think I should raise my boys, don't you. They keep me busy enough."

He raised his hand with a gesture. "I'm just asking. Hey, nothing wrong with me asking, is it? I don't want you messing with my woman if you're some kind of lesbian."

"No Johnny. I'm not gay. I promise. You don't have to worry."

Kathy chimed in. "Damn, Johnny. I can't have no friends."

"Well Kathy, why she don't have a man?" He spoke like I wasn't right there in front of them. Matter of fact, Johnny liked me as a friend just like Kathy. He thought I was smart. He just couldn't figure me out is all. The guys thought I wanted their women and the women thought I wanted their men. I was hoping I meet somebody soon, a friend or something, just to shut them up.

There were a lot of guys that liked me, but I didn't want to be one of their women who was passed around because there weren't any real feelings for anybody in the group. No real love connection. I was fine by myself. Everybody else is the ones with the problem. I was okay with me.

I was taking the boys to church but kind of let up since I started hanging out at the after hours club with my new friends. I had to get back into it. The boys and I had been church hopping, trying to find us one that we felt comfortable enough to join. Actually, I was hoping to find a church like my church in Oklahoma.

I found this one church on Jackson street. Ms. Helen, who owned the soul food restaurant, went to that one. I felt comfortable there because she smiled at us when we first attended. My friends didn't go to church.

We ate at Ms. Helen's restaurant a lot. She recognized us. That's where I found out Matt was allergic to shell fish. He threw up gumbo all over her table. Yeah, she recognized us which made it nice. I liked going to church with my boys. I wanted them to know God. That's one thing I prayed about, all the time, that they grow up knowing God. Lord knows I've seen so many weirdo's in my life. I didn't want my boys like that. I prayed so hard for them. I also knew that I had to take them and I had stopped going to church. I needed to do better.

C. Oakes

Chapter 16

Phyl called.

"Phylis, girl what's up? Everybody alright?" I got nervous because getting a call from home, out of the blue like that, well you naturally think the worst.

"Yeah girl, we're fine. We're doing good, just taking care of these kids."

"I know that's right, me too."

"Sharell, I called because Val's coming up there."

"She is? When?" This was good news. I was excited.

"It'll be a while, but start looking for her a place to stay."

"Awh man. . . that's no problem. I got some friends that have all kinds of houses for rent. They're good people. She'll get a nice place."

"That's good. I told her you probably know somebody with a place or something. At least you would help her find a place to live."

"Sure, sure. I'm happy to do that for Val. I'm happy she's coming here. At least somebody that's knows me will be close for a change."

"Okay."

"Hey, tell Val not to worry about it. I got it."

"You sure?"

"Phyl, I got this. I'll give you a call in a couple of weeks to let you know something."

"Girl, thanks."

"Hey, you're my sister."

"Love you!"

"Love you, too."

I was so glad to hear Val was coming to Seattle. I'll have some family here. Valerie is Phyl's older sister. In school, I was scared of Val. I don't know why, for some reason, she just intimidated me. I hadn't seen her since we were kids. She got married after high school. Her husband was quite a bit older than she. They're still together. I think it's been over ten years for them. That's nice. I wish I had married somebody good like that. And I was still married to the same man all my life. Man. Her husband's in the military. I was finally going to have a homie with me. I was so happy. I'll have to let Johnny know that she's going to need a place. I didn't ask about her kids. Shoot, I don't know how many kids Val has now. Well, I got time.

Lana, the babysitter, found her a little boyfriend and she's been messing up with me. Seems like that girl grew up over night. When I first moved next door, Lana was kind of homely. She didn't wear makeup, she didn't have much of a shape. But now, Teri, her mom, has her hands full. I'm glad I have boys. Lana has fire red hair and real fair skin. She's a pretty girl with all legs.

I know that boy has her doing this crazy shit. She's been wearing my sweaters. Just helping herself to my things. My white Angola sweater, I didn't want anybody wearing that. I saw one like it on the soaps. One night, I went to bed and my sheets were dirty. "They've been screwing in my bed. Damnit." I was so pissed. "Damn, I don't like that." Then my ceramic piggy bank, it's big, it sat on the floor because its was so heavy; somebody chiseled a hole in the bottom of my piggy bank and was taking my quarters out as fast as I was putting them in there. That boy has her doing this shit or she's letting him do it. He's going to get her in trouble. I didn't want to say anything to her mom, but this has got to stop. I'll talk to Lana first.

The boys and I were going to church pretty regularly again, well almost regularly. I liked the church on Jackson. I was checking out the preacher and thought maybe he was a little too fly, that's cause he has a long jeri curl and he was kind of young. He may be thirty something. But after I looked at his shoes, I didn't think that he was so "fly" anymore. He wore granddaddy shoes. This guy was real. He could teach and preach like they did in the south. I liked the way he would explain situations that happened in the biblical days. He would dramatize how it must have been. He could paint a mental picture for us with all the history of why people thought as they did. The customs they had that regulated their lives. He was a good teacher.

What made it really good for me is the time I spent in prison and read the Bible for myself. For the first time in my life, I knew what the preacher was talking about. I was following what he was saying. It's terrible that I had to go to prison to finally read it, but that understanding I got while I was there, was worth it. I know God better. This understanding makes church better. The singing was great. I can even understand church folk better. They try to do good. They try. That's all anybody can do is try. They try.

Man, I was getting it, then he said something I hadn't heard before. My antennas jumped up. I sat straight up. What is this he's saying. I listened more closely. This preacher was going on, loud.

"If you give ten percent of what I have given you, and bring it back to the store house first, that's to the church first, sisters and brothers . . . Give to God first. If you give ten percent. That's all. One dime of every dollar. Then I will open up the windows of heaven and pour you out a blessing that you won't have room to receive it. Can you imagine that, God, blessing you so much, so much, that you don't have room to receive it. Then He goes on to say. Try me now. See don't I do it. God will . . . brothers and sisters. He's God, He's Almighty. Try him now. He will pour you out a blessing from heaven, that you will not have room to receive it. Let's pray. Father, we thank you for your word . . ."

I had never heard that before. I read it again and again. That's what it says. I'm going to try it. Give Him ten percent first and the windows of heaven will open and He will pour me out a blessing, that I won't have room to receive it. I'm going to try it.

Every week whether I went to church or not, I stopped by the church office to give my ten percent. It wasn't hard, I just took my money after work each night, count what I'd made, take ten percent out and put it in my Bible. I'd give a little extra for good measure. Nothing to it. I noticed that every week a little more was going in the pot. When I didn't get to church, I gave my tithes the following Monday. Then I'd run out of the office before anybody said anything to me. It had gotten kind of hard for me to work, knowing I'm going to do some table dancing later that night, after I praised God that morning. So I stopped going to church on Sundays. I needed to work. But I still wanted to give my tithes. I wanted God to pour me out a blessing. I didn't know what kind of blessing, I just wanted something.

"Hey sister, Sister Sharell, . . is that it. Sharell?" I turned to see who it was and it was the pastor.

"Yes sir?"

"Girl, I've never met anybody like you, . . . you don't come to church, but you're paying your tithes every week. That's the first. Why aren't you coming to church, sister?"

"Well, pastor." I hung my head and wasn't saying anything.

"I want to see you more often in church."

"Yes sir."

"How's those boys?"

"They're well."

"Good, good." He left me alone, I was sure glad he didn't press the issue. He sensed something, I know he did, well whatever. I turned and ran out the door.

I have stopped going so much cause the more I went to church, the more trouble I had working in the club. I got to where I could hardly dance for a customer. Doing those lap dances got tough. Things were picking up, though. I really didn't have to work so much. The little money Gus was giving me helped. Then I got these customers that were giving me real money with no strings attached. I got a thousand from this one guy that's a butcher. He just handed me ten one hundred dollar bills, then it happened again. This old man gave me a couple thousand. I was thinking, this tithing business works. I started just being a hostess, waiting on tables and managing the other dancers.

There were two billboards across the street from the club. I asked Gus to lease those billboards and advertise for the club. That's what the clubs did in Oklahoma. Have giant girls hanging on billboards, advertising the clubs in Oklahoma. These billboards weren't used. They were waiting for us, Gus got the signs and advertised for the Sands. We had customers lined up around the building to come inside the Sands. I didn't have to dance anymore. I waited tables. Dressed pretty. My tips were a couple hundred a night. I don't know where all this money was coming from but it was coming. I couldn't figure it out. It just happened.

One day, Teri, Lana's mother was sitting on the front steps waiting on me. She was very upset, looked like she was crying.

"Hey, Sharell, I need somebody to talk to." I thought for sure it would be about Lana and her new boyfriend. Maybe Lana was pregnant or something.

"What's up, Teri." Yeah, she's crying. " What's wrong, girl."

"Sharell, I found this." She showed me some paper.

C. Oakes

"What's that?"

"Girl, it's a letter that my son wrote." Teri has a older son that seems to be a cool kid. He was about fifteen. Good looking kid. He never said too much to me, but he and his group of friends were always playing with my boys. They took them trick or treating on Halloween. He and his friends all seemed like normal, cool teenagers. They weren't the mischievous type, at least that's how they acted around me.

"Sharell, it's written in blood."

"Written in blood? Why?"

"It's to the devil."

"Whaaaaat? Girrrrrl!"

"What would make him want to write something like this, Sharell."

"Teri, girrrl . . . I don't know."

"I know I haven't been the best parent in the world. My kids don't see their father at all. Maybe we should have gone to church more. I don't know what to do." She was blaming herself. "I'm sending him to stay with my parents for a while." She wanted me to listen. I did, I just listened and felt so bad for her. I felt her pain. I wanted to cry with her. I know she tries to be a good mother. She is a good mother. I really didn't know what to tell her.

I hadn't been around anything like that before and couldn't imagine why someone would want to do that. Write a letter to the devil, man. Why would he do that? He's such a quiet, nice kid. I was baffled. Growing up in Oklahoma and especially when my daddy was living with us, we were in church every Sunday, all day. Church and God had a big impact on me. Faith in God is what I was taught. I'm not perfect, no not at all, but I want God with me. I didn't know what was in the letter, didn't want to know. All I know is this . . . It's time to move!

"Johnny, I really need a place to move and my friend is coming here, she needs a place, too."

"I got a house that's ready, but it's too much house for you by yourself."

"What you mean too much house for me?"

"Sharell, it's big."

"How big?"

"It has five bedrooms."

"How much are you asking for it."

"I'll let you have it for $500 a month."

"I can pay that."

"Yeah, but I'm not letting you move in by yourself."

"Well, let me move in, because my friend is coming and we can stay there together."

"How you know she'll want a roommate? You're making plans for that woman. She might need her own place." He was right, I didn't know that.

"Well, Johnny, keep it for me. Let me make sure."

Phylis was glad I called. "Girl, I was worried to death. You said you would get back with me in two weeks."

"Time passes so fast, Phyl. When is Val coming."

"She's on her way now and you hadn't called me back. I didn't know what to tell her. They were getting a hotel until I could contact you."

"How is she coming?"

"Girl, they're riding the Greyhound."

"Awh, man. I know she's going to be tired. That's about two or three days on the bus. When will she be here?"

"Tomorrow."

"Okay."

"You got something for them? I told her not to worry about a place, that you'll have everything worked out. Then I didn't hear from you."

"How come you didn't call me to let me know she was on her way."

"I tried. I couldn't get you. Girl, I was so worried. I told Val you had everything ready for her. Did you get them something?"

"Yeah, but I need to talk with her about this arrangement I got."

"What arrangement?"

"I want to know if she mind a roommate."

"Who you got for her as a roommate?"

"Me."

"Awh, she wouldn't mind that."

"You sure?"

"Yeah, I'm sure."

"My friend Johnny has this place that he won't give me unless I got somebody there with me. He said it's too much house for me by myself."

"What kind of place is that?"

"It's a five bedroom house."

"Oh, that should be big enough for y'all."

"Well. I'm going to go ahead and get it so we'll have it when they arrive. I'll try to have everything together for her."

"Girl, that's wonderful. How does this place look?"

"I haven't seen it yet."

"You haven't?"

"Nope, but I know Johnny, if he says it's big, then it's big. I know it's nice. He ain't giving me nothing that ain't right."

"I hope so."

"Girl, you should meet these people, they're top of the line."

"Well, call me and let me know how things go."

"Okay, I'll have Val call."

She laughed. "Okay girl, let me know something."

"Okay, bye now."

Val and the kids looked crazy when they got off the bus. They looked completely wore out. We had to make a bunch of trips back to the station to get all their things. Just my luck they arrived in the middle of the night. My little car was packed to the gills.

I was so happy to have Val here and she was glad to have me there, too. Val's husband was still in Panama and he was being stationed in Tacoma when he comes back to the states. Val said she was tired of living over there and wanted to come back to the states, have a place together for them before he retires in about two years. They were in Panama for over five years.

Val has three kids and our house was perfect. Just perfect. We weren't crowded at all. It has three stories, with spiral stairs up to the top floor. The downstairs was a unit by itself. Val and her kids took the downstairs unit. Only their kitchen area was a mini kitchen. There were three bedrooms on the bottom floor, a den or living room area, and a full bathroom. On my floor is the master bedroom, it has the main kitchen, a living room area, full bathroom and a huge dining room. Then on the top floor, which was formally the attic, was a huge bedroom and a separate game room. That's where my boys stayed. It was perfect for us. Val was happy with the house, and me and my boys love it, too.

The elementary school was on the corner, maybe half a block. Ronnie went there. Val's two older kids, Edward and Veta, caught the school bus with my big boy, Matt. Then she had a younger son, Charlie, he was only two years old.

Val didn't waste any time getting herself together. She put an ad in the newspaper for housecleaning and got customers right away. We went to the car auction and she found a nice car. Kathy gave us extra bedroom and living room furniture. Val's stuff was in storage in Oklahoma City. We were settled in no time. I loved having Val in Seattle. We were perfect roommates. The kids got along great. Val cooked dinner every night. I was used to making enough for leftovers. She didn't believe in eating leftovers. She really spoiled us.

I was able to work and party with my friends more because Val was a home body. All she did was take care of the kids and the house. I felt guilty so I paid the rent and we went half on utilities. I volunteered to pay the utilities too, but she wouldn't have that. The way she took care of the kids was priceless. Every night she helped with homework, cooked, made sure they had their bathes— she did everything. She went to the school functions with my kids, as well as her kids. I was in hog heaven. That's probably how husbands feel when they don't have to worry about nothing but bringing home the bacon.

Kathy and Johnny liked Val, too. She cleaned their house and some of their friends houses, too. She was trustworthy. That's important. Val minded her own business. Everybody was happy, especially me.

I was at the after hours one night. There was a older gentleman, about forty years my senior, playing poker with the gang. He won this really big pot. I was sitting on the sidelines watching. I've been playing poker for about five or six years now, but there's no way I would play with these cats, cause part of their game was to cheat. These guys try to cheat every hand. They mark the cards, there's so many ways they cheat. He won about one hundred thousand dollars that hand. He was taunting them.

Everybody wants to break Presley. Everybody wants to get Presley's money. I didn't have but a pair of fives. Before I knew it, I grabbed the cards to see. Everybody at the table stood up. . . except Presley. He just looked at me. These guys were about to have my head on a platter. I dropped the cards as fast as I grabbed them.

"Oh, I'm sorry." I was embarrassed. I don't know what got into me to grab those cards like that. I guess I was caught up in the moment. Presley just smiled at me. Johnny and BoBo were fussing at me.

"You keep your little ass over there. You don't mess with these cards." Johnny was kind of smiling. He couldn't believe I grabbed those cards.

"You got some money, Sharell? You want to get in this game?" The guy that was running the game was rolling his eyes at me, then looking at everybody, fussing, too.

"Where did you get her from? Y'all better control y'all's friends."

Kathy was cracking up. Tears were rolling down her face, she was laughing so hard.

This booster came in with some coats. Cashmere coats, leather coats with fur collars. Some were just plain long wool coats. They were all nice, all colors.

"Hey let me see what you got there." Presley looked at me. "You see anything you like."

"Let me see here." I went through the merchandise looking for something that I might like. They were too big. I'm only size five on a good day. The only one that might fit was a camel colored, full length cashmere coat. It was nice.

"How much?" Presley was handing the guy some money. I thanked him. Presley got up from the poker table and came to sit with me.

'What's your name?"

"I'm Sharell."

"Hi Sharell, please to meet you. I'm Presley. Where is there to eat around here? Can I take you to breakfast?"

"Well sure. That'll be nice, let's see. . .there's Thirteen Coins. I like that place."

"I want breakfast food. They have breakfast."

"No, maybe we can go to Deano's place."

"It's open now?"

"Yes, he's open."

"Will you have breakfast with me?"

"Sure and thanks for the coat."   Before we left for breakfast, I quietly slipped over to Kathy.

"What's up with this guy?"

"Girl, he's rich. That's Presley. He's one of Johnny's friends. He lives in California. He comes up here a lot. Girl, you want to catch him."

"Oh yeah."

"Uh uh. Girrrrrl he's one of the main ones."

I looked him over. He seemed nice.

Chapter 17

Presley was really good to me. He never had those doubts about me like everybody else, he didn't think I was gay and liked women. Never thought I was some kind of police, like everybody else thought at one point. Presley was real. He gave me only one rule, he said I was never to let anybody put a sack of dope in my hands to sell. I could live with that. Presley warned me and warned me.

"Now, Sharell, if you ever take a sack, I'll have to stop seeing you."

"Presley, you don't have to worry about that. I'm not the type to sell drugs." I knew that I can't sell drugs cause I'm not slick enough. People play a lot of games when you're in that business. You have to have a tough heart to sell drugs. Dope friends would run all over me. Presley was serious and I wasn't going to sell any drugs and mess up a good thing.

Sometimes the gang would say things to make Presley jealous. Since he was gone so much, they liked to shake his confidence a little in me, also they knew he liked me. I just hated when somebody would tell a ball-faced lie or insinuate something was happening with this person or that person, just to get next to Presley. They thought that stuff was funny. Presley did have a jealous streak and that was okay. I wanted him to be a little jealous. Once I went to see a friend from Oklahoma. He was promoting his book at a local television station in Seattle. Of course, Presley said he knew the guy and didn't want me to see him. He complained.

"I don't know why you want to see him. He ain't got nothing. He's broke."

"Presley, he's a homie. We use to hang out back in the day. We were friends."

"Well, I'm the one that broke his ass. I got all his money."

"Why are you jealous of Thomas, Presley? Stop throwing salt on Thomas." Thomas did play ball in California. Presley probably did know Thomas. But I left that alone and went to see Thomas anyway.

Presley came to Seattle every month, then he'd stay about 10 days to 2 weeks. He absolutely spoiled me. I had stopped smoking cocaine but started back while I was hanging out with Presley. I thought it would be okay if I smoked it only with him. He would have so much that we never ran out. The time we spent together, I wouldn't work. He'd give me so much money that I didn't have to work. Every day he would give me two to four hundred dollars, sometimes he'd forget and give me more. Or sometimes he wanted to play around a bit, needed some space, so he'd give me enough money so I wouldn't complain about him playing around with somebody else. Sooner or later he'd come back, a little worried, looking for me.

I really liked Presley, too. I was never involved with a man this much older than me. I never thought I would go for someone this old. But I liked Presley. This had to be the most elegant man I've ever met. His mannerism was elegant. He walked elegantly. He was tall, dark, and handsome.

Presley said he played poker all over the world. He said he invented some of the ways to cheat. Presley has red and blue chalk behind the buttons on his shirts that he uses to mark the card when he plays poker. He's so funny, he'd have these thick bifocals on looking at cards in people's hands. Trying to see the marks from across the table. Sometimes he would lean so far across the table, you'd think he's going to fall over. You had to know he was looking for something, he'd just play if off, like he's counting the pot. He'd tell me everybody cheated some time, some way.

On the other hand, he was so smooth and so sweet. He always wanted to know what I was thinking. It mattered to him what I thought and how I felt or how I saw things. We'd talk about politics. I liked that. We were connected. I could tell when he came to town, seems like the air was different. I got excited for no reason. Then it hit me. Presley was here.

Yep, times were good. I was enjoying life for a change. Gus was great. He paid off my little car. Since I was half way managing the club and since it picked up so much, he rewarded me with the title to my car. The girls at the club treated me like I was a big sister. That's because I would stand up for them. Gus would get mad at somebody and fire them, then I'd argue all night till they had a second chance. I wasn't scared of Gus. I liked Gus, he use to wear black everyday. Gangster style. He couldn't help it, he was just a gangster. It was his Greek nature.

The club was running good. Every body was making money. But the drugs had gotten out of hand. Girls were smoking and snorting in the dressing room everyday. All night. They couldn't leave the dressing room to get the money that was out on the floor, taking hit after hit. We called it the white ghost cause it was up in smoke. I was begging girls to come down.

"BJ, Sugar Cane, get down here. Lillie, please help me, can you get on stage now. Dorothy, the customers are leaving, nobody's out there dancing. What are y'all doing? Man, BJ get a grip." I tried to reason with the dancers to put the pipe down and come out the dressing room.

"Nikki, girl, come here and take a hit of this." Tess was an Asian dancer, she always had the good powder. I took a quick snort and continued to beg them to come down. I was trying to keep them from getting too high up there, but White girls and Asian girls were snorting like crazy till they got nose bleeds and Black girls were smoking their brains out.

Gus knew things were out of hand but he didn't know what to do. He'd stay in his apartment. Some of these girls were like his daughters. A few had been on the streets since their preteens, twelve or thirteen. And Gus felt protective of them. I felt he really loved all of us. He was going crazy worrying about everybody.

I was worrying too. Alycie was my friend, she snorted heroin. She was the only one that got sick. Sometimes she was really sick. She'd just say, "Oh I'm fine, I'm just feeling a little weird today." She'd make a call and go home for the evening. Alycie was one of the older girls. She was so pretty, a smooth, dark skinned sister with coal black, long, wavy hair. This was her real hair, no hair pieces. She had eyes like an Asian or Hawaiian. She was just pretty. I always wondered how somebody that looked like her become a heroin junkie, but then, people always wondered how I became a dancer.

Then BJ. She was the baby of us. This was definitely one of Gus's babies. When I met BJ, she was only sixteen. She had been working on the streets a few years already. I didn't know she was so young. BJ had been on the streets since she was twelve, maybe younger. Gus gave her a job in the club to keep her off the streets. I guess the streets had taken its toll on BJ because she didn't look young at all. Shoot, BJ had more street smarts than me. Mostly all these girls in Seattle got turned out at a young age. Ruby and Sharon, all of them had been out there a while, grew up out there on the streets. Although I was older in age, I was the baby as far as experience.

But BJ had my heart. She was really sweet, with the prettiest smile you want to see. Her teeth were perfect and white. BJ was a tan colored sister. She kept her hair dyed blond. She sort of kept to herself, didn't mix with other dancers too much. She had lots of regular customers. BJ would make her money and was out the door. I would really worry about BJ cause she got too high. She got slow motion high.

For some reason, smoking cocaine made you look toward the ground. Even when you're talking with someone, you keep looking off or at the ground. You can't have any eye contact while on that stuff. I wonder why it's like that. You just can't hold your head up. You can't talk, your lips don't work right. Cocaine has you tweeked out. BJ came in the club, barely moving, staring at the ground, picking the carpet for pebbles of rock cocaine that wasn't there. She couldn't work like that. I stayed in the dressing room with her. I had a bottle of rum, so I fixed us a drink of rum and coke, hoping the alcohol would help bring her down off the cocaine. We were there all night till closing, just talking about every thing.

"So why they call you BJ?"

"Girl, you know what BJ stand for."

"BJ," I thought about it. "No I don't know."

"Nikki, stop lying. You know what BJ stand for."

"No, tell me."

"Blow Job. BJ stands for blow job."

"Whaaaat!"

BJ started laughing at me. "Nikki, you're so crazy, everybody knows that."

I was stunned. "Why you call yourself that?"

"Cause when you tell a trick your name is BJ, they automatically think about a blow job. Then I can get more dances and dates. Oh! You know I don't do it, but the tricks don't know that."

I was thinking, . . yeah, that's a real working girl, promise the world, get the money, and don't do a damn thang. I didn't say anything else about it, but I wondered why she would call herself that. I guess she's just a hustler.

"Nikki, you ever pray?"

"Yeah, I pray, do you?"

"Naw . . .I've never prayed."

"Why not?"

"Girl, I don't know how to pray. I've never prayed. I don't know what to say."

I knew what she was thinking. She's looking at herself wondering what would I say, how can I explain this, to God. But, at least, she wanted to know! I used to be the same way. Wondering what could I say, to God, for me, for my actions.

"Nikki, how do you pray?"

I was thinking . . . "Wow, this is my chance. I'm going to tell somebody about God. I'm going to tell somebody about Jesus." When I went to prison, I really felt a connection to God, I felt like he had me. . . I belong to him. I felt like I had the understanding that I've never had before and now I'm ready, for my mission. This was my chance. I have to be careful not to blow it.

"BJ, it's like this, God loves us. He wants us with him. . .so much that he gave Jesus, his Son, to bring us closer to him. There is this bridge between us and the Father, it's called sin. Because of sin, we need help going to the Father, that's because the Father is Holy.

So when you pray to God, you ask Jesus to take you to the Father and Jesus will take you, in spirit . . .it's like he's taking you, by the hand, and walking you to the Father in prayer. Go to God in everything. Just ask in Jesus' name. You know Jesus was the sacrifice for us, because we're sinners. Just ask and Jesus will be right there walking you to the Father. Girrrrrl. That's real."

The next time I saw BJ, she looked like a different person. Shoot, she was a different person. BJ had dyed her hair black, she was glowing. BJ's whole essence was radiant. Bright. She looked pure.

BJ was so excited. "Nikki, Nikki, girl guess what. Guess

what!"

"What, what?"

"I got saved."

"Whaaaaaat?"

"I got saved." BJ was so happy.

"What happened?"

"Girl, I went to this church and I got saved." BJ was changing into her costume, moving fast, trying to get on the floor. "I'll talk to you later, I'll tell you all about it."

I left without talking to BJ. I'll catch her later, I couldn't wait to hear what happened. I wanted to hear every word.

I went straight over to Kathy's house. I wanted a hit. She always wanted me over, I was somebody for her to get high with. Kathy started smoking coke, too. We'd smoke, talk, I'd try to go home, but she'd entice me with more coke. Daylight would break, then I'd run to the house before the kids woke up. That was our daily routine. I got to where I didn't want to work. That's another thing about coke, I didn't want to work. All I wanted to do was snort and smoke that stuff. Then I wanted to live like Kathy. She had plenty of money.

One thing's for sure, I wasn't going to spend my hard earned money on cocaine, they always gave me what I wanted. When it came to money, Presley told Johnny to give me what I wanted and he would take care of the bill when he came to town. But that shit got old to Johnny. I would go to Johnny, tell him I needed a few hundred, then he'd make a big deal. Call down to Presley, Presley would give him the okay, but Johnny hated to give me the money. I guess he had to work for it and I wasn't his woman.

Johnny would complain, "tell that nigga to buy that house for you. He got the money. I'll sell that house to you right now for sixty thousand." I knew that was a deal, so I called home to my folks.

"Momma, I'm staying in this five bedroom house, they said they would sell it to me for sixty thousand. Momma, it's a nice house."

"Baby, I can't invest in something like that without seeing it."

"Well, y'all need to come up here and visit sometime. I always come home, every year I come home, nobody's ever come here to visit me. I've been here over five years now and nobody's come, not one time." I wanted to get that house. I knew it was a bargain. What could I do? I didn't have any work history. I danced for a living. It wasn't two months later that a big story came out. "Seattle, America's Best Kept Secret." Housing doubled, tripled. My house was appraised for over 200 thousand dollars. Johnny didn't raise my rent. He's a good guy.

I didn't like going to the club anymore. Everybody was high. Then I got high, it was out of hand. There was no control over the drugs, it was wild. Frankly, I was scared too, because the police may decide to come through any time. Gus sure wasn't hanging around either. He stayed in his apartment. Plus, the Ballard neighborhood decided to launch a crusade against the billboards in the neighborhood.

Gus was very adamant about supporting his neighborhood. He always supported the Ballard community, and the community always put up with Gus and his club. But they weren't having the billboard signs any longer, making their neighborhood look like the strip. They launched a campaign against the Sands advertising in the neighborhood. They said it was too close to schools.

I think what happened was the traffic, well, maybe it was the club traffic, cause a beach was right down the street. The community didn't want those billboard ads any longer. All those guys, hanging around at all times of night, for those dancer girls, messing up the neighborhood. As long as it was quiet, it was okay. The signs were too much.

BJ died. I couldn't believe it. BJ died. Gus went ballistic. He was storming around firing everybody. It was just the three of them there. BJ, Alycie and one of the local disc jockey's from another club. Alycie was crying uncontrollably. BJ was her friend. Alycie watched her grow up.

"Nikki, we didn't know what to do. You know how high BJ would get." I just listened. I couldn't believe what I was hearing. "Nikki, she took a really big hit, you know how BJ would do, and she went into convulsions. We were all high, we were trying to help her, then she died."

"You could tell that she died?"

Alycie nodded. "Yeah, you could tell. She started shaking then she just stopped. I tried to help her." Alycie was quiet. Just crying. "Nikki, we left her in the room."

"What? How long did you leave her there? "

"I don't know. It was at night. We were trying to think." Alycie was crying so hard she couldn't talk. "We left her in the room. She was dead. BJ died right there in front of us."

"And y'all just left her like that?"

"No, well, when it got daylight, we called her mom's boy-friend."

"You did?"

She was nodding. "He's a cop. We told him what happened. He came and got her."

Oh, I felt so sorry for all of them. I can't imagine that. My friend dying in front of me like that. I know one thing. It could have happened to any of us. Everybody was getting high.

Gus was so pissed, he banned Alycie from ever working in the Sands again. Alycie worked for Gus over twenty years.

Man, all I could do was think about my last conversation with BJ. She told me she was saved. She looked saved. I wonder if what she did, her little backslide made a difference to God. I don't think so. What I really think is our Father was preparing BJ to go with him. I decided to visit BJ's mom. I felt like I needed to share my last conversation I had with BJ. I wanted to tell her mom what we talked about. Her mom had a nice house.

"Hi, I'm Sharell. I was BJ's friend." She looked at me like she didn't know who I was talking about. "Your daughter was my friend, and I just want to tell you about our last conversation."

"Oh, you were one of Angelique's friends?"

Angelique . . Angelique, I was listening to her mother say her name. Whow, BJ had a beautiful name. She was an angel. "An-gelique told me she got saved. Ma'am, Angelique looked saved too." I told her about our conversations. I think BJ would have wanted me to tell her. BJ's mom was just as beautiful.

"Would you like to visit with her. She's ready for visitors." I thought about it for about a second.

No ma'am, I don't think so. I want to remember Angelique the way I last saw her, happy, with that pretty smile. She had a beautiful smile."

Then I said goodbye to Angelique's mom, and bye to my friend.

Chapter 18

I can't remember the last time I took my kids to church. I ought to be ashamed of myself. Its my responsibility to teach my children about God and teach them values and morals. Boy, I need to get a grip on things. I got to do better. I need to spend time with my babies. They both worry about me. They don't need to be worrying about their momma. They don't know I do drugs or anything like that. They haven't seen me with some man either. I know they wonder what I'm doing at all times of night. They know I work in a club. They've always known that. But I use to come home at night. Now, well. . . I just have to do better.

The other day Matt was giving me the third degree.

"Mom, where were you?"

"I was out."

"Well, what time did you get in?"

"I don't know, Matt, why you ask?"

"Because I woke up and I was up a long time waiting for you. You never came home."

Ronnie was listening, then he started. "Yeah, Mom, one day, I waited for you, too. I was up all night till the sun came up and you never came home."

"You what?"

"I stayed up all night waiting for you. You never came home, Mom."

I stopped right then and started hugging and kissing both of them. I love them so much. I don't want them worrying about their momma.

"Momma, I was waiting for you but I fell asleep and it was morning already."

"Oh, I'm sorry, baby."

It was Matt's time again. "Momma, are you over Kathy's house all night?"

"Baby, I'm sorry I've been gone so much. I'm not going to stay out like that anymore. Okay?"

"Okay, Momma. We just don't know where you're at all night long. You got to be careful these days, Momma." I listened to my big boy. He's telling me to be careful. He sounds so old.

Val's always there. She just spoiled me. Well, I got lazy. The drugs and partying kept me up all night, and when I do come home, I'm tired. Too tired to see about my babies. I sleep. I stopped doing a lot of things with my kids. I'm taking advantage of Val. She's so good. Never complain, except one time she made me stop buying her things. She was getting all teary eyed, calling herself fussing at me.

"Sharell, you got to stop."

"What Val?"

"You always buying me things, paying for everything. I can give you money for bills and food. I can pay my way, Sharell, I'm a grown-ass woman. I can carry my own weight."

I was thinking . . .What's wrong with Val. "Damn Val, I just appreciate you being here with my kids. You cook, you see about them, you do everything. I just want to do something for you, for a change. You do so much for me."

"Well, you need to spend time with your kids, Sharell."

"I know."

"I don't mind the boys, they're just like my kids. We all do things together. Homework and everything. So it ain't no problem with them. They're good kids, you just need to spend time with them yourself."

"I know Val. A few minutes ago, they gave me the third degree."

"Well, you know the boys ain't no problem with me."

Val started crying again. "What's wrong, Val. Why you crying?"

"I came from the doctor today."

"Everything alright?"

"Yeah, everything's alright, it's just that I'm having twins."

"What! What! You're having twins? You sure?"

"Yep. You can see them. The ultrasound shows both of them."

"Can you tell what they are?"

She smiled. "Yeah, they're both girls. Sharell, what am I going to do with twins? Charlie's already a hand full. Girl, at the doctors today, Charlie was making that grinding noise he always make, and was driving the nurses crazy. They asked me, if I could please shut him up." She was laughing.

C. Oakes

"What did you tell them?"

"I just told them, I've tried. He always make that noise." We laughed about Charlie. He's a trip. She's right, that boy's a hand full. I thought it's great she's having twins.

"So, when are the babies due?"

"Girl, I got a few months, I'm only four months now." She looked six months. Val's going to be big as a house. "Eddie should be retiring by the time I have the babies."

"He is?"

Val laugh, she knows I'm not ready for her husband to come home and break up our family. We have a great arrangement. "Sharell, will it be a problem if Eddie stays here with us until we find a place?"

"Girl, no. That's not a problem. Take as much time as you need. When is he getting out?"

"I'm not sure, I'll let you know."

Val's husband, Eddie came to Ft. Lewis a few months ago. He stays on base. I remember when they first met, he took Val away quick. So I only saw him a couple of times. They've been living the military life every since they got married. She was only eighteen. He's going to get out and mess up everything. Me and Val's living arrangements were perfect, at least for me. She and the kids visit Eddie at Ft. Lewis on weekends, that's how she got pregnant. I'm happy that her family can spend time together, I just know he's going to take Val away from me. This is the first time I felt alright about living here, in Seattle, with only me and the kids. It felt like home.

Things were becoming unglued for me. There, the Lord showed me He was true to His word. That tithing thing works. I was getting a lot of blessings at first, but I couldn't hang. I stopped tithing. It's hard to continue to tithe every week, especially when you're doing things you shouldn't do, like smoking coke everyday. Not taking your kids to church like you should. When I stay away from church, it was easier to make excuses for working in the club, partying all night, not spending time with the kids. When I go to church, it's a constant battle going on inside me. I was in straight contrast with my being and my heart. By not going to church, I don't have to think about what's right so much.

Johnny was getting tired of giving me money, too. I couldn't see the big deal. Presley paid him the money back. Then it hit me, Kathy was complaining that Johnny was giving me money, too. Then one day while I was over Kathy's, Presley called to talk with Johnny, then she said it right in front of me, while on the phone with Presley.

"I should be with you, Presley." Kathy was looking straight at me, dead in my face and then she said it again only louder. "I said, I should be with you. So I won't have to do nothing but ask Johnny for some damn money when I wanted something." Kathy eyes were glued on me. She was tripping. Kathy knows exactly what she's doing and saying.

I got up and stood by her, then whispered so Presley couldn't hear me. "Girl, what is wrong with you. Why did you do that?" I watched and listened while Kathy knocked me off the pot.

She smiled, "Here Johnny, the telephone."

"Why did you do that? Kathy, what made you do that?" I couldn't believe my friend would purposely ruin my relationship with Presley, but she did.

"I got to work and take chances on going to jail, and you don't have to do a damn thang, but ask my man for some damn money. I'm sick of that shit."

That was it. Why didn't she just say something to me, instead of going crazy like that. She messed me up. Man. I guess I won't see Presley anymore. I know he's not putting up with this bullshit. And I know he's not going to let Kathy's jealousy interrupt his business with Johnny. So, I'm the one out.

Johnny got off the phone with Presley and went straight for Kathy's throat. I left. I wasn't going to be in the middle of that mess. I was out the door, in my car, heading down the street and could hear fussing and cussing and screams. Damn, why she nut up like that.

I really like Kathy and Johnny, but it was time I backed up a bit. They were more than nice to me and my kids. Kathy gave me a birthday party, the first I've ever had in my life. She gave me a mink. Her and Johnny always included me in their family functions. They're good people, but my welcome had run out. I might have been wrong, over stepping my bounds a little, asking Johnny for money like that. Even if Presley gave it back. They could have said something to me. I would have understood.

C. Oakes

Mike called. He wanted to see me and the kids. We talked a while. He told me Dwight died, back when I was in Texas.

"Why didn't you tell me, Mike."

"I tried. I called you. Some man answered the phone and hung up on me."

"Well, why didn't you call back. I would have come home for that."

"I didn't want to cause you any problems. I was having a hard time anyway. I went in the hospital."

"Why, what was wrong with you?"

"I don't know what was happening. They say I got sick cause of Dwight. I couldn't cry, so I guess I was crying inside or something like that. I don't know. They said I was bleeding internally, I was real sick. Anyway, I don't do drugs anymore. Do you?"

"No!" I lied.

"I stopped all that shit. Everybody couldn't believe me, I told them I quit and everybody kept giving me rocks, trying to get me to take a hit. Talking about if I just hit it, I'll start back. So I proved it to them. I said, here, give it to me. I took a big hit, then I stomped on that shit, and told them, Now, I don't want it. I quit! I haven't had anymore since."

"Man, Mike that's good."

"So when are you and the kids coming to visit?"

"You're sure I'll be safe."

"Girl, how long has it been, four or five years. I've gotten over you. I want to see you, though. I want to see my kids."

"You send for us, we'll come visit."

"Okay, I'll call you with your ticket reservations."

"Hey, around how long are you talking about."

"You can stay as long as you want to stay."

"We'll come stay a few days."

Mike was late picking us up from the airport. Typical. He just can't do right. The kids went crazy when they saw him. I couldn't believe Ronnie remembered him.

Ronnie jumped on him. "Dadddddy."

Matt was too big. "Hi daddy."

"Hey man. Look how big y'all are? Man, Matt you're as big as me."

I rolled my eyes and got in the car. "Sharell, the traffic is so bad out here."

"That's no excuse Mike. You knew we were coming."

"Y'all hungry?"

"I'm sure the kids want something to eat."

"Sharell, you sure look good. I see you've been taking care of yourself."

"Thanks Mike. I try. So how far is it to your place?"

"Not too far. I want Mom to see y'all first. I told her you were coming."

"Okay. It'll be nice to see your mother."

We drove in silence for a while. I looked at Mike, he still looks the same, too. He hadn't aged one bit. "So, how did Dwight die?"

"He OD'd."

"Whaaaat, Dwight? Man. That's hard to believe Dwight would OD."

"Well, it was some bullshit, but nothing was done. The police could have saved his life, but they didn't call the ambulance until it was too late. They waited till he died. He laid for hours. When they brought him to the coroner, they said his body was warm. He had just died. Police ran a check on him, found out who he was, and that was it. They let him die. Man, Mike, that's cold."

Mike still had his entourage, or his family. I was surprised but happy to see Jolynn was there. I was real happy to see her.

"Girl, what are you doing here."

"Visiting Mike and LaPonz. You remember my daughter Cora don't you? You know LaPonz's her dad."

"That's right. How old is she now?"

"She's the same age as Matt. I think you had Matt about three or four months before I had my baby." For some reason, when Jolynn was in Hawaii, I forgot all about her baby was with LaPonz.

"So she's eight."

"Yeah, my mother raised her."

"Oh, that's right. I remember that."

"I was only sixteen when I had Cora. Girl, that's one of the reasons I left Hawaii. I had to get back to my child."

"Yeah, I finally went and got Matt. He stayed with me till we left Hawaii. It got crazy there, as soon as you left."

C. Oakes

"What happened?"

"Star and some other girls jumped on me."

"What? They jumped on you?"

"Yeah."

"Was Yvette with them?"

"No, not Yvette, it was the Hawaiian crew."

"You know they wouldn't have done that shit if I had been there."

"Naw, probably not. It got wild. We had to leave. It got pretty dangerous."

"So, how long you been here, in California?"

"I've been here about six months."

"What are you doing?" She kind of smiled. "Nothing right now." I was thinking . . . that's Mike. He takes care of every body. He takes care of the family. The house was full of people. Mike introduced us to everybody. There were mostly new members in his entourage. All young. Still, nobody made a move without Mike's instructions. I watched for a while. I was trying to figure this stuff out. It was strange to me before, and stranger to me now. These cats didn't eat unless Mike said eat.

I'm not the type to be here with Mike. I watched everybody ask Mike this and that. Not knowing what to do next. He has patience. But then, he always had some scheme going on. He was planning something, it was a reason everybody was there. Either they sold his drugs or was part of a plot to get some money, beat some insurance company, there was something going on. I couldn't deal with this environment. Mostly everybody were just kids. I guess I was a kid too when he met me. I guess we both were kids.

It must be gratifying to be idolized so much. Mike told me he showed his family, the movie, SuperFly. They told him, "That's why you're so cool. You saw that movie a long time ago." That's funny.

A girl was there that was pregnant. She looked ready to have the baby any minute.

"Mike, it that your baby?"

"Naw, I just let her live here cause she has no place to live."

"Oh yeah?" I went straight to the girl and asked her. "Hi, what's your name."

"I'm Myra."

"Is that Mike's baby?"

"Yeah, it's Mike's."

"When are you having your baby?"

"I should have it next month."

"That's nice."

I went back to Mike. He knew I had asked her. "You're still a dog, Mike. I don't want to hurt that girl's feelings by being here. I remember how you did me. I'll stay at a hotel. You can find somewhere reasonable for me and the boys, close, can't you?"

"Don't worry about her. She don't mind. She really doesn't care."

"Right, Mike. I just bet. We're staying at the hotel."

That's when I realized that I'm a woman. I've been holding my ground. By no means have I been perfect. Shoot, I dance for a living. That's definitely not the best way to live but I've been making it. By myself. Taking care of my business. I've been living without a man for four years now. I decided I wouldn't bring another man in my children's lives until they were older, at least teenagers. I realized that I'm a bonafide woman. I pay the cost to be the boss. My mistakes were mine to make and I'm responsible for the consequences. My actions must take in to account that I have two little beings that depend solely on me for their livelihood.

Seeing Mike again, let me know how much I had grown. And I must have been really stupid back then.

"Mike, me and the kids will be leaving Monday. Okay?"

"Sharell, if that's what you want to do. . . Hey. I'm sending Jolynn back with you. Can you help her find a job, is there something out there for her to do?"

"Sure, that's no problem. I'll be glad to have Jolynn with me for a while." So that was the reason Mike sent for me. Jolynn was getting in his pockets too deep. Mike was selling drugs but not indulging. Jolynn was smoking up his profits. He couldn't charge her, she's real family. I didn't mind, I'm too happy to take Jolynn back with me.

"Jolynn, where are you staying. I stay at Mike's other house. I hang out with his other woman, Donna. She has a nice place. She's real cool. Wait till you meet her. She's the one that handles most of the drugs."

"Did she know I was coming?"

"I don't know."

"Well, I'm only staying a few days. I'm leaving Monday or sometime early next week. Mike said you might want to come with me. Girl, it would be nice if you came to Seattle with me. I was thinking Val would be leaving me soon. Jolynn could stay downstairs. I manage this club in Seattle. I sure can use your help. You'll make a killing, Jolynn. Girl, you'll love The Sands."

"Oh yeah? I do need a job."

"Well you're going to make good money there. Damn good money. I promise."

"I'm ready to do something. Just come back with me."

"Where will I stay?"

"With me! I got this big house. Anyway, my roommate's moving in a couple months. The downstairs is a whole unit, three bedrooms, a kitchenette and a full bathroom. Wait till you see it."

I called Val to let her know that Jolynn was coming back with me. Val didn't know Jolynn, but was excited that she was coming. And the fact that she's from Oklahoma made everything good. Val was glad just to have company.

"When will y'all get here?"

"We'll arrive Wednesday night at nine. Let's see, we're coming on Southwest Airlines, we'll be at gate C22. Can you pick us up?"

"Yeah, I'll be there. You think y'all will be hungry?"

"Val, I'm so sick of food. We ate so much in California."

"Your kids might want something, Sharell."

"They probably won't. We'll eat something before we leave. Girl, don't make a big deal."

Jolynn's family was real glad she was coming back with me. Me, Jolynn and the kids were on the plane, on our way back to Seattle. Me and Jolynn had us a few drinks, and were talking about old times with Lucky. We talked about Mike and LaPonz. I told her everything that happened in Hawaii. We talked about the club, my friends in Seattle. We talked about everything.

"Is Ronnie Lucky's baby?"

"Ronnie is my baby."

"I thought so. He looks just like him."

"Mike always claimed him. He always said Ronnie was his

baby. You know me and Mike got back together a little while when I came home. Let's see, Matt was around five or six and Ronnie was around two. Then I moved to Texas. I never saw you then. Were you in Oklahoma?"

"Yeah, I was there. I saw Mike and the kids. They came over a few times with LaPonz."

"Sharell, did you recognize Myra?"

"The pregnant girl?"

"Yeah, did you recognize her?"

"No, not really." Jolynn started laughing. "Why, Jolynn?"

"Girl, did you ever see the girl that was babysitting for Mike in Oklahoma?"

"Babysitting my kids?" Jolynn just nodded. I looked at Jolynn . . "You got to be kidding me. Come to think of it, I did see her a couple of times back then. She couldn't have been no more than fourteen or fifteen. That's her?" Jolynn was laughing harder. "He took that little girl away from home?" Jolynn nodded.

"Yep. He sure did."

"Man, Mike's a dog."

Chapter 19

Jolynn fit right in at The Sands. Everybody likes her. Gus likes her, too. Jolynn went by the name Samone. She really loved the fact that we didn't strip.

"Girl, nobody takes nothing off?"

"Nope. We dance on stage in full costume."

"Sharell, I like that. I've never worked in a place like this where we don't take anything off, that's good. Well, Jolynn you know the deal, you don't make your money on stage anyway. You make your money on the floor, with your conversation." Jolynn was smiling, sporting that gold tooth. She knows how to talk for her money.

"We flash a tit sometimes when we're doing a ten or twenty dollar table dance, but that's it. Nobody sees it but the guy that's buying." This was right up Jolynn's alley.

Some of the younger dancers didn't like it. They couldn't compete with the hustlers. I guess it's hard keeping the attention of the customers with only your conversation. To compete, they felt they needed to show some skin, show their more tighter bodies. So most young dancers quit and went to work at the more traditional nude strip joints. Some stayed, the natural born go-getters stayed. It was only real hustlers at The Sands and we were making real good money.

I had to give her the scoop about the freak that was killing girls in Seattle.

"Jolynn, you need to be careful around here. Don't go on any dates without letting me know who you're leaving with, okay? Now, Jolynn you have to promise me that you won't go with anybody without letting me know."

"Okay, I won't."

The Green River Killer was terrorizing all of us. This had been going on since the early days, when I first came up north. Girls were disappearing before, and nobody was paying attention. Now, at least, it's a serious investigation. We hear something on the news about the investigation weekly, well almost everyday. At first, it was a big task force working on the cases, now it's down to only one investigator. But he's serious about it. Still, there weren't any suspects. There must be a suspect, somewhere, I just don't know about it. But bodies were still being found. Strangled, left on the side of the road, or in the Green River.

"So how many has he killed so far?"

"Now, it's over 40, maybe 50 girls."

"For reaaal."

"Yeah. They call him the Green River Killer. He dumps the bodies near the Green River. That's not too far from here. I'll show you. It's close to Highway 99, that's the ho stroll. We come up Highway 99 everyday."

"They don't have a clue who this guy is?"

"Naw, girl. We think it's a cop. That's what they say on the streets, cause the girls are going with him. But, then they say it could be a taxi driver, too."

"A lot of girls leave with taxi drivers. Man. I'm not going on any dates unless I'm positive."

"Let me know Jolynn if you do that. I need some ID, car tags, I want a deposit on your return. You hear me?"

"Yeah girl, I said okay."

"You know what Jolynn, I haven't turned a date since I came back to Seattle. You don't have to do that working here. You can get the money without all that. You know what they say in Oklahoma, the more you give, the less money you get." Jolynn was nodding, agreeing with me. "That's true, girl."

"I know it is, Sharell."

"Anyway, you don't want to take a chance and get that stuff that's going around. That AIDS stuff is crazy. They say it stays in your system for twenty years. Just work in here, Jolynn. You don't have to turn no dates and you'll still get paid. In fact, you will get more. You'll see."

Jolynn was doing it again. Making thousands to my hundreds. I couldn't for the life of me figure out what in the world she was saying to get that kind of money. Guys were coming back the next day, bringing her money that they had promised her the night before. Unbelievable! How does she do that? Damn, she's good. The other dancers were amazed. Gus loved her.

We were all living together, Me and my kids, Val and her kids, and Jolynn. It was like we have known each other for years. Everybody respected each other's privacy, we helped around the house and with the kids. Jolynn liked to cook. Everything was perfect. Then it happened. Val went into labor.

Val was at the foot of the stairs. "Sharell, what are you doing right now?"

"I'm just playing the nintendo." Me and the boys were having a good time, I was screaming, getting too excited about Super Mario.

"Well, can I get you to take me to the hospital?"

"What?" Me and the boys just looked at each other. We were stuck. Our eyes were big. "It's time? Mom, she's ready to have the baby?"

"You're going in labor, Val?"

"Yeah, I think I better head on to the hospital." We were up in a flash. I was running around, trying to be organized and trying to act like somebody sane.

"You got your bags? Where's my keys."

"Yeah, I got everything. I can't find my keys. Where's my. . ."

"Here, mom, here's your keys. Thanks."

"Come on girl. I got to go." Val was getting impatient.

I drove my car. I had Val, Veta and Charlie with me. Jolynn drove Val's car with Edward and my boys. We were all there to welcome the twins. I'm not the type to watch the babies come out. So Val had the twins, by herself, with no one to hold her hands. But when she finished. We were all there, happy and loud. We couldn't believe they were here.

"Oh Val, they're so pretty." You couldn't pay enough money to get the grins off our faces. "Girl, they're so precious. Oh Val, name one Sharell."

"Yeah, right." The kids were in wonderland. They know how the babies come, but this was they're first time experiencing a real birth. From the big fat stomach to the world, . . . with eyes wide open, they had arrived. They were so beautiful. This was great! The nurses had to put us out the hospital. I didn't want to leave. Man we had fun that night. She named the twins Taylor and Tyler.

Val was on the march to find them a place. They found a place in West Seattle. That's across the bridge, looks like another city, looks like another state. I was about in tears when they left.

"Sharell, you know we'll come around to visit. I'm not leaving the state." Eddie was strutting around like a proud turkey. I was pouting like a kid. Eddie was laughing at me. I was starting not to like him. I know he realizes how bad I hate for Val to leave me and my boys. Well at least Val's happy. Her husband's now home and at last, her family was all together

Things were so different now. My boys missed Val. They looked sad. They were lost without Val, Edward and Veta. Their family had broken up. Seattle is not like Oklahoma where they have lots of cousins to grow up with in the same neighborhood. My boys were lonely. Matt was getting up there. Close to ten years old. He started hanging out with some of the bad kids. Well, I don't think the boys were bad, they didn't have a lot of guidance. They called themselves being in a gang. All the parents were on drugs. These were just children hanging out together, leaning on each other. Lord only knows what it's like at some of their homes.

I've always wanted my boys to be independent. I make them ride the bus, learn the routes. The bus was right on the corner, it comes around every five minutes. I wanted them to know how to get around and do things, like go to the movies, go to ball games and school functions.

When we were little, the whole neighborhood went to the skating rink at Bryant Center. The neighborhood looked out for each other. That's the way it was back then in Oklahoma City. That's the way it is with these kids around here.

Well, I'm not around like I should be. The kids are hanging out together, one might need a little help paying this or that. I didn't mind helping, so Matt and Ronnie know where I keep my stash. I have a drawer full of money. They know they can get five or ten dollars, no problem. My boys have never taken advantage of the situation. Plus, I want them to have spending change in their pockets. So why did the police bring them home for shoplifting. Matt stole some beef jerky. Some damn beef jerky and he had five dollars in his pocket.

"I have preached and preached to you Matt about not ever getting yourself in the situation where the system can come take you away from me. Haven't I told you that, haven't I. . . . Matt, look at me when I'm talking to you. You want the police to take you away from me? Do you? I'm not going to let that happen.

C. Oakes

Do you know what happens once you're in the system. Do you? You get a record. Matt, they put it on your record. It doesn't matter how old you are. The police will always mess with you once you got a record. Shoplifting will always be on your record from now on. Matt, then you won't be able to get a job, you can't vote. If you can't work, you can't ever buy anything, no car, no house. Nothing, you'll never have anything. Matt, I don't want you getting started with the police. Do you understand me. I'll split my family first, I'll do it, before I let the system take you out of here."

That night I prayed about my babies. "Lord, I need help. I'm not a good mother. Father, I'm giving them back to you. I'm giving my babies back to you, Lord. My Lord, My God. I know you're the best. You know what's best for them. You can teach them and guide them, to be strong men that knows you and love you. I know you won't let nothing happen to them. Lord, they're yours. Take my babies, Father, raise them. I'm not a good mother. Please Lord, help me, help us."

All of a sudden, there was a weight that lifted off my shoulders. It was profound. I felt it. It was like stress and weight, all in one, came off my chest and shoulders. "He's God. Thank you God. Thank you Father." I slept peacefully.

I talked to my dad. He lives in Bessemer, Alabama, where he was raised. He asked if the boys could come visit him this summer. I thought that would be great. At least they would have a man, a positive man, to do things with them. I know daddy will take them to church. He's the pastor.

"Y'all will go fishing with daddy. Then there's all our cousins that lives there that's you guys age. Ronnie you and Matt can go hiking in the woods. There's animals, chickens and pigs and cows, there's so many animaaals. You're going to love Alabama."

Matt wasn't buying it. He was too protective of me. "Mom, I just don't know about leaving you here by yourself. You got to be careful mom." My big boy feels he has to be with me.

"Well, you won't be there long, you're just staying for the summer. Then you'll be back with me when school starts." I took by babies to the airport and they were on their way to Alabama. I didn't let them see me cry.

I watched as the plane flew away with my babies. I watched

till the plane was long gone.

Things were getting out of hand around here, in the hood. I never noticed all the people standing on the corners selling rock cocaine.

"Why haven't I noticed this?"

Jolynn liked seeing them. "Girl, look at them. They're on fire."

"What?" I was thinking that sure sounds evil.

"They're on fire, selling rocks. Let's stop and get some."

"No girl, I don't do that."

"Ah . . Sharell girl. We can just get a fifty. That's not going to hurt nothing."

I was scared somebody would see me copping rocks on the streets. "Tell him to meet us down the streets." Jolynn motioned him to meet us down the street, off the main drag. Jolynn got the fifty dollar sack. I guess she knows what she's doing. I see why Mike was getting her away from California. Jolynn was on fire. She's really bad.

"Girl, police might bust us trying to cop some rocks on the streets like this." Guys were standing on every corner, selling that stuff.

"Look at him, what's wrong with his pants? Why he got his pants hanging down like that?"

Jolynn laughed. "That's the way they wear them now."

"Whaaat?"

"They call that sagging."

"You got to be kidding. He wants his pants hanging off his ass like that?" Jolynn thinks I'm funny. "But he can't walk. Look at him. They won't stay up. He looks like a bum, holding up his pants with his hands like that. Where's his belt? If he gets a belt, that would help."

"Sharell, they hide the rocks in their crack."

"The crack of their ass . .You're lying."

"No, I'm not. Their pants sag so they can get to the rocks faster."

"Girl, this is a mess. I don't want that shit."

"Girl, it's in a bag."

"So, I don't want to touch the sack that was inside the crack of his ass."

"Come on girl, we got it now."

Every night before we would go home, me and Jolynn would get us some rocks to take with us. We'd smoke it up. Then Jolynn would want some more. "Come on Sharell, let's go get one more."

"Naw, girl. I don't want nobody seeing me doing that."

"Come on, Sharell. I'll buy it."

"Jolynn, I'm embarrassed out there getting rocks off the streets. Everybody knows my car."

She would beg and beg, "Let's get some more."

"I'll call Joe and have him bring us some. I don't like getting stuff off the streets like that."

I started losing weight. The girls at the club thought I looked great.

"Nikki, you have a perfect body. Look at you. There's no fat anywhere." I had to admit, I was looking good. Joe said I looked like a little doll. My clothes were fitting good. But I was getting bad on that stuff. I had my own tweek thing that I would do. For some reason, I would put a piece of rock cocaine in one of my clothes pockets, then go through my entire dresser, emptying all my clothes, to find the piece. Sometimes, well, mostly I would take a razor and cut the pockets of my clothes, looking for the piece that I stashed. All my clothes were cut around the pockets and around the buttons.

As soon as I got to the club, I was ready to leave. I hated to work. I couldn't wait to get out the club. There was just as much cocaine in the club as it was on the streets. The atmosphere was wicked. Cocaine was everywhere. I couldn't deal with the customers. I couldn't deal with the other dancers. I didn't want to talk with anybody. I had to leave so I could smoke my rocks in peace. I wanted to be in my bedroom, locked up. I wanted to dig through my drawers, I wanted to cut up my pockets, dig through my closets, crawl on the floor . . looking for my rocks in peace.

I couldn't smoke coke with Jolynn anymore. She would snatch the pipe out my mouth. She stressed you out, making you rush your hit. She couldn't wait for her turn to hit the pipe. "Damn Jolynn, can I finish my hit."

"Okay, okay girl."

"Don't sit there with your hands ready to take it from my mouth, Jolynn. It's not fun if you're going to rush me like that."

"I'm sorry. I'm sorry."

"Then why don't you stop. Here take it. Jolynn, just take it."

Jolynn could still go to work everyday. She stayed out the dressing room until we closed. Jolynn had too much money on the floor to be messing around with us upstairs. Plus, she didn't want everybody seeing her tweek, snatching pipes from people's lips.

"Sharell, I met this guy. He's from Alaska."

"Where did you meet him?"

"In the club. I met him in the club. Girl, he's really nice. He's quiet. I'll introduce you to him."

"You like him?"

"Yeah, I like him a lot."

"When did you have time to meet somebody."

"Girl, he started coming in the club everyday, then when you weren't there, he'd give me a ride home. I've been to his house. He has a nice place in Auburn."

"Really?"

"Yeah, he lives with his sister. He lives downstairs. His mother owns the house. She still lives in Alaska. They don't pay anything for rent."

"Really?"

"He wants me to move in with him."

"Are you going to do it?"

"I'm thinking about it."

"Well, if you decide to move, I wish you luck and be careful. Anyway, you know you can always come back here if it doesn't work out."

It was time for school to start. "Hi daddy, where's the boys."

"They're around here."

"Daddy, I don't have the money to send for them right now."

"Well baby. I was hoping they could stay here and go to school for a little while. Those boys are doing fine. Let them stay with me a while. You can get them when school is out, right now they're fine."

"Okay, Daddy, you're sure it's okay."

"Hey, these are my babies. You take care of yourself, let me take care of Matt and Ronnie a little while."

"Okay, Daddy. You sure you don't mind?"

"Hey, I'm loving it."

"Are they around?"

"Yeah, hold on, I'll get them. Matt, Ronnie, your mom's on the phone."

"Hi Mom,"

"Hi baby, where's Ronnie, tell him to get the other phone."

"Ronnie pick up the other phone, it's Mom."

"What are y'all doing?"

"We're just playing. Hey, Mom, we ate a possum."

"What!"

"We ate a possum, Mom we had to feed it everyday till we ate it. We kept it in a barrel, I was scare of it." They were laughing. "That thing would growl at us."

"Did you like it?"

"Naw, I was just tasting it."

"Ronnie, what have you been doing?"

"Nothing."

"Well, why aren't you talking to me?"

"I'm not doing nothing."

"You guys will probably go to school there and I'll get you when school is out."

"We got to go to school here?"

"Well, yeah, just this year. I don't have the money to send for you yet. Hey, I'll send y'all some school clothes and shoes, okay?"

"Okay mom."

"I love you and I miss y'all so much."

"I love you, too."

"Bye"... click

"Dang, they just hung up."

C. Oakes

Chapter 20

Jolynn moved in with her friend, Calvin. She seems happy. They're already talking about getting married. I can only wish the best for them and hope she's okay, jumping in marriage so fast. I don't think this guy has enough positive influence to keep her in check. She needs someone that'll get her off the madness. She needs someone strong. Calvin's too passive. He drinks too much. He smokes just as much coke as Jolynn. She's right, he's quiet. Too quiet. You wonder what he's thinking. Jolynn just wants a decent place to live, she wants somebody that'll half-ass take care of her. She can make money. That's not a problem. She just wants somebody in her corner. I can't blame her. That's what I want.

I need someone that'll help me get off this mess, too. They call it crack now. I guess cause street dealers stash it in the crack of their asses. Whew!! That's disgraceful. It's a damn shame. Cocaine used to be for players. It was the social drug for smooth people. It was the top of the line party drug. But this crack, man. . .it has no class and no shame.

Now I'm living in that big house by myself. Everybody's gone. Calvin, introduced me to one of his friends, Lawrence. Actually, I saw Lawrence in Alaska. I didn't really know him in Alaska, but I saw him around. Every now and then, he would come in the Bush Company and buy a dance or drink from me. Lawrence wasn't my type. He's nice and all, but not for me. However, I was lonesome. I was really lonesome. My boys were gone. I didn't have anybody to care for now. That's when I'm at my best, when I'm looking out for someone else.

It's funny, I never knew that about me. I need to be taking care of my boys. I do better when I'm responsible for them. I do better when they're depending on me. Then I'll shine. My boys looked good, dressed good. They got the best toys and bikes. I got to take better care of myself. How can I take care of them if I'm in the dirt. I can't. My boys have been gone almost a year. Now, it's just me and I'm not doing so good.

Lawrence sold drugs, too. He had more balls than Calvin.

Not that he walked around like he's bad. In fact, it was just the opposite. He didn't have to prove anything to anybody. I liked that about Lawrence. What I didn't like about him is this. . . He has one of those expensive mobile phones. They looked like a great big walkie talkie that's hooked straight to the police station. I don't trust those phones. Seems like the police can tap into one of those things and hear every word. I didn't want to be around him when he was making deals on that thing. Then, to make it worst, Lawrence dressed like a bum. Rich folk could afford those phones, he sure didn't look rich. Those phones cost about a grand, then the bill was close to a thousand every month. Police had to know he was selling drugs walking around talking on that thing. I never saw any of my other friends with one of those mobile phones. I didn't trust it. Sometimes I wondered about Lawrence.

Lawrence and Calvin had another friend from Alaska named Rusty. This guy gave me the creeps. He has long stringy un-combed hair. He looked dirty. He is dirty. His eyes are dark and evil looking. I wish they had never brought him around me. He shouldn't have known where I lived. I was always complaining about Rusty.

"Lawrence, I don't trust him."

"Why? Sharell, he's alright."

"No he's not."

"He's one of my home boys from Alaska. I grew up with him."

"I don't care, Lawrence, it's something about him that's not right."

"Why do you say that?"

"I can tell. That guy's dangerous. Look at him Lawrence. Why did you bring him around me anyway. Don't be bringing these weirdo's to my house."

"Well, I won't bring him around anymore."

"Please don't. There's something wrong with him, I'm telling you what I know. He's weird."

After a few days, I come home from shopping and running a few errands, I pulled up to the house and was immediately pissed off cause there's Rusty working on one of Lawrence's raggedy ass cars in front of my house.

"Lawrence!"

"Yeah? Why is Rusty over here? You said you wouldn't bring him over here anymore."

"I needed him to do some work for me."

"Why are you paying money for that raggedy car."

"That's a classic, Sharell."

"It's junk and it's leaving oil stains in the driveway. Lawrence, I'm not use to this mess, all these raggedy cars parked in front of my house. The neighbors are going to complain. You got to move this shit."

I could feel Rusty looking at me, all mean, rolling his eyes, saying something under his breathe. He knows I don't like his ass. Why does he come over to my house?

"Lawrence I need to talk with you. Can you come in here for a minute." I was pissed. "Lawrence, why?"

"Why what?"

"Why you got that freak, Rusty, at my house?"

"I need him to do some work for me, I told you he's working on my car."

"Well, you and that freak need to find another spot to work on your cars. I need you out of here. I want you and Rusty away from here today. Do I need to do anything to help you leave."

"Sharell, why are you tripping?"

"Lawrence, I'm not playing, you need to leave. What can I do to help you. You need anything?"

"No, I can go."

"I need you to take the cars away from my house today."

"Okay, I'll move them."

"When Lawrence?"

"I'll be gone today."

Lawrence was alright, but I couldn't have him bringing any old kind of guy to my house, where I lived. He act like he didn't care what he brought around me, messing up the neighborhood with those ugly raggedy cars parked all over my block. I wasn't use to that and was glad when he left.

I was staying by myself again. Lawrence came around every now and then. We were still friends. We'd get high together, then he'd leave. I was kind of scared in the house by myself. If no one was with me, I'd wait and come home in the morning. If I had to come home at night, I'd have someone do a walk through with me.

I was getting strange feelings. Like someone was in there. I told Jolynn about it. That I think someone was in the house at night. I don't think she believed me. Like I was paranoid.

"Jolynn, I'm not kidding, somebody's been in here."

"Sharell, how are they getting in?"

"I don't know, but they're getting in. I've checked all my windows and doors. I had sticks and wood blocking the windows from opening. The doors had double and triple locks. I can't figure out how they're getting in here."

"Girl, you better be careful."

"I am. I'm changing my all my deadbolt locks tomorrow." At night, I barricaded myself in my bedroom. I stay in my room till morning, then I'd call Joe or somebody to get me.

"Girl, you sure you're not being paranoid?"

"Jolynn, when I walk in my door, I can tell if they've been here."

"How do you know?"

"I can tell. I can feel it."

Kathy came over. I was so glad to see her. I hadn't seen Kathy in a while.

"I thought I'd come over and check on you. You stop coming to see us."

"Girl, I thought I better give y'all some room."

"You know you're always welcomed any time."

"I know that my welcome was getting ranky."

"Sharell, I miss you."

"I miss you, too."

"Here! You want some coke, I brought you over some snort."

"Thanks. Let me fix you a drink, all I got is Hennessey. Is that okay?"

"Yeah, sure." We both laughed and was happy visiting with each other. It had been a while.

"So how's everything?" I felt Kathy was truly concerned.

"I'm good. How's everything with you?"

"We're fine."

"Good."

"When are the boys coming home?"

"I'm letting them go to school in Alabama, with their grand-daddy, this year, I'll get them when school's out."

"I know you miss them, huh?"

"I do."

"Presley asked about you."

"He did? How's he doing?"

"I guess he's good. I haven't seen too much of him lately. He calls. He keeps asking about you, asking us if we heard from you."

"Tell Presley, Hello for me."

Kathy stopped talking, she was looking around. She looked at me, her eyes were big, like her antenna's were on overload. Kathy was whispering, "Sharell."

"What?"

"Somebody's in here."

"What?"

"Somebody's in here."

I went straight to the kitchen and got my two knives. The ones I take with me to my bedroom at night, so I can sleep. "You see these two knives, girl, nobody's going to mess with us."

"Girl, I'm leaving, somebody's in here."

"Don't go. Why you say that, Kathy?"

"Cause somebody's in here, I can tell. You better be careful, Sharell. I got to go."

"Okay, well, thanks for coming."

"Call me later. Let me know you're alright."

I went back to the kitchen and laid the two knives on the countertop while I walked Kathy to the door. I sure didn't want her to leave.

"You lock your doors good, Sharell. I'll call you when I get home."

"Okay Kathy. I'll talk to you later."

"Damn, I hated she left. Let me get my knives." I headed toward the kitchen to get my knives. "Damnit!" My heart dropped. I was scared. There was only one knife laying on the counter. I flew out the kitchen and went straight to my room to barricade myself inside. There was no way anybody could get in my room. My king size bed blocked the closet and the door where neither one could be opened. I had wooden sticks blocking the windows from opening. I figured if someone came through the windows, I'll have enough time to knock 'em out with all my weapons strategically positioned around my bedroom. That was the only way I felt safe enough to sleep.

The next morning, I called Lawrence to come over so I could come out my room. I was really scared. I started walking around the house, looking for evidence of the intruder.

"Look Lawrence. What is this shit. Somebody scratched up my furniture. They used the knife that was taken last night and scratched the furniture with it. This is crazy. Kathy was over last night, she said the same thing."

"What's that?"

"That somebody was in my house."

"Did you mention it to her or did she just say it."

"No, she could tell just like I can tell, somebody was in here last night. Whoever it was, took one of my knives. I had two knives on the counter. Somebody took one and scratched my furniture with it."

Inside my bedroom closet is a door that once lead to the attic The attic is now my boys room and a game room. But I still have the trap door in my closet. Somebody could be in my closet hiding. The intruder left a picture in there for me. I guess he just dropped the picture cause it was on the floor around my shoes.

"Look I got this out of my closet. Lawrence, look at this. I was holding a picture from a nude magazine. This picture was of a girl with her legs opened, leaning back on a bed, only there were added drawings, exaggerating body parts. It was sick!"

"Sharell, I'll stay with you a while."

"Okay?" I nodded okay. This was no time for me to be stubborn. Lawrence stayed a few days. I didn't complain about his raggedy classic cars. Matter of fact, I was enjoying his company. We have always been friends.

It wasn't long before I was getting those scary feelings again. "Lawrence, Lawrence, where are you?" I went to the front yard, I didn't see him. I walked outside. He was deep in oil and grit, under a car hood. I was feeling it again. I went straight to my kitchen and got my knife. "Lawrence, I can feel it again." I started checking around upstairs, downstairs, then I saw him. Jumping my fence. He was in my backyard. It was Rusty walking across my backyard. I got the same feeling. The exact feeling when someone was in my house. It was Rusty all the time.

"Lawrence, it's Rusty. It's Rusty coming in here."

Rusty was walking on the side of my house, coming to the front yard.

Lawrence started cleaning his hands. "Where is he?"

"He's coming, he just jumped the back fence."

Lawrence was looking, not knowing what to do or think. "What are you going to do?"

I was so pissed off. "Lawrence, tell Rusty I know it's him. Tell that man the next time he comes in my house, I'm shooting him. Let him know. Let your buddy know, Lawrence." I jumped in my car before Rusty could speak to me.

"Sharell, where are you going?" I turned toward Rusty, giving him a real dirty look, making sure he heard me.

"I'm going to buy me a gun."

Chapter 21

Rusty took his po-ass back to Alaska. Lawrence went to Alaska, too. He said he got a job working in the oil fields at Prudhoe Bay. At least I wasn't a nervous wreck anymore. Man, a girl has got to be careful. Now Lawrence was alright, but his friends and associates, I don't know about them. Why in the world would he bring a maniac like Rusty to my house. He knew about that man, he being his home boy and all, he just didn't care about bringing him around me. There's no telling what that looney has been doing in a remote place like Alaska. For all I know, he could be the Green River killer. I don't know. They haven't caught him, he could be the killer and Lawrence got him running around my house. But, if Rusty would have come around me one more time, if I had caught him doing that crazy stuff in my house, I was going to shoot Rusty in his sneaky po-ass.

It sure is good to feel safe again. For a while, I was desperate, trying to explain to folks what was happening based solely on my premonitions. Trying to make somebody understand that I wasn't hallucinating on crack. Kathy is the only one that believed me. She knew right off somebody was in my house. She felt it. Kathy has strong intuitions too. I'll never forget the way she looked. Kathy flew out the house. She left me right there, scared by myself. I should have left with her. Well everybody else thought I was just being paranoid. Even Jolynn. I still haven't figured out how he got in the house. The windows and doors were rigged shut. Nothing was opened, nothing seemed moved. I don't know how he got in.

Calvin has been keeping Jolynn to himself lately. I never see her anymore. I hadn't seen her working at The Sands or around town. Jolynn don't call, she won't come by. I hope she's alright. I hope Calvin's not as crazy as Lawrence's other friends. You know what they say about birds of a feather, flock together. I probably need to go by her house and visit her, just to check on her. I don't know, I feel a little responsible for Jolynn. After all, she came here with me.

Val's entirely too busy. I never see her either. At least she has reasons. They're looking to purchase a home. She has the twins and Charlie. And now, her husband is retired from the military. She's busy. At least we get to talk. Val will call at least once a week; just to check on me and let me know she's alright. I don't have to worry about Val. Eddie don't like her hanging around me too much. I know he makes her uncomfortable when I'm there visiting. He shouldn't be like that. What's he worried about anyway.

My friend, Kathy decided I needed some protection. After that night, she's been checking on me. Calling and wanting to know my whereabouts. She told Johnny about the incident with Rusty, that somebody was in the house when she was over. Now he's been coming over inspecting and checking on the place. He brought a few of the old gang, MC and Joe. I felt thankful that they cared so much.

"Sharell, you sure you can handle being here by yourself?"

"Yes, Johnny. I'm alright."

"What are you going to do if somebody else comes in on you."

"Johnny, trust me, I'm alright. Anyway, I got me a little 22." They started laughing at me. Joe makes me sick sometimes. He started on me.

"Sharell, baby, that ain't going to do nothing but get you shot cause they gonna just take that away from your little ass."

"Shut up Joe."

MC was cool. "You know how to use it?"

"Yeah, I can use it. Anyway, I let the problem know I had a pistol and I was waiting on him to come back. He left town. I wanted to shoot him."

MC spoke up for me. "Ah, she'll be alright, won't you?"

"Yeah, like I said. He left town, I'm not worried about that problem any more. I was hoping I'd get a chance to shoot him in his ass." They all were laughing now cause I was demonstrating my eagle eye shot.

We tried to figure out how the guy was getting in, I don't think they know. This is just rental property for them. I did get new deadbolts. Some times I see MC or Joe riding pass the house, looking, keeping an eye out, just in case.

I miss hanging out with those guys. For a while, we really partied. It was fun going to the after hours clubs, The Cotton

C. Oakes

Club and The Royal Esquire Club, being treated like VIP's, we were special. That was fun. Then Johnny and the gang always brought shows to town. They brought Millie Jackson, Lakeside, just lots of old school groups. Me, Kathy and Kathy's sisters would meet the celebrities at the airport, in two or three limo's, take them to the hotel. Then party with them the entire time they were in town.

But it's hard work socializing with the gang. They're good people, they have good hearts, but they're stressful. You have to stay alert with these guys. And now since Presley's not around to protect me or my honor, I have to be distant. I have to stay quiet. I have to keep everything and everybody in check. I can't get too friendly or loose, somebody might take it wrong and think it's their turn to be with me and I'm not going to be passed around in anybody's circle.

Kathy still comes around. Matter of fact, she's around a lot. She comes to my house to smoke coke in peace. I don't blame her for not wanting do it at home, with the kids and Johnny around. He don't do anything but snort anyway. He's so much older than Kathy, he wouldn't like seeing her high on crack. I don't think he even knows that she smokes it every now and then. I don't mind her coming here to hide her little secret. Plus she leaves so much for me, for being available to her. She leaves a lot. With what she leaves me, I end up smoking all night. Just what I want to do, smoke coke all night, by myself, tweeking in peace. Between Kathy and Joe, I never have to buy crack.

I think Joe likes me too much. He says I'm cute. He's always joking with me, talking about my cooking.

"Sharell, don't bring anymore food over here for me to eat. I gave my dog that soup you fixed. After my dog finished chewing on that soup, he jumped the fence and ran away. I've never saw that dog again."

I was cracking up. "Joe, your dog didn't chew my soup."

"You know what, I dreamed about you."

"You dreamed about me? What did you dream, Joe?"

"That I was tearing that thing up."

I like Joe too, he brings me coke just to hang out with him. Joe's alright, but I can't keep this up. He jokes around a lot, he's never crossed the line. He likes my company and he'll feed me all the crack cocaine I want, . . .all night. I won't leave as long as he's giving me rocks left and right. I got to stop.

In a way, I'm being controlled by the people that gives me crack. It's sad that I do this, I hang around like a rabbit with a carrot being waved in my face. Waiting around for another hit. I won't spend my money, but what's the difference. I'm not trying to make any money either. I'm at their beck and call, they're flunky for some rocks.

It's terrible that I'm allowing this crack to destroy me. After what I went through in Hawaii, my soul was actually trying to leave my body. I remember fighting hard, with all my might, to stay inside myself, inside my body. I was so scared. Man, that's heavy, my soul didn't want to be with me anymore. I must be really bad.

I'm getting so pathetic. I lost so much weight. My size 5 wardrobe is too big. I can't eat. I don't have an appetite. I only work now and then, to pay a bill when one's due. I'm not taking care of my responsibility with my boys, I'm not sending money to them in Alabama. I'm getting so bad. I don't even call my boys anymore. I don't know how I got this far gone. Sometimes I'd stay in the house all week long, only opening the door to let Kathy in, cause she wanted to get high and I know she's bringing more for me. I'm a shame of myself. I need help.

My car was on a flat. I don't have any men friends anymore that'll fix my flat. Joe and those guys aren't the mechanic types. They're not going to get dirty. They'll pay to get their cars fixed and that's what they would expect from me. Only thing is, right now, I don't have any money. I need my car to make some money. Maybe I could borrow some money from Kathy or Joe and get my car fixed. I need to go to work tonight. I'm broke.

You know, I really don't want to start borrowing money from any of these guys. I don't want to change the dynamics of our relationship. People change when you start borrowing money from them. They might start charging me for drugs. I'll just ask Joe. He's cool. I'll ask for a C-note till tonight. I just won't tell him I got a flat. Damn I hate to borrow money. Usually, I'm loaning money to somebody. Look at me now.

I left walking to the convenient store to get a beer. There's a mechanic shop across the alley, straight behind the building, I'm going there, I'm going to ask somebody to fix my flat on credit. Who knows, it's worth a try. I live right here in the neighborhood. I'm not going anywhere. Maybe if I promise an extra twenty for his troubles, he'll fix it on credit. As I started walking toward the back of the convenience store I noticed this guy eyeing me. Um, he's kind of cute. He's just staring. He need to wipe that grin off his face. I headed toward the back, I acted like I didn't notice him. He's still looking at me! Damn, he's fine! If I turn around again, and he's still staring at me, I'm going to ask him to fix my flat.

"Hi, what's your name?"

"I'm Aaron, what's yours?"

"I'm Sharell." Aaron was gorgeous. Tall, thick straight-curly hair. He's a smooth tan, articulate brother or other. He talks black but he certainly don't look totally black. Maybe he's one of those Black Canadians, mixed with French or Indian. I don't know but it's a good mix.

I asked in my best damsel in distress voice, "Are you busy?"

"No, not really."

"Why? What do you need."

"Well, I got a flat."

He was flirting, shaking his head, "You do!"

"Yeah and I don't know how to fix a flat."

"Where's your car?"

"It's on the next street over."

"Come on, get in."

"Well, I have a problem, I don't have any money to get a tire but if you can help me out, I can repay you tomorrow. I promise I can get you the money . . ."

He had that stupid grin again, just listening to me rattle on. "I'll see what I can do for you."

"You sure you don't mind? I really appreciate it."

"Don't worry about it. I might need you one day." He seemed alright. I didn't get any negative vibes. If I did, I didn't notice them cause I needed help. I wanted my tire fixed so bad. Plus, I wasn't in the mood for any foolishness, I'd probably hurt him if he tried anything..

This guy drove a silver sporty two-seater Nissan. I jumped in the seat and directed him to my house. Whew! Relief. Something told me everything was going to be alright. I could tell he was impressed when he got to the house.

"You live here?"

I nodded. "Yes."

"Who lives here with you?"

"Just me and my kids. I usually have a roommate. It's a big place."

"Oh yeah, I might be looking for a place pretty soon."

"Where do you live now?"

"At a hotel. I'm here contracting with Boeing."

"Oh okay! What do you do?"

"I'm a engineer. I'm working on the design side of the new triple 7 airplanes."

"How long will your contract last?"

"I don't know yet."

"Well, I got room for rent. You can stay here if you want."

"That'll be great. The company is paying all my expenses. I'm staying at the company's hotel. It's not very private. Let me check, see if I can set it up, I don't know what's their policy on housing but I would like to get out of that hotel. I share my room with another contractor. He's from Fiji Islands. He's cool, it's just that I've been sharing my space for four months now. I want some privacy. Can I call you and let you know?"

I was thinking that's a good way to get a telephone number. Yeah, here's my number. I scribbled my number on a piece of paper and handed to Aaron."

"How much are you talking about per month?"

"I'll be looking for half on everything, I have a complete unit downstairs, three bedrooms, full bath and kitchenette. That's what's available. If you like, you can take a look around?"

"That'll be great." I gave Aaron the once around then let him get to work on my car. I needed to get to work on my finances. Aaron got dirty and fixed my flat, paid for my tire and was on his way. Man, just when I thought chivalry was dead.

I saw Aaron driving by my place a couple of times through the week. I guess he was checking out the environment, seeing if anyone else was around. I wasn't alarmed by any of this. Actually, he's not guilty for being careful. He called every now and then, keeping the coals on the fire. I can't blame him for that either, this is a good place to live, a good neighborhood, a really nice house for this price.

After a couple of weeks Aaron came back confirming that he wanted to move in.

"You sure you want to move here?"

"Yeah, in fact, I was just notified that my living expenses were ending and I need to find a place to live. I was just offered a long term contract."

"That's good. Isn't it?"

"Yeah, that's real good. It could lead to a permanent position."

"Hey, where's your kids?"

"My kids are in Alabama. I'm letting them spend time in the country, around some men for a while. They don't need me nagging at them all the time, sometimes it's good to hear a man nag at them." I smiled.

"They're staying with my dad. I'll get them this summer."

"That's good. Everybody's not able."

"No. I guess I'm blessed."

"You sure are. Well how old are they?"

"My boys are eleven and seven, soon to be twelve and eight. They're really good kids. I miss them."

"That's great. What's their names?"

"Matt and Ronnie."

"Those are neat names."

"Thanks."

"I don't believe I mentioned to you that I have a daughter, Tiara."

"Oh yeah?"

"Yeah, she's six."

"I bet she's pretty."

Aaron was shaking his head agreeing. "Yeah, she's real cute, at least to me. It'll be my daughter and me moving in."

"Really! You're raising your daughter."

Aaron nodded. He seemed to be a humble man. He just smiles and seems pretty laid back. "Why are you raising your daughter?"

"Her mother's hooked on drugs and I'm not having my daughter around that kind of environment."

I thought to myself, "Oh oooh!"

Aaron continued to tell me all about it. "I took her to court and that woman came to court high. The judge took one looked at her and granted me custody."

"Whow. Who's keeping her while you're here."

"She's with my mother in California. That's where I'm from, San Bernandino.

"Oh, okay. I don't think I've ever heard of that place. I never asked you, when will you be ready to move in?"

"I can't move in till I get my new contract, that's in a few months. Will I need to leave a security deposit?"

"No, that's alright. If you move in that's fine, if you don't, that's okay too. Stay in touch and if you change your mind, just let me know."

"Well I'd rather give you something, so you won't rent it to somebody else."

"Here's a couple hundred. I want you to hold my place, cause it'll be a few months before I can move in. I'm going to California for a month and bringing my daughter back with me. I really am counting on this space."

We talked all night, about everything. After listening to his horror stories with his kid's mother, I was having second thoughts about him moving with me.

Chapter 22

I decided I would get my finances together. I'm tired of being broke, this isn't me. To tell the truth, I must be crazy letting myself get into this predicament. It's too easy for me to make money. There no excuse. All I have to do is go to work. Well, I'm getting out of this rut and I'm going to buy me some new clothes and some new shoes. I'm going to treat myself with something other than drugs.

First, I got to send my kids money. They need school clothes. My dad said they've out grown everything. I bet they're so big now. They got to go shopping. Then I'm stacking for a few months. I'm going to work everyday and staying till the club closed, so I can stack. It's time for me to be consistent with my work. It's time for me to see about me. I need to stay away from Kathy's house for a while. I can't get anywhere hanging around those guys.

You know what? I'm tired of being high. It's really not fun. I'm tired of feeling bad about it. And I'm sure tired of tweeking, cutting up my clothes. Locking myself up for days, peeking out windows and doors, crawling around the floor looking for more crack. Never being satisfied. After taking that first hit of crack, it's a constant feeling of dissatisfaction. It's a disappointing high. A mad race to get that first hit rush again, you hit it, and you hit it, you put more on the pipe, then nothing but plain ole frustration. You're running and running, but there's no finish line. There's no peak, and when its gone, depression sets in. You feel stupid. Kicking yourself for being so weak and dumb and especially broke.

I did call my boys. They seemed to be alright. I got a little upset cause of what Matt said. They're not use to getting a lot of whippings. Matt filled me in.

"Hey mom, Aunt Bea can sure whip good." Aunt Bea is my dad's sister. She's pretty, but robust. I remember when I was young, Aunt Bea didn't play. She meant what she said and said what she meant. She's tough.

"What are you talking about, Matt? What do you mean by that? Who did she whip?"

"She gave Ronnie a whipping. She sure whipped him good."

"She did?"

"Um huh."

"What did he do?"

"He was with our cousin Gary, playing in the woods by the house and they caught the woods on fire."

"They caught the woods on fire?"

"Yep, and the fire trucks came to put the fire out."

"How many fire trucks came?"

"It was about three. The police came, too. Granddaddy and everybody was helping the firemen put out the fire. It almost burned up all the woods around the house."

"I bet she tried to kill my baby, didn't she?"

"Yeah momma, she whipped him good."

Dang! My heart was broke, I didn't want my kid beaten like I know he probably was whipped. "Where is he?"

"He's here."

"Let me talk to him."

"Hi Ronnie, how's my baby?"

"Alright. When we coming home, Mom?"

"Well, I don't have enough money to get you home right now, but as soon as I do, I'm sending for you. Okay? Is everything alright?"

"Yeah, I'm just ready to come back to Seattle. I miss my friends."

"Do you miss me?"

"Yeah mom. I miss you, too."

"I'm sending you some money so you can get school clothes. Okay?"

"Okay mom. We're going to school here again, the whole year?"

"Naw, I don't think so."

"Hey Ronnie. Will you do something for me?"

"What?"

"First, tell me you'll do it."

"Yeah mom, what?"

"I want you to be good so you won't get in trouble. I don't want anybody giving you any more whippings, it hurts me when I hear that you got a whipping, it makes me cry, so please be good so you won't get in trouble. Can you do that for me?"

"Yeah mom."

"Y'all are coming home real soon, I promise."

"Okay mom."

I cried when I hung up the phone. My kids need to be with me. I just planned on them being there for a few months, now it's been close to a year. I haven't done anything since they've been gone. I've just gotten worst.

I hurried to work. I wasn't talking much to any of the dancers. . . cause nothing's changed, still drugs everywhere, not so much smoking but still a lot of snorting. I was glad to see everybody. They seemed glad to see me. But, I need a break from all the drugs. Seems to me, I should be able to go to work and not be around drugs. I need a little time away from all the madness.

Gus was giving me a hard time. He's pissed at me, mad about me taking off like I did. I get tired of dancing. Dancing for a living can mess you up. I don't have a decent man in my life. One that's normal. One that has a square job and will accept me as a dancer.

What happens is there's this stereotype attitude about dancers. Guys all think we're not good enough. I've dated square guys before, but once they find out you're a dancer, the change is automatic. They treat you like a whore and it's been almost a year since I've had sex.

Then on the other hand, I won't date a guy that buys dances. I think they're tricks. I think they're weird to be buying lap dances, spending hundreds. I don't want a man like that and no decent man wants a woman like me. I'm left with nothing, no options. Sometimes I just have to get away.

Gus gave my position away to this Asian girl, China. I was okay with that. It didn't bother me at all, but I think China was trying to let me know she was in charge now. I hope she doesn't push it too hard. I just want to make my money and not be bothered.

"Jolynn, girl where have you been?"

"You mean . . . where have you been? Cause I've been here working."

"Well you could have called me. You use to come by every

now and then."

"Girl, I've been staying home with my husband. Guess what?"

"What?"

"I'm pregnant."

"Dang Jolynn. You going to have it?"

Jolynn just shook her head. "I don't know. I don't know."

"What does Calvin say?"

"He says it's up to me."

"Well, if I was you, I'd have it."

"Girl, I don't know about bringing a baby in the world, especially the way I live."

"Jolynn, you'll do good. Have you ever gotten an abortion?"

"Naw girl."

"Well, if you've never done that, don't start. Don't put that on your record. I promise, it'll bother you later. So when are you having your baby?"

Jolynn gave me a little smile, "I'll have to see."

It was my turn to dance. It's been a while. I got nervous. I didn't know what song to dance on. The music has changed. China's been doing the juke box. Dang, I don't know any of these songs.

" Jolynn, come here."

"Girl, what's a good song?"

"Dance on Whitney."

"Which one."

"Any of them."

"I want something slow."

"Gap Band is on there. Here's one."

"That's good?"

"Yeah, that's a good one." I settled on *Wishing Well* and showed out.

I don't know why I get so nervous. I've been dancing close to fifteen years now, I've danced all over, and I still get nervous. I can put on a show whenever I want. Some days are better than others. Sometimes I'll connect with the customers, have them eating out my hand . . .then other times, it's like I'm an alien from another planet. It doesn't matter how long I've danced, I'll always feel strange dancing on stage, exposing so much of myself. The way a girl dances, the way we move our bodies, is very inti-

C. Oakes

mate, it's personal. When I dance, it's like I'm showing the way I move when I'm making love. That's giving a lot of yourself away to complete strangers.

But I can deal with it. I've produced a mental barrier, protecting myself. I feel like it's not me. It's not me at all. Some how I'll separate myself from my actions. My name isn't Sharell when I'm on stage. It's Nikki. Hearing yourself called something else really helps. I've been called Nikki for years now. I joke that Nikki is my split personality. She's my alter ego. She doesn't care. That's probably why it doesn't bother me so much, cause I don't feel like it's me sitting on laps, flashing tittys. It's Nikki doing that.

Aaron called again. He sounds so nice.

"Sharell, how are you?"

"I'm good, Aaron. How's everything with you?"

"Good, by the grace of God, real good. I'm calling because I want to give you another two hundred dollars to hold my spot this month. When will be a good time to come by?"

"I'll be home until about eight tonight. You can bring it anytime before eight, okay?"

"Yeah that'll be fine. I'll see you around seven."

"Okay, I'll be here."

"Hey, Sharell!"

"Yes."

"God loves you."

"Thanks Aaron, see ya later."

Aaron came right on time. He always has this little boy grin. I think it adds to his attractiveness.

"When do you plan on moving in?"

"It'll be a couple more months." He gave this nervous laugh, "Just don't give my place away."

"Don't worry, I won't."

"I'll be going to California for about a month. I got to get my daughter and visit with my mother, then I'll be ready to move in. That's at least another two months before I actually move in. I promise to call a couple of weeks ahead of time, so there won't be any surprises. I'll give you two hundred every month to hold it for me."

"Okay."

"You sure that's enough."

"Well, I'll take more."

He gave me that little boy smile,   "No. . .no, that's alright."

I'm glad he didn't listen to me and gave me a deposit. I need all the money I can get. I'm sending this money to my boys in Alabama.

Aaron is a neat guy and a Christian too. That's good. I need someone positive around me.   Every time I talk with him he tells me God loves me. Man, that's good to hear.   I appreciate that attitude. And he's smart. I have a weakness for smart men. He's a real gentleman and fine, too. I wonder why he's not married.

I continued to work. Everyday, I went to work and stayed to closing. Stacking my money. I need my boys. It'll cost a little over six hundred for airplane tickets. I'll pay all my bills then I'll buy their tickets. When they get home, I don't want to be worried about bills. I want to spend time with them. I want to laugh and play with my boys. Just us. Man, I got to get my boys home. I feel so guilty for them being gone so long. After work, I went straight to the house. I didn't want to be persuaded off my mission, so I stayed away from friends, clubs and drugs. I've been doing good and I didn't want to turn back by doing something stupid.

The phone rang, it was Kathy.

"Hey Girl, how you doing?"

"Okay. Where have you been? Why haven't you called us?"

"Girl, I've been working. I got to send for my babies."

"I know they've been gone a long time."

"Yeah, too long."

"Sharell, I'll give you the money to get your babies. I miss them too."

"Naw Kathy, that's okay. I'll have enough in a couple of weeks. Thanks though."

"Well If you need to borrow some money, just let me know. I'll loan it to you, whatever you need."

"Naw, that's okay, I don't like owing money. I appreciate you and thanks for the offer."

"Come over, we haven't seen you in a while, stop being a hermit."

"Naw, I can't come over there, I won't go to work and I need

C. Oakes

to work tomorrow."

"I told you I'll give you what you need. Come over and have a snort with us. Everybody's been asking about you, . . .even Johnny. Come over for a little while."

"Well okay, I'm not staying long."

One day of snorting and drinking, turned out to be two days. I enjoyed my friends. We partied. On the third day, I was home, by myself too high to work. Kathy got tired of my company and sent me home with a rock the size of a pop bottle cap. I tried to smoke it up. I didn't want to have any left that would get me started again. I was up already for three days. I was tired, so tired, but so high. I couldn't sleep. I was shaking bad, but I kept hitting the pipe. I didn't have to share with anybody. I smoked and I smoked.

Damn, I was getting down to the last few pebbles. "I think I put some in my pockets." I started taking clothes from the closet and drawers, digging in pockets. My room was a mess. "I know I hid some rocks in my pockets. I always do." I started feeling the pockets, "Damn, it's gone in the corners. I have to cut it." I started cutting my pockets. "There's something there, I can feel it." I didn't know if it was crack or cotton balls in the pockets, but I was finding out. I know what I'm doing. I just wanted one more hit. I couldn't believe all that crack was gone. Maybe some was on the floor. I could have dropped some. I started picking the carpet for hope. Maybe just a little pebble that I could have dropped. "What's that? Um. . .Nothing. Well, I got this last little hit."

Just as I was crawling on the floor, looking for pebbles, taking the last hurrah of my private party, it started. I was on the floor, shaking and shaking, crawling around the floor, picking the floor for possibilities that I might have dropped something, determined to take that last good hit. Then the singing started. I could hear it. The singing was for me. Where did that come from?

"Praaaaay ay ay for me e. Praaaaay ay ay for me e. Oooooh my mother, she prayed for me e e. Wheeeen en en I'm down. Aaaaat a at the altar, pleeeease don't forget et to pray ay ay for me."

There I was, on the floor, pitiful. I couldn't do anything. The song continued. . . for me. My soul left my body again. This time, it ministered to me. . . along with everybody else. "How could that be?" It must have been angels and saints and ancestors and my own soul. Praying for myself when I wasn't able. I was looking at myself on the floor. I saw me, I saw me. . . I was sad, on the floor like that. I could feel everybody there. People had encircled me, singing for me, ministering and praying for me. They wanted me to live.

What was I doing? This wasn't fun. I didn't enjoy this. I didn't like it at all, feeling like this. I'm pitiful. I begin to pray . . .I was rocking back and forth, trying to connect with God. I didn't want this anymore. "Lord, I know I'm high, and I know what I'm saying. I'm never going to do this again. If I'm going to continue to smoke cocaine, I don't want to live. Lord, just take me out now. Why should I continue to sin against you. Lord, I don't want this life. I don't want to be high like this. I promise Lord, my God. I'm never going to do this again. I won't smoke cocaine again. I promise you. I promise you. I promise you. . . I know exactly what I'm saying. And I'm saying to you, Lord, Never again. I won't ever smoke cocaine again."

C. Oakes

Chapter 23

It was morning. Last night was so eerie. I remember that song, but I never sang it. That was a song I used to hear when I was young. It's an old spiritual that my parents and grandparents sang. Whow . . .I can't believe what happened. I like that song. Pray for me, that's the song I heard. Somebody must love me. People were praying for me. "Thank you, who ever you are!"

I don't know how to feel just yet. . . I mean, I don't know if I'm a new person. I know what I did, I promised God to never again smoke crack again and I meant every word. I'm never doing that again.

First of all, I'm not going to make frivolous promises like that to God. I respect God and what I promised Him. I going to keep this promise, I'm not ever going to bring a crack pipe up to my lips again. That's all it takes. Just don't do it.

I'm disgusted with myself. I was so pitiful last night. . . I hate that stuff.

I need to call my children. Right now!

'Hello . . Hello, how's everybody?"

"Sharell?"

"Yeah. Is that you?"

"Yes. How's everybody?" It was my Aunt Bea. She sounded worried and concerned.

"Where have you been? We've been trying to contact you. Everybody been looking for you."

"What do you mean, I've been here."

"We've been trying to call you. Nobody has been able to get you."

"Why . . What's wrong?"

"Momma died."

"My grandma?"

"Yeah baby. Momma died."

"When?"

"She died last Tuesday."

"What?"

"Yeah, we had her funeral today."

"Oh my goodness. My poor grandma."

"Sharell, everybody's here."

"They are?"

"Yeah, everybody but you."

"What?"

"Yeah, your mother's here."

"She is?"

"Uh huh. Let me talk with her."

Momma was short with me. "Yeah?"

"Hello, momma?"

"Yeah?"

"Momma, it's me, Sharell."

"I know who it is."

"Well, how's the kids and daddy?"

"Everybody's fine. Your dad did a good job on Mothers' Eulogy. It was a beautiful service. I asked if I could buy her gown to bury her in, and they let me. . . so I was able to dress mother . . . you know. . . get her ready. She was beautiful."

I started panicking.

"She saw me. Oh my goodness . . . Oh my goodness. My grandma's spirit was probably there last night and she saw me. She saw me tweeking and being pitiful. Oh Lord, there were others there, too. Who were all those people praying for me. Oh my goodness. My grandma saw me like that." I was praying and praying hoping it wasn't her that saw me like that.

"Momma, I got to get my boys home."

"I've already talked with your father about that, I'm bringing the boys home with me."

"What did he say?"

"He acted like he wanted to keep them with him, but . . hey, I just told your dad that I'm bringing the boys to Oklahoma, so he agreed."

"Okay momma. Let me speak to daddy."

"WC, the telephone."

"Hello, Daddy? Hi Daddy."

"Hi baby. How you doing?"

"I'm fine, Daddy. How you doing Daddy?"

"Hey, me and the boys are doing great. Your mother tell you? She wants to take the boys back with her."

C. Oakes

"Yeah, she told me. Well, I guess that'll be okay. I'll be getting them pretty soon anyway. So grandma died?"

"Yeah, baby. We're having a good celebration for her."

"That's good daddy. All your cousins are here. We tried to reach you. I think there's a ticket waiting for you at the airport."

"It is?"

"Yeah, It's probably expired by now."

"Man, oh man!" I was so disgusted with myself.

"I wish you could have been here with us."

"Me, too. I wish I had visited grandma before she left us."

"Well, you know your grandmother, she's gone on to be with the Lord."

"Yes, she is, Daddy. She's with Jesus now."

My grandmother was so special. She saw things, she had visions, and she saw spirits. My grandma could even communicate with animals. Once when I was a little girl, we would go to Alabama every summer and stay with our grandparents. This particular year it was a terrible storm, maybe a tornado had come through, and all our animals got scared and ran away. My grandma left, she was gone about a couple of hours, then she came back, walking up the hill to our house, all our animals were behind her, she was clucking, and squealing, and loving those animal back up the hill. All our animals were behind her, following her home. I'm going to miss my grandma. Everyone say's I look just like her.

My grandparents had been married over 65 years. They were always laughing together. My granddad would have her crying laughing at his stories. She would always tell me not to believe granddaddy.

"Baby, you believe your granddaddy?" I was sitting right next to him absorbing every word. "Baby . . baby, your granddaddy's lying." She'd laugh again, then start crying because she couldn't stop laughing. That'll just make granddadddy keep going. He'd swear everything was the honest to God truth. They were happy together.

Aaron finally called. He left a message on my machine.

"Hello, Sharell, How are you doing? I'm just calling to give you a heads up. I may need a ride from the airport. Can you pick us up? We'll be ready to come there, . . in Seattle, by the first of the month. I'll have to call you with the specific time and airline. I'll have Tiara with me. I didn't ask you about the school system. I'll have to find out about the schools in the neighborhood? That school at the end of the street looks like a good school, I should have asked about their programs. Tiara's always gone to a private school or been in a gifted class. Well, I hope everything's alright with you. Take care of yourself. I'll see you soon. Hey, God loves you and I do, too."

I listened to my message over and over. "Is he serious with that God loves me business." He always says stuff like that.. Maybe I should be grateful. Well, I need some positive messages. It sure doesn't hurt.

Aaron will be here in a few weeks. That'll work out great because I'm planning a trip to Oklahoma by next month. The house won't be empty while I'm gone to get my kids. It's been a while since I've been down stairs. It shouldn't take too much to get it ready. After they move in and get settled, I'll leave to get my boys.

I need to gain weight before Momma sees me. I'm so skinnny. I look like a skeleton. Well, I should fill out a little by then.

I was waiting at the gate and watched Aaron and Tiara as they departed the plane. Tiara is an absolute doll. She has long, very thick, kinky wavy hair. She's skinny with knobby knees. She's going to be tall. Tiara saw me and almost ran into my arms. How cute. Aaron and I held her hands as she skipped through the airport. She wasn't shy. This little girl liked me the first time I saw her. I liked her too. Tiara was excited about her move here. I have to admit, I was a excited too. I've always had boys and foot-ball and baseball. It'll be fun to do nails, dolls and dress up.

We arrived at the house and I showed Tiara her room.

"Now, here's your closet. I'll help you hang up your clothes, if you like? Upstairs, all the way at the top, is my boys room. Wait till you meet them. I have an eight year old, Ronnie and a twelve year old, Matt. You're going to love them. I guess you and Ronnie will be going to the same school." She was all ears, listen-ing intensely.

Tiara is so sweet. She wasn't saying too much, just listening. She didn't asked any questions about my boys. I showed her our family pictures. Still she didn't say anything. She was soaking it

C. Oakes

all in.

We went through the house. I think she loves it. I didn't have much furniture downstairs. Val and Jolynn took what they needed when they moved out. I didn't mind because it was old furniture. Nothing great. I think Kathy gave us most of the stuff. We'll just have to get more. I told Aaron about the Penny Saver newspaper. We can find good things in there. Anyway it's an option.

It was time for me to go to work. I told Aaron that I worked in a bar and I waited tables. I wasn't ready to trust him with my business. That's something I don't tell everybody. I might not ever tell him what I really do. I don't know how he might take living with a dancer, he might flip. He acts so square, so religious. For now, I'll just keep it as my little secret.

My friends couldn't believe I quit doing coke. I was over Kathy's house. I missed her. I missed everybody. It's been weeks since I had seen my friends. They didn't know that I had changed, I was a new person. I hadn't been high for weeks.

I didn't have any problems quitting because my mind was made up. I didn't want any more. Never. I hate what it did to me. I especially hate that I didn't see me grandma before she died. I blame that on cocaine. If I wasn't using that stuff, I would have gone to get my boys and I would have seen my grandma. I'll never forgive myself for that. I let cocaine take an irreplaceable opportunity from me. Seeing my grandma again was priceless. Now it's gone.

But I still have my friends. I don't know how my friends are going to take me now, with my new attitude. Cause I ain't doing anymore cocaine, period.

Cocaine was it. It was the life of the party. I loved the stuff. The people were fun, I enjoyed the life. I had fun as long as I wasn't smoking crack. To tell the truth though, I was getting just as bad when I snorted coke. I'm an addict. I've changed.

We were all classy, straight from the heart, good people. We didn't want any bull around us. We looked after each other. I loved the environment. But what was after cocaine. Would they still want me around. Me, being the only one not snorting, or getting high with them.. I didn't have any other reasons to party. I can't handle getting drunk. I don't go dancing, I get enough of dancing at work. I don't meet guys. I just didn't think anyone would understand me or even want to try to understand or get to know me once they find out I dance for a living. But, these guys accepted me. We were friends. If I truly needed anything, I could count on them and that means a lot to me.

I told Kathy I quit cocaine.

"Johnny, Sharell said she didn't want anymore snort." Kathy was telling Johnny, she didn't believe me. She just laughed like I was joking.

"You don't even want a hit on my pipe?" Kathy whispered with a little challenge in her voice. She wanted to know if I would sneak a quick hit.

"Kathy no. I don't want it. I quit." She don't understand, I'm not doing it. I don't want any of it.

"You really quit Sharell?" Johnny asked although he wasn't buying it either. He got a plate from the cabinet and filled it with prime powder. "Here, you can fix a cigarette."

"Naw, that's okay. I don't want it."

"You can have a cigarette. That's not hurting anything." Johnny reasoned with me.

"I quit. I really quit. I don't want anymore."

"Not even a cigarette?" Kathy said defensively. We would remove about half of the tobacco out of cigarettes and replace it with powder. Cigarettes were good like that.

"Naw, I quit." Now they were offended. Kathy and Johnny looked at each other with their personal eye signals. They felt challenged to make me fail. I saw what they were thinking. They didn't want me to win. They silently questioned me.

"Who does she think she is," with their eyes. But then, their love for me won them over. They want what's best for me. I believe they could accept me not getting high with them.

"Sharell, you can have a cigarette. That's not going to hurt you." Kathy sided with Johnny. They could accept me not getting high with them anymore but they want me to party with them one more time. Only thing, they didn't know about my promise to God.

"Okay." I agreed. I packed me a cigarette with the good powder stuff and lit the cigarette. It wasn't good. I smoked it and basically ran out the door.

God was angry at me. I felt it. I felt dirty. I felt a dark cloud

C. Oakes

above me. I wanted it to go away. I wanted to run. I ran into my shower. I tried to wash the dark cloud away. The shower confined me to where I had to face what I did. God was not pleased with me. Out of every thing I've done in my life, out of all the things I failed at, out of all the gritty things I've done. This had to be the worst. I felt his anger. It felt like he was frowning down on me. I never ever want to feel like that again. I knew he was angry. I knew he was disappointed. I don't want to ever make a promise to God that I don't keep it. Ever.

I washed and I washed. I wanted to make myself clean. I decided I wouldn't do that again. Any of it. I'm not going to smoke it, snorting, put it in cigarette, I'm not going to be around it. I'm finished. But I needed forgiveness. I prayed and I prayed.

"Lord please forgive me." I washed and I washed. "Lord please forgive me. I'll never do it again." I much rather disappoint my friends than to disappoint the Almighty and I'll never break a promise to Him again

Chapter 24

Aaron was doing everything around the house. He worked on the plumbing, he put up night lights, he made sure the yard was cut perfect. He worked on my car, fixing the brakes, checking the oil, and just tinkering, making sure it was in good condition. He was Mr. Fix it.

He had a hobby of rebuilding computers and had a couple of systems that he hooked up around the house. One was put downstairs in his room, one upstairs in my room and one in the kids playroom. I thought that was cool. I know my boys will think it's really cool. He tried to teach me how to use a mouse. I didn't like it.

Aaron seemed perfect. He was handsome and smart. He had a good job. I thought maybe he was sent to me. Maybe God had sent me a man. But why was this man single. I know he has somebody. He couldn't be without anybody. I thought I would ask when the time was right.

Aaron said that he didn't drink. That was something new, everybody I knew had a social cocktail every now and then. He was adamant. No drinking what so ever.

Aaron explained. "Sharell, you don't want me to drink. I'm terrible when I start drinking, I can't handle it. So I don't do it. You wouldn't want me around while I'm drinking. I promise you. I can get pretty terrible."

"Okay, Aaron. I'll remember that." I assured Aaron that it was okay. Well, he didn't have to persuade me. I'm going to respect him. I know he knows better than anybody. If he can't drink, then he won't get it from me. He seems so honest about his problem.

"Will it bother you if I drink, I mean, I don't want to influence you?" I wanted him to be comfortable.

"No, it won't bother me." He assured me. "I'm not going to drink. You don't have to worry about that. But, I don't want you to feel self-conscious about you having a drink if you want it." Aaron was looking at me with his wholesome look and religious mannerisms. He was sweet.

I had let the cocaine and crack alone but I wasn't ready to quit drinking or smoking marijuana. I wonder how he felt about that, me smoking marijuana. Since we were being so honest, I decided to ask about his personal life. Where was Mrs. Fix it?

"So Aaron, how does your friend, your woman . . . feel about you moving here." I caught him off guard. He wasn't ready.

"She's okay about me moving to Seattle. But I hadn't told her that I would be moving with another woman. She doesn't know that." He laughed nervously. I don't feel that he wants that secret out.

"She might make you move?" I asked jokingly.

"Right now, she'll have to understand. I don't think I'll have a problem." He sure can look innocent. But I knew better, I just decided to let it go, cause he should have said something to his significant other especially about moving him and his daughter in with me.

I was upstairs, sitting on the sofa watching the evening news and a special report about the Green River Killer was on the set. They showed pictures of the victims that were attributed to the killer. It listed 46 deaths. It's now the year, 1987. The police finally had a man of interest. Finally, I thought. Maybe that's him. I hope they'd catch his ass. They had taken body samples from some guy but didn't make an arrest. I didn't know Aaron was standing behind me, watching the special report too.

"Sharell, what's that about?"

"Haven't you heard about the Green River Killer?"

Aaron shook his head, "No."

"Well, there's a man that's killing working girls. He's kills them and then dumps their bodies in the Green River. That's only a few miles from here, in Tukuilla. This guy's been doing this for years now. Every since I came here, back in the seventies, I've been hearing about girls disappearing. At first the police wasn't paying attention because it's been only prostitutes that were being killed. Now since its been so many bodies found dumped in this community river, there's an whole police unit working on the case."

"You're kidding. I wonder why I hadn't heard about any of this in California."

"I don't know, but they haven't heard about it in Oklahoma either. I guess it's a Seattle thing. You'd think it would be all over the country. Something this big, that's so terrible. What does it take to make national news, anyway. I mean, this guys been killing for close to a decade now."

"Well, I don't think they would want anything like this to get out without someone in custody. One reason I would think is, they would have to answer a lot of questions, like what took so long, and I know the police wouldn't want that type of questioning. Then again, you wouldn't want anyone else to get any big ideas. You know, like a copycat killer. If I were the detectives, I wouldn't want this news in the national media either, under any circumstances." Aaron is so analytical. I thought.

My kids were now in Oklahoma and I was determined to get them home with me before school started. I love my mother. I know she means well, but sometimes my mother can be so bossy.

"Sharell, these kids are doing fine. I planned on enrolling them in school down here. Let them stay here this year and you get them when school's out. It's only a few months. I was hoping they could stay with me. I want to spend a little time with my grand babies before they get too old. They never spent any real time here in Oklahoma. We're all settled and everything. We're going to church every Sunday. I was kind of enjoying them. They'll be okay till you're ready for them. You're not ready to take care of these boys right now. I know you're not."

I was thinking, what is she talking about, I'm ready for my boys now. "Momma, they've been gone too long, they want to come home, especially Ronnie, you know he wants to come home. I know Matt wants to play football. There's a good football program here. All the police and firefighters work with the kids here at Rainier play field, it's a big deal. They're mentors to these kids. I want to get the boys around this kind of stuff. You know, it's such a good positive athletic program. I don't want them to miss it. This one coach, Danny Copeland's been asking about Matt. He wants him to play."

"Sharell, let these boys stay here. You can visit them anytime you want, . . .and when school's out, then you can get them."

Momma put her foot down. The boys were staying. It has always been a losing battle when it came to my mother. Anyway, she probably knows what's best. I really don't want to challenge her decisions after my downhill spiral of bad decisions, like the one I made with Mike, and me not going to college, and me ending up as a dancer and everything else, after all that. Whatever she says is probably right. I decided to visit my boys for the summer.

"Where are they now?"

"They're here, hold on . . .Matthew . . . Ronnie . . .Come here. You're mom's on the phone."

"Hello, hey there, how are y'all doing?"

"Hi mom, . . .

"Hi momma." They both were on a phone.

"How are y'all doing? Hey, I want to talk with you guys about something. Momma wants you guys to go to school there this year. What do you think about that?"

"We'll get to go to school with Quincy? Yeaaa! Mom, we're having fun. We're playing with Quincy and Ericka. It's fun here."

"I'll be there in two weeks. Okay? We'll go shopping. I know all y'all's school clothes are too little by now." I was thinking I could get a good price on plane tickets with at least a two week reservation.

"Momma, you'll be here in two weeks? Yeaaaaaaaaa. Momma is coming. Momma is coming." Ronnie was excited. I was excited too. I cried when I hung up and began calling for my plane reservation.

It was a beautiful Sunday morning and Aaron invited me to go to church with them. They were all dressed up in their Sunday outfits. Aaron sure looked handsome. Tiara is just a doll. He sure dressed her up homely. Yuk! Why he got that little girl looking like that? Homely.

I thought about the invite. It sure would be nice but I declined and explained.

"Aaron, I hadn't told you but I'll be going to Oklahoma for about a month or so. I want to make sure the rent is paid up for two months before I leave. So I'm going to work a lot in the next two weeks. I'll be working today and probably staying all day. Thanks for the invitation." I got some money saved but I needed to work as much as possible so I can have a big bank roll when I get to Oklahoma. Since I stopped smoking crack, it's easy for me to make money. I don't mind going in the club and working ten or twelve hours.

When I got to the club, I saw Jolynn. She looked terrible.

C. Oakes

This crazy fool has been beating her. Jolynn had scars all over her face. "Dang, Jolynn, what happened to you?"

"Calvin did this to me. Sharell, I'm scared of him. I was in the hospital for about a week. He beat me with a rifle in my face and head. He said he was going to kill me. I looked so bad. The police told him if he did it again they were going to arrest him."

"Why didn't they arrest his ass then. Why didn't you call me?"

"I didn't press any charges. He only does it when he's drunk. When Calvin don't drink, he's the sweetest man ever. Alcohol makes him violent."

"Jolynn, that's no damn excuse. A drunk does what he wanted to do all the time but doesn't have the balls while he's sober. He wanted to beat you up. That's the truth, Jolynn. He wanted to jump on you. He used drunk as an excuse to really do it. Where's the baby when he's fighting you like that? What does his sister say? Don't she still live upstairs? I didn't want to upset Jolynn but she started crying."

"Sharell, usually the baby is in his room. I shut the door so he won't hear us fighting. I don't know why his sister don't come down and stop him. You know, Calvin's the only boy in his family. He is so spoiled. His sisters and momma let him get away with everything. Anything he does is alright to them."

Jolynn was defending his ass. I didn't want to hear that bullshit. Since I stopped getting my ass beat, I don't have any tolerance for any other woman getting beat. I've grown out of that shit. I'm strong now and I'm not scared of any man. This kind of abuse is not acceptable. There's no reason for it. Especially fighting someone like Jolynn. She is so sweet. She would never do anything that deserves this kind of brutally. I can tell he must have beat her severely cause she has scars on her head and face from stitches.

"Look, you got to call me if it ever happens again. Jolynn, you know your family. They would come here and kill that man if something happens to you. Then one of your brothers would have a murder rap because you didn't stop Calvin from beating your ass half to death. If this ever happens again, Jolynn, you have to call me. Do you understand. I'll put an end to this shit, I'll stop his ass."

I felt so bad about this. Jolynn came here with me, I can't let anything happen to her. I promised myself if she gets beat like that again, I was calling her folks and sending her back to Oklahoma. That man could kill her. He put her in the hospital, beat her with a gun. I was sick to my stomach.

"Val, girl that man Jolynn married put her in the hospital for a week. He beat her with a gun in her head and face. She had to get stitches in her face. Man, I'm sick. Jolynn is so sweet, how could he do that to her."

"Where's Jolynn now?"

"She's back with him. Talking about he only does it when he's drinking."

"Now Sharell, you know you can't do anything if she's going to stay with his ass. Jolynn can come here and stay with me, I know she can stay with you. But until she's ready to get away from his ass, there's not too much you can do about it. You just have to pray for Jolynn and hope she can get away before it too late."

I called Jolynn before I got on the plane to Oklahoma. "Hello, is Jolynn there?"

It was Calvin. "Hold on."

I really didn't have anything to say to him. "Hello, hey girl how's everything? I'm on my way to Oklahoma. You know I got to check on you before I get out of here. You're going to be alright?"

"Girl, yeah, everything's fine. Girl, Calvin is so sorry he did that. He's been apologizing. He wouldn't have done that if he hadn't been drinking and getting high for days. That man was so high when he did that. He was too high. Calvin wouldn't have done all that if he was sober, it was the drugs and alcohol. He brought me a diamond bracelet. You know one of those tennis bracelets. It's pretty." Jolynn was upbeat.

"Well, I was just checking on you before I left for Oklahoma. I'll be gone about five or six weeks. I'm staying with my boys for a while."

"That sounds nice. Well tell everybody hello for me and have a good trip. I'll see you when you get back. Girl, don't worry about me, I'll be alright."

I hung up with Jolynn and said a little prayer under my breathe

C. Oakes

for her. Lord knows, I would be so so sad if anything happens to that girl. I just feel protective of Jolynn. Lord, I remember when I was getting my ass kicked by Mike. Then he would buy me presents, jewelry, wanting me to forgive and forget. Those days are over.

C. Oakes

Chapter 25

My older brother, Kenny, picked me up from the airport.
Kenny turned out to be a good husband for my friend Vicki. She
has never had to work. They just started their family. They have
two daughters. Their first daughter, Zshoni is now three and the
baby, Zoe is only one. It's funny cause my oldest boy Matt, is
already a teenager. I'm glad that I'm able to come home to visit,
I can go to my church, I can see my old friends. I'm going to
enjoy this trip.

When I got to Oklahoma City, I was shocked. How long has
it been since I visited home. It looked like a ghost town. The
neighborhood was deserted. The houses on our street are boarded up. These are brick, three and four bedroom houses all boarded up and abandoned. All these houses are empty. What happened?

"Kenny what happened around here? Why are all these houses empty?"

"Sharell, these knuckleheads all got on crack. It killed the
neighborhood."

"Crack cause the neighborhood to go down like this? I
couldn't believe what I was seeing." It was terrible seeing my
beautiful neighborhood looking all broke down. Boarded up. I
love Oklahoma City and the little suburb we live in called Park
Estates. It's a nice neighborhood, but this didn't look like my old
stomping grounds.

"Girl, this ain't nothing. You should have seen it a couple
years ago. That stuff damn near destroyed Park Estates. A lot of
people lost their property. Houses were getting repossessed. People weren't going to work or they were getting high on the job. It
was nuts. If I had the money, I would have brought all these houses. I got me a couple of them. But I almost went broke myself,
cause nobody was paying rent. It was real bad around here. Now
it's better. It's a lot better. They're still on that shit, but not like
they were a few years ago."

I didn't admit it to my brother that I too was on crack. I hope
it's not noticeable. At least, I was able to get back on track. Thank

God!

"Man, take me to see my babies."

"Those big old knuckleheads aren't babies. You hear that Vic? Sharell called those big, corn fed boys some babies."

"Did momma tell you that she wanted to keep them this year? I want to take them back to Seattle with me. They really need to be with me. They've been gone so long. I'm their mom. I should be taking care of my own kids.

"Sharell, leave those boys here. They're doing fine. They can stay one year. Let us keep them a little while. I didn't get to see my nephews grow up. Now they're almost grown. You can get them next summer. You know the family reunion will be in Wichita next year. Get them then." I gave up and resolved within myself that I was only visiting my boys. I would enjoy my time with them. Get them ready for school, then go home.

"Okay. That's it. Just this year."

"Mommmmmmmmm. Hi Momma."

"Hey, hi baby. I hugged and kissed Ronnie. You look so big. Look at you. Ronnie had grown more than I ever expected. All his baby looks were gone. He looked like a little man. I bet Matt is really big too. Where's your brother?"

"He went with Quincy to Douglass Center. Momma, how long are you staying? You're going to move here. We should live here in Oklahoma. I want to stay with my cousins."

"I don't know Ronnie. I'll have to think about it. I thought you missed your friends in Seattle?"

"Well, I like it here too. I like seeing my cousins. Momma, come here, let me show you my room." I visited a while with Ronnie, by himself, in his room. I let him tell me all about it. I let him have me all to himself. And I held my son. I cried a little too, cause I missed him so much.

Matt and Ronnie were staying in my little brothers rooms. The twins are gone to college now, but they're home every weekend.

It's fun when everybody's at home. It is nice having the feelings of a tight family institution. While I'm in Seattle, I never feel like I'm home. First of all, I can't find a church like my home church in Oklahoma. Then while I'm here, I have the closeness of my family right at my fingertips. Man, that's enough right there to move back here in Oklahoma and never look back. I sometimes feel my children are missing out on our family unit. We are a close knit family. We're clannish. I know they are missing something that's non replaceable.

Then too, I'm in a place where nobody really knows me. They don't know anything about me. Not like at home, where all someone has to do is ask, "Who's your folks?" Man . . . then they know all about you. Well, I'll take that back, there's Val and Jolynn living in Seattle. They're from Oklahoma and if it weren't for them, I would be so very lonely.

On the other hand, Seattle has so much to offer. My children will have an opportunity to grow with the experiences of cultural differences, and it's expected to know and respect those differences. They won't grow up in a box. They will be trained for change and understand diversity. I think that's important. The schools are fantastic in Seattle. Then I want my boys to enjoy all the activities, like the Bumpershoot, and the Hydroplane Races, and the professional teams. I had to face the truth, I'm taking my boys back to Seattle with me. I'll just have to find a good church home where we can feel good enough to become members.

When I saw my big boy, I was knocked off my feet. He was taller than me.

"Where's my boy, Matt? What have you done with him? I want him back. Give me my baby. Is he in there somewhere?" I was playfully beating on his chest. Matt's smile was brighter than the biggest star in the universe. He was so proud that he was now taller than me. He couldn't wait for me to see how tall he had gotten.

"Oh oh. Put me down. Put me down boy." I screamed. Matt had picked me up and was spinning me around. I know I'm small but dog gone it, he didn't have to pick me up like I was a little rag doll. Matt didn't have any problem throwing me over his back.

"Look at my big boy. Look at you. Ah, man." I started crying again. This boy is big. He has big feet. I had no idea he had grown so much. I knew right then that I needed more money.

We partied during my visit. Me and my sister Carol, took all the kids to Tulsa, Wichita, and Dallas. We had so much fun together. We fried chicken, packed picnic baskets, and left the city to visit other relatives and to enjoy each other. We went to family game rooms, Frontier City and water parks.

I showed the boys what a real pool shooter can do.

"You got to concentrate. Look at the pocket, not at the ball." I shocked them. "Look where you want the ball to go, then send it there. That's the secret." They didn't know their mom and auntie were pool sharks. "You got to talk a good game, too. Don't win without letting your opponent know how good you are, even if it's luck. Tell 'em you can't lose, you're too lucky. That's it. You can talk some people out of their game. Don't be rude, but shake their confidence. It works."

My visit was coming to an end, I only had a couple of days left in Oklahoma City. My mother loves to shop, so we went together to buy school clothes and supplies. It was kind of uncomfortable cause I know she wanted to tell me what was on her mind. I really didn't want to hear it. I know she was going for the main artery to my heart. Momma has a way of getting to the gut of things, without giving me any preparations.

"Sharell, what are you doing with your life? Why do you feel you got to drag these kids through the mud while you decide to get yourself together. It's just not right. Why don't you move back here, get yourself together and raise your boys around something decent. I was thinking we could get one of those houses and keep disabled adults. We can go into business together."

Whow, I wasn't thinking she would go there. That's a great idea. But then, my mind was already made up. I wished she had of said that earlier, before now, so I would have had time to think about it. Then, on the other hand, when I looked at the city, I thought "no, not right now." I wanted to get back to Seattle.

"Momma, we do pretty good in Seattle. Why don't you come visit us some time?" Momma didn't push it, she let it go. I was appreciative of that. We actually had a good time shopping.

It was hard as nails to leave my boys. I don't understand why it was so important for them to stay there and not come home with me. Everybody thought it was better for the boys to stay with momma this year. I don't know, but I gave up the battle and walked away crying all the way to the airport.

My kids weren't too upset. "Momma, stop crying, we'll be home when school's out. Don't worry, we're going to be okay. Ronnie was trying to comfort me."

C. Oakes

"Mom, you sure you're going to be okay while we're gone. I don't want to let you go back by yourself if you need us home." Matt was looking out for me as always.

"It's okay, I promise. Anyway, I got two roommates. A guy I met and his little girl, she's six years old, real cute. So I won't be there by myself at all. They'll probably be there when you come home this summer. You'll get a chance to meet them. They seem to be good people. He builds airplanes for Boeing."

"Oh, yeah. Momma, why didn't you tell us about this man living with you before now?"

"I don't know. I guess I forgot. It wasn't all that important. I was so glad to see you that I wasn't thinking about anything else. I should have mentioned it to you. I just forgot."

There was a flight assistant talking over the intercom giving boarding instructions for handicap and families with small children. I listened for my seat number before I began lining up to scan my boarding pass. It was finally time for me to head back to Seattle.

"Well, guys, it's time for me to go. Be good for grandma, okay? Give me a kiss." I kissed everybody, my boys, my niece and nephew and my sister, Carol. As I boarded the plane, hot tears were streaming down, fast. I was going home. Lord, please protect this flight.

During my trip, I read magazines, listened to music, and had a couple of drinks. As we approached SeaTac, I began to get myself together by touching up my makeup and gathering my things. I grabbed my bags that were packed underneath the seat in front of me. Okay, I'm here.

I'm home. Seems like it was a short trip. I was a little tipsy. Val was there to pick me up. Hey Val, thanks for coming to get me.

"It's okay. Come on girl, let's head for the baggage claim area before the crowd gets there."

I had my bags and we were driving down I-5, toward my house. "Val, how's the twins?"

"Girl, wait till you see my babies. They're huge. It's already been two years. I can't believe how time flies. Sharell, why didn't you bring your boys home?"

"I had planned on bringing them home, but my mom wanted

to keep them this year. I don't think she believes I have a stable home for them. I don't know. She kept talking about getting myself together before I bring them home. Val, my home is stable, isn't it. I mean, I take care of my babies, don't I? I don't know why she thinks I'm not taking care of my boys. I know what's the problem, Momma thinks just because I'm a dancer, I don't care for them good enough. I may not be the best mom, but, I take care of my boys. I'm not that bad."

"Girl, I think I would have brought my kids home. Let's get some Ivar's seafood before I take you to the house."

After a great meal, I went home. I thanked Val again for picking me up at the airport. Home, sweet home. I got my bags out the trunk of her car and headed inside. The house has separate entries for me and Aaron. I got upstairs and he has downstairs. I got inside and was putting my things in my room. I could hear giggling from downstairs. Aaron had company. I was jealous. I didn't say anything, I didn't acknowledge that I was in the house. It was late, too late to visit, so I just pouted.

The next morning, Aaron was knocking on my door. I opened the door and there he was acting so innocent. His mannerism's so humble like he was concerned about me. I didn't want to see him.

"Sharell, how was your trip?"

"It was good, Aaron, real good. I enjoyed every bit of it."

"So, where's the kids?"

"Well, it's a long story. We decided to let them stay this school year. I'll get them when school's out this summer."

"Whow, that's too bad. I wanted to meet your boys. I was hoping to have someone to go to school with Tiara."

"Yeah, that would have been nice. So who's your company?"

"My girl, Patricia's here visiting from California. I told her about you. She wants to meet you."

I was thinking to myself. . . . I'll bet. I don't want to meet his girl. If she know's what's good for her, she'll get her man out of here.

"Oh, I'd love to meet her. How long is she here?"

"Actually, she's leaving tomorrow night. She been here, visiting about a week now. "

"Well, that worked out well. You had a little privacy. I hope you took her around to explore the city's treasures. Did you show

C. Oakes

her the underground city?"

"Not really, I don't know the treasures myself. I need some-one to show me around."

"Where's she now?"

"She's sleep right now. We were up pretty late." Aaron gave me a little naughty smile.

"Oh okay. I'll be around." I returned his little naughty smile then hurried to shower so I could get dressed. I wanted to be out the house before she woke up. I didn't want to meet his woman. I didn't want to see what she looked like and I didn't want to be her friend. Anyway, I don't think she would want to spend her last little moments here in Seattle, visiting with me.

C. Oakes

Chapter 26

What happened between me and Aaron seemed so natural. I forgot all about his girlfriend. I forgot she was here visiting him a few months ago, while I was in Oklahoma City.

With him being around all the time, fixing things and Tiara needing her hair combed, we were like a family. We went grocery shopping together. Then, Aaron was handing me money to pay the bills. We seem to have things in order. I cooked dinner and help Tiara dress for school. It was fulfilling and I felt secure.

Aaron and I were friends, good friends. We laughed a lots together. He respected me and didn't flirt too hard. He was cute and shy. At least, I think he's shy. He's probably just acting because he can take charge too. Once when we were at a gas station, two young men were arguing and ready to fight. Aaron jumped right in the middle of the situation, listened to the parties, then gave judgement. He proceeded to instruct them on just what they were going to do.

"Now, you guys aren't going to be fighting around here. So you need to go home and chill out. Man, you're suppose to be friends. This man didn't steal your money, okay. It's three dollars? That's what it is? Here man, take this. Here's three dollars, now take this and go home and forget this mess, man. Tomorrow, you'll forget all about this little stuff. Shake hands and go home." After the altercations, Aaron walked back to the car like he was "the man." All I could do was sit in the car and watch him, then talk to myself.

"Look at him. Who does he think he is?" He finally got in the car. I tore right into him. " Aaron, you'd better be careful getting involved with stuff on the streets like that. These guys these days don't care."

"Oh, I wasn't too worried. I can take care of myself. I can take care of you, too."

"Okay, Mr. Man. You take care of everything. I don't think I'll let you take care of me, though. Not the way you walked in the middle of that mess over there. . . .You have to have a big chest for this job. I don't think you're ready." I was teasing him, cause if he wanted to take care of me, I'm ready to hand that ball over immediately. I'm tired of doing everything, worrying about everything, paying all the bills. I'm ready to give the responsibilities away forever. Let someone else do it.

"You'd be surprised about me, Sharell. I can take care of myself real good and I've had some close calls too."

"Oh yeah. Like what?"

"See this! See these scars." Aaron took off his shirt and wore only a sleeveless t-shirt. Then he raised the t-shirt. "Look at this." He continued by uncovering a scar hidden by his hair. Then I saw all the evidence of a rough life. Burn scars on both his shoulders looked like melted skin. There was a long scar across his chest and back. He had a scar across his skull, I guess his head must have been busted open at one time. How did he live through all these catastrophes. This guy is a cat with nine lives.

"Damn, What happened to you? You look like Frankenstein."

"Sharell, I use to be rough. I drank back then. It almost killed me. I was blessed to live through all this mess and turn my life around. I died once. Yep! On the operating table, I was pronounced dead. Its funny cause I heard them say I was dead. I remember how peaceful I felt. I knew I was with God. So I just laid back and enjoyed the peacefulness. Then I hear a voice telling me that I had to go back. Then I remember waking up in my room, looking around, then realizing that I was still here. It was real disappointing. Cause I was with God. Can you imagine that? They said I was in a coma for three weeks."

"Man, Aaron, I'm glad for your sake you've changed. I don't think you could take another traumatic blow. You're dangerous. Look at you. How did your shoulders get burned up like that?"

"In a car accident. I was drunk. I think angels pulled me out of that situation."

"Really? Why you think angels got you out?"

"Cause I was caught in a burning car. I couldn't get out. It was fire everywhere, so I laid back on the seat to try to kick out the window or open the door, but I couldn't get in opened. The glass didn't break. I passed out. Next thing I knew, I was out the car, laying on the grass, then the ambulance came. Somebody pulled me out. I couldn't get out by myself. I was unconscious and the car was on fire. Think about it. Who would approach a

C. Oakes

car, blazing, on fire? No one was there when the ambulance came, so I've always had the feeling that it was angels that came to my rescue. I've always had that feeling. . .that it was angels. You see why I'm always praising God?"

"Whow, Aaron." I didn't ask anymore questions. That was enough for one day. But I had a new appreciation for him. I felt sorry for him, too.

I didn't know what to do about me dancing. I wanted to quit but didn't know how. I've been dancing almost fifteen years. I could pay my bills. I could buy me things. I didn't have to worry about living expenses. But now was the time to escape this way of life if I was ever going to get away from this profession. With Aaron paying half on everything, I now had help with bills. I could afford the drop in my income, at least until I got use to making respectable money. Yes, this was my chance to go through the transformation to a more normal life.

But then my criminal record would show up. I was too embarrassed about my record to apply for a real job. They would find out that I was in prison. I couldn't take that. I rather live with my secrecy and dance for a living, than for someone to know that I had spent time in prison.

I hadn't even told Aaron that I was a dancer. He still believes that I'm a cocktail waitress at some fancy restaurant. I got to tell him the truth cause he's acting like he likes me. I don't want to mislead him and if he's going to change on me, then I want him to change now, before I let my guard down.

"Aaron you got a minute, we need to talk" I was kind of nervous, but decided whatever happens, will happen. I wasn't going to hide the truth about my life anymore. I think we're friends. I believe he's had enough time with me not to judge me too harshly. "There's something I think you should know about me." There's that look again. The I'm so humble look.

Aaron could tell this was important. He stopped tinkering with the computer and sat next to me on the sofa. I was twirling my thumbs and fingers. I took a deep breathe.

"Sharell, don't worry. It can't be that bad, can it? You didn't kill anybody, did you?"

"No Aaron," I gave a nervous giggle. "I didn't kill anybody but when I told you that I was a waitress, well, I was lying. I'm not really a waitress. Actually, I'm a dancer. I dance at a club."

"A strip club?" Aaron acted excited. He was shocked too.

"No, not exactly. It works like a strip club but we don't strip."

"What kind of place is that?"

"Well, we wear costumes and table dance. We dance on stage, sometimes we dance with the customers. It's just like a strip club, we just don't strip."

"Can I come see you?" He sounded like a little boy, acting innocent.

"Nooooooo. You can't. But I just thought you need to know."

"Well, I can't blame you for keeping some things to yourself. You're cool. Don't worry about it. I appreciate your honesty but don't worry about it. God still loves you."

"Thanks, Aaron. I was a little worried. Thanks for being so cool."

I went to work that evening. It felt good that I was able to share this part of my life with my square roommate. I danced that night thinking of Aaron. I played on the juke box, *This Is For The Cool In You*, every time I had to dance on stage. I was happy, having fun and by the end of the night, I made lots of money.

Jolynn called. She was whispering. "Sharell can you come over here?"

"What's wrong? Is he fighting you?"

"Yes! Come right now." She sounded scared.

I heard a scream. Then the phone hung up. I got in my car and drove as fast as I could to Jolynn's house. A police substation was only a couple blocks out the way. I decided to stop there first to get help.

"Hello, sir. I need your help. My friend just called and her husband is beating her up. He put her in the hospital six months ago. She just called me crying. He's fighting her again."

"What's their names? I need their names and address."

"Jolynn and Calvin Brown. I don't know the address by heart, but can you follow me? He beat her with a rifle just a few months ago and put her in the hospital."

The police followed me with their sirens blowing. We came to Jolynn's house. Her face was messed up and Calvin looked stupid.

The police and I walked in the house like we owned the place.

C. Oakes

Calvin wasn't saying anything. Then his sister, Sonya came down the stairs.

"Can I help you? What's wrong? What's going on Calvin?" She wasn't concerned until the police showed up. Sonya had the nerves to roll her eyes at me, looking at me crazy. The bitch. I ignored her. Why didn't she bring her ass down earlier, when Jolynn needed help.

"Come on Jolynn, I'm taking you and the baby out of here. You can come stay with me at my house."

Jolynn started packing fast. Poor thing, she was hurt and she looked terrible. She wasn't crying. Jolynn wasn't saying anything. She kept getting her things with her head down trying to hide her face.

"Ma'am you need to get checked by a doctor. You don't look so good."

"I'm okay." She said, but she wasn't. Jolynn had a black eye and a swollen jaw.

Calvin chimed in. "She's okay. Ain't nothing wrong with her."

"Ma'am would you like to press charges against your husband? You don't have to take this kind of abuse. We can't do anything if you don't press charges. Do you understand? You know ma'am, domestic violence can be stopped. You have to stand up for yourself before it's too late. Think about your baby. You wouldn't want your baby to grow up in this atmosphere. We can take your husband away right now. At least give him time to think about what he's doing."

She looked terrible and scared. She listened to the officer intensely, but still refused to press charges. Calvin started laughing like he wasn't worried about going to jail.

"Listen to me, boy." The officer had about enough of his ass. "You better be glad I don't take you for a ride. If I ever hear you have caused injury to your wife again, I'll prosecute you myself. You understand me, boy."

Calvin didn't say anything. Sonya paced around like she was going to do something. She kept looking at me like I did something wrong. All she cared about was protecting her fool of a brother.

Sonya finally spoke up, "Jolynn, I can keep the baby for you if you want a few days alone."

I know she didn't think Jolynn was really going to let that baby stay with her evil ass. I couldn't believe she asked such a ridiculous question. That heifer has nerves.

"No. He's going with me." Jolynn wouldn't look at her. She held her head down when she spoke to Sonya. Jolynn was mentally and physically whipped by this brother and sister gang.

I took Jolynn and her baby to my house. We called her folks in Oklahoma and told them she was coming home. But she couldn't come right away, she needed to get over the black eye and swollen jaw. Then she needed money for a plane ticket. I told Jolynn not to worry about anything. I would take care of her until she's ready to leave.

Jolynn stayed with me about two months. She began acting like her old self. She laughed with me and Aaron. She cooked for us outside on the grill almost every day. She completely spoiled us. We went shopping for clothes for her and her son. You know the baby has to look good when his grandmother sees him for the first time. I enjoyed her stay with us. Aaron enjoyed her too.

It's funny cause Aaron didn't have any prejudices toward me or Jolynn and what we did for a living. He liked the fact that he was living with two dancers. Tiara was happy too. She was so glad to have the baby around. She was a real good helper too. She babysat while we worked. It was cool cause the baby slept through the night and Aaron was always there while we were gone to work.

"Sharell, where did you meet Aaron. Girl, you ought to get with him. He's cute and he's got a good job. Girl, he asked me to go to church with them. He's really nice. I should have gone with him. Have you ever gone to his church?"

"Naw. But, I'll go to church with him, one day. Aaron is cool but he has a girlfriend. He goes in his room talking with her for hours. I'm not going to get in the middle of that. If he becomes single, then I might. Right now, I don't think so."

"Well I don't blame you. He might not be such a good boyfriend. He acts a little possessive. Shoot, I've had enough of that mess, jealous hearted people in my life. Come to think about it, you better keep your roommate." Jolynn started laughing. "Don't mess up a good thing."

Jolynn was finally long gone. She left Seattle and I hoped she would never come back. I didn't want to worry about her. She might get back with her husband. If she does something that stupid, then I was going to wash my hands of her. I wasn't going to worry about her anymore. I did my part.

I couldn't stand the sight of Calvin. He was a sorry excuse for a man. A momma's boy that was nothing but a drunk that fought his wife. He put sweet Jolynn in the hospital. Another man would probably beat his ass.

I saw him one day at the gas station while I was pumping gas. He acted like he was going to confront me. He continued to walk toward me like he was going to start something. I just stood there, hoping he would try. I already had a plan for his ass. Calvin was smoking a cigarette and I was pumping gas. When he got close enough, I pulled the hose out my tank and looked at him, with dare in my eyes, hoping he would take another step. Calvin turned his punk ass around and I never saw him again.

Chapter 27

I decided I would visit Kathy and Johnny. We were getting so distant and I didn't want to be distant from my friends. I missed my friends, so I decided I would spend the day with them. Johnny was cool. He had me some weed to smoke.

"Sharell, Kathy said you liked this. I've been saving it for you. You know we don't smoke weed over here."

"Thanks Johnny. This is some good buds. Thanks."

I stayed all day. I got wasted and couldn't drive home so I spent the night in their guest room. The next day, I started all over again. Enjoying my friends without cocaine.

One thing about it, I could sleep and I could eat. When I snorted cocaine, I couldn't eat or sleep. Kathy always had a beautiful food spread for her guest, then the next day, it all got thrown away. We couldn't eat while doing coke. It wouldn't let you sleep either. We were miserably too high. I'm glad those days are over for me. I can enjoy Kathy's fantastic food, then passed smooth out.

Everybody seems the same. They were doing the same thing. Listening to the blues and snorting cocaine till they had nose bleeds. I think Kathy was a little jealous cause I quit all that mess. She said a little remark but I know she didn't mean anything by it. She don't have the will to quit cocaine right now and she don't know how I quit. I thought I should tell her, then she would know it wasn't me by myself, I had God's help. I had divine intervention that prayed for me. On top of that, the promise I made to God, the promise that I would never indulge in cocaine again. If not for that, I might get weak and fall off the wagon. Not now, I have the fear of God in me and that's one promise I won't break.

"Kathy, I never told you what happened to me, that made me quit doing cocaine. Girrrl it was a trip." I shook my head cause I never told anybody about that night. Nope I don't think I said anything to anybody. "Wait till you hear the real reason I quit."

"Why? What happened?"

"Girl, one night when I was getting high, I got too high. I was shaking and tweeking but still trying to take that final hit. I put the last of my stuff on the pipe, I was thinking this is going to be a whopper. It was too much. I was already shaking. I was a mess. I started tweeking and looking around the floor for more to smoke, then all of a sudden, people were there, around me, singing and praying and moaning and going on for me. It's a trip because . . . well, I was watching all of this, I was watching myself crawling around the floor, tweeking. Girl, I got as low as you can go. I was at the bottom. What really scared me is . . . well, it was like my soul was asking for help without me. Then, I prayed to God and promised him I wouldn't do it again, so I didn't, till that last time when I smoked that cigarette full of cocaine at your house. After that, no more for me. Girl, I got so scared because I had broken a promise to God, I'm not ever going to break that promise again. I don't care what anybody says. I don't care. I'm finished with it. That's it."

Kathy started laughing at me. "Girl, you made a promise like that to God? What's wrong with you? You should never make a promise to God."

"Well, I won't do it again. But I'm not doing coke again either."

"I don't blame you. Don't worry, you won't get any from me that's for sure. I don't want to be standing by you, if the Lord decides to strikes your crazy ass down, with lightning. Why did you make a promise like that? You're so crazy."

We both laughed then went back to our friends. Kathy asked me to stay again another night. I decided I would but I needed to tell my roommate something.

I called Aaron to let him know that I was okay and not coming home again.

"Hi, Aaron."

"Hey, where have you been? I was kind of worried about you. I hadn't received a call. I didn't know if anything had happened to you. I had to comb Tiara's hair myself." He was joking but I could tell he wasn't happy.

"Oh, I stayed with friends. I'm sorry if you were worried. It's been a long time since I've had to check in. I guess I wasn't being very considerate. Forgive me? I should have called. But I'm calling you now, I'll be staying again tonight. So, I'll see you tomorrow."

"You are! Well, have fun." (click)

"Damn, he hung up. What's his problem. That's really rude. I'm going to talk with him about that when I get home." All night I was bothered by Aaron's rudeness. What is wrong with him? I can't help it if he has a woman. He needs to get it straight. I'm not his woman and I'm not going to feel guilty about hanging with my friends.. I decided to continue with the party. I continued to eat, drink and be merry.

All good things must come to an end. It was finally time to go home. I felt like I've been on a vacation. I didn't do anything the whole three days I visited with Kathy. She always had a house-keeper, so I didn't wash one dish. We wore the same size clothes, so I got treated to a couple of jogging suits. These are sharp, expensive jogging suits too, that still had the price tags on them. I really had fun.

As I walked in the house, Aaron was there tinkering with one of the computers. "Hi Aaron" He didn't speak. Wait a minute. He still has an attitude. He really needs to lose that. He's not my man, I don't have to report to him. He's tripping.

"Hi Tiara, how's my little friend. Ooooo girl, your dad did that to your hair?"

Tiara nodded. "Will you comb it for me? In Living Color is coming on, can we watch "In Living Color" while you comb my hair? It's coming on next, in thirty minutes."

"Sure baby. Get your hair box and we can watch it in my room."

I wasn't going to be intimidated by Aaron's silent treatment or rudeness. I live here and he's not going to make it uncomfort-able for me to be here. That's so unfair. I'm not use to having a man that I got to check in with, Tiara's not my responsibility. Man, some people can really take your kindness for granted. I never asked for this. He's treating me like I'm his woman, only no sex. I got to get our roles back on track. He's only a roommate.

"In Living Color," was too funny. Tiara and I lost it. We laughed so hard that we cried. They did a thing on Prince playing basketball. For a minute I thought it was too wild for Tiara to watch. But her humor was on target, she laughed just as hard, and her stomach hurt just as much as mine. We came unglued. Where did they get these guys? Then Fire Marshal Bill came on. Fire

Marshal Bill was a walking disaster. His face, hair and ears were burnt up. We cried laughing.

Tiara was finally bedded down and I wanted to chat with her father about his attitude. I've always needed to get my conversation straight or my points down before I start. So I made sure I had all my points together. These were my issues. This guy was making me feel guilty for staying out when I never asked him to look out after me. He's only my roommate. He doesn't have any other role here besides roommate, and I'm not giving him any reasons to feel differently. He has a woman.

Aaron was walking around, with his innocent look but being defiant. He knows he was out of line. I feel I have to nip this in the bud before it gets out of hand.

"Uh, Aaron, what are you doing? Are you busy, cause I have something we need to talk about."

"Uh, no Sharell, I'm not busy. What's the problem?" Aaron was acting like he's the man again. I can't put my finger on his attitude, but he's not as innocent and humble as he tries to project. He's acting like I did something wrong. But I just decided to look over that.

"Aaron, I don't think you're treating me right. I don't understand your attitude. I called you to let you know I was staying with friends and you basically hung up on me. I don't appreciate that. Why are you giving me a hard time about my personal business? My children are not here right now. I like Tiara, I like being there for her. But I was just being helpful and I don't mind that, when I'm available. Aaron, don't make me feel uncomfortable being your roommate."

"Sharell, Sharell, hold it. Hold it. You're right. I was wrong. I'm sorry. But it's not that I was wanting you to take care of my daughter. My problem was the fact that you weren't here. I got so use to you being here. We wanted you home. I'm sorry if I was being unfair. I was mad that you stayed gone three days. I'm sorry. Will you forgive me. I won't take you for granted anymore. I promise."

I smiled at Aaron because I didn't expect such honesty. He must have been practicing his speech too.

"Well, Aaron. It's okay. It may have been my fault too. But, if I'm not around, you need to have a plan B in place. Cause I may

C. Oakes

leave town any time, and that was terrible what you did to Tiara's hair." He had to admit that was bad, real bad. He should never attempt to comb that child's hair again.

Aaron was standing a little too close. He was smiling a little too much. It's been a long time for me. Too long. Look at him, he's trying to seduce me. Since I got it straight, it's best to keep it that way. I better get out of here.

"Well, I think I'll just turn in for now. I'll see you tomorrow."

"Sharell don't go. I want to hear about your friends that kept you out three days. Who are they?"

"You want to hear about my friends? Why?"

"I just want to know about them."

"Well, my friends are a couple. Their names are Kathy and Johnny. They're good people, in fact, they own this house we live in. It has been a while since I visited with them, once I got there, to their house, I didn't want to leave. I just relaxed the whole time. She absolutely spoiled me. We ate fantastic food. Her husband, Johnny makes his own barbeque sauce, I had to eat as much as I could cause he won't let me bring any sauce home. We just had a little unplanned party that lasted three days. That's it."

"Whow, that sounds nice."

"You thought I was with a man didn't you?"

"Well, . . .I didn't know. I thought maybe you were with your boyfriend or something."

"I don't have a boyfriend, man friend or anyone that I'm inti-mate with, not right now. I just decided that I would wait till my kids were older before I would have a serious relationship. Don't get me wrong, I want adult company. But while they're young, they don't need men entering their lives. I can wait."

"So, when's the last time you had a boyfriend?"

"What are you asking me, when's the last time I had a boy-friend or the last time I had sex?"

"Both, I'm asking you both."

"That's none of your business, Aaron. But I'll tell you any-way. The last time I had a boyfriend was about a year ago. He wasn't a real boyfriend, I slept with him a couple of times, that's all. I don't lead an exciting life. I just work in a club. That's mostly my only contact with men. I don't get to have a serious relationship. Like I said, when my boys are older, then hopefully,

I can have a man in my life."

"Whow, you sure are a beautiful woman not to have a man in your life. These guys must be crazy in Seattle. You wouldn't last like that in California."

"I don't think I would last like this in Oklahoma either. But since we're here and we don't have any relatives living around us, it's best. Don't you have to go to work in the morning? You'd better stop being so nosey and get some sleep."

"Since it's been such a long time for you, I'm willing to help you out. You can join me. I'll treat you right."

He knew better than that. "Thanks for the offer, but no thanks. Aaron, I quit having sex. I've decided to wait for something more. I'm just tired. I'm tired of sex. I'm tired of faking. I'm tired of the whole game. I want a commitment. I want to be in love. I want to be married. Maybe I'm really old fashioned, I don't know, . . . I don't want another "boy" friend. I want a man in my life. I'll just wait for the right one. You better be good. What about your friend in California. How's she doing these days?"

"That's the point, she's in California. She has a great career there. I doubt if she will leave all that to come here with me. I don't think our relationship will last with this distance between us either, me being here and she's there. We're just friends anyway. She wants to get married, but I don't think so, not right now. I love her but I'm not in love with her. Not enough for us to get married."

"Dang Aaron, does she know that?"

"Hey, I've tried to let her know, but she won't listen. She thinks she knows what's best for me."

Well, you should take care of your business. I mean, straighten out your life with your friend. She thinks you guys may get married at some point. If you're not, then let her know so she can get on with her life. That's only fair. . .It might hurt but I'm sure she would want you to be honest and not waste her time."

Aaron agreed. "Yeah Sharell, you're right. Man I don't want to hurt her. Did I ever mention to you that her brother is married to my baby sister."

"No you didn't. Oh, you guys are one big happy family."

"I guess. But I'm getting my business together. I got to talk with her."

Lately Aaron has been flirting harder than ever, especially since I told him he didn't have a chance with me. Why are guys like that? You say no, and they go crazy. He's been hanging around my bedroom. Coming in my room uninvited.

"You better be good. Get some sleep Aaron. I'll see you tomorrow."

"Okay, Okay, I'll see you tomorrow. Hey, God loves you and I do too. Good night. Oh I forgot to tell you, your boys called today. They sound like grown men. One was giving me the third degree. He asked me about my job, where I worked. He asked about my daughter. They sound like some strong young men."

"Thanks, they are. I'll give them a call tomorrow. Night Aaron."

It was a few months that past before Aaron got out of line again. This time, I was visiting with other friends, I stayed gone over the weekend. Hey I got great friends. It was nice to be out visiting without cocaine. I enjoyed my straight friends. I finally had to make new friends and break away from the old ones.

I went to Mercer Island, man I enjoyed that place. I ate great food, smoked great salmon and smoked great weed. I had a ball. So why did I have to come home to Aaron's distorted face? He wasn't quite slamming doors but he was walking around hard, close to stomping. He wanted me to know he wasn't happy.

"Aaron, what's your trip?" I didn't wait for an answer. " I'm going to bed. I'll talk with you tomorrow. Good night!"

"Sharell, I don't think it appropriate for you to be staying out two or three days at a time."

"What are you talking about? I can stay with anyone I want, when ever I want. You need to stop."

"It just doesn't look right for a woman."

"Aaron I don't care about your little stereotype or your little attitude about what a woman should or shouldn't do. I pay my own way. Stop it. . . .Just stop." I started laughing cause this guy was unbelievable. "When's the last time you talked with Patricia? How's she doing? Maybe you should visit her. Take a trip."

"We broke up."

Damn, I hadn't thought about that. I hope he's okay. I felt concerned. "Aaron, when, what happened? You finally had that heart to heart talk with her didn't you?"

"Well, that relationship wasn't going anywhere. I wasn't moving back to San Bernandino, and she wasn't coming here to Seattle. It was best. She can go on with her life and I can go on with mine."

Damn, I hope he's not going to take it out on me. Naw, I'm tripping now. "Well, if there's anything I can do for you, let me know. I don't have anything planned."

I started looking at Aaron in a way that I never allowed myself to do before. I looked at him with a "maybe we can get together look in my eyes." I stole a look between his legs. Ummm . .. there's definitely something there. I wonder if he knows what to do with all that? He's got a good job. He goes to church. He's really good looking. He's smart. He needs to brush and floss those teeth, but maybe I can help him with that. He doesn't trip over me working in a club. He's a pretty nice guy with good values and morals, at least that's what I've noticed in him.

I went over everything that I thought was positive about Aaron. I came to the conclusion that he was definitely a good catch. Besides, I don't want to grow old by myself. I can't imagine being alone the rest of my life. I don't think I'll ever fall in love again. Not really in love like before, I was crazy in love. That's not in me anymore. I can't remember what real love feels like. It's been so long. But, these days people get together for other reasons. We're good friends. We can make a good home for the kids. I can learn to love him. We could learn to love each other.

It's about time for me to get in a serious relationship. Matt's going on fourteen and Ronnie's already nine. They should be big enough now for me to have a man. They're too big for anyone to take advantage of them. That's why I waited in the first place, for them to get older.

Aaron must have been thinking the same thing about me. He started talking with me about quitting the club business. Man that was music to my ears. I started praying about it.

"Lord, help me. Lord you know I want a real job. Lord, what if . . .I started working for temp agencies and I went to the club on weekends." Aaron taught me a lot on the computers. I already knew how to use a word processor, but I wasn't familiar with any of the other programs. I finally got use to using the mouse. But I didn't want a real job until I got my boys home this summer. I want to spend some time with them. We could go on a trip together. They've been gone so long.

Things were looking up. I felt maybe I could be happy.

C. Oakes

Chapter 28

After finally agreeing to visit one of the worship services with Aaron, I fell in love with his church. There was only a few members in the whole congregation. I'm talking about fifteen to twenty people at the most. I've always belonged to a big church, a few thousand members. That's pretty big to me. Anyway I felt comfortable at Aaron's church. I started attending every Sunday, then I joined. They nominated me to be the treasurer. I've never held a position at a church. This was absolutely opposite to anything I've done in the last eighteen years of my life. Can you imagine me? An officer in the house of God. But the preacher didn't know about me. He didn't know that I had fallen from grace a long time ago. All he knew is the fact that I was marrying Aaron. Yes, we were getting married and that was good enough for Pastor Carter.

Now I plan on taking good care of my position, I'll do everything I can to be a good treasurers. I just needed to know what to do. Aaron and Pastor Carter promised they would groom me and tell me everything I need to know because I have to give a annual report to the national body. I wasn't too worried, I can learn the job.

When I joined the church, Pastor Carter was approximately seventy years old. He was swift on his feet like a twenty year old. This has to be the most caring and giving man I've ever met in my life. Most of the congregation is from the streets. Exactly the people that needed God the most, including me. Pastor preached love and forgiveness. He's so kind, I've never met anyone like him, outside my grandmother. He didn't judge anybody. That was good. Pastor was glad that we were available to hear the word and he had a congregation where he could preach. Every Sunday he told us how much God loves us and we needed to hear exactly that.

I never would have imagined that our church would have so much money stashed away. Frankly, I was shocked. They had previously purchased land for a new building. Land in Seattle is pretty expensive. Then there was money saved to start construction. But the members needed their utilities paid, they were getting eviction notices, everything was going on, their car's were being repossessed, they had to get out of jail. Everybody was in a crisis. I was scared to death signing all those checks for so much money. Every check I signed was around a thousand dollars or more. What about the new church? We were spending the money fast. I didn't know what to do. Who was I to question the actions of the Pastor? I don't think he cared too much about the building fund. He wanted to help his people and they needed him right then. I can see his point. He's their shepherd. I just didn't know about these sheep around here. They were more like hungry wolves.

They understood the Pastor. They knew he was oh so kind, they were only attending church to get their bills paid and Pastor Carter wasn't going to let anyone down. So I signed the doggone checks. Who knows what the Lord might do through Pastor Carter. Hopefully they'll remember his kindness.

My boys are coming home, I'm going to get them this summer after the family reunion. I'm bringing my babies home. Yeaaaa! I'm never letting them stay away like this again.

They already knew I planned on marrying Aaron. In fact, I asked them if it was okay. I wanted to know what they thought about it.

"Matt, tell me what do you think about me getting married?"

"Mom, he has a good job? He goes to church? He might be alright. You need someone in your life mom. We're not going to be around when you get old. You'll need someone to take care of you. Maybe he'll work out." That's my little man, always thinking about me.

"Ronnie, what do you think?"

"I don't know mom. What does he want us to call him? I'm not . . ."

"Daddy, call him daddy." I cracked up laughing. "His name is Aaron, that's what you'll call him."

"He's coming to our reunion this summer, right?"

"Yeah, he's coming to the reunion and his daughter's coming too. I want you to meet them both, before we get married. We'll get married after the reunion, in Oklahoma, with just a few of us around. I want to know what you really think about him. I think you'll like him. Anyway he wants to marry me, that's a plus. His daughter is sweet and cute and she likes me, too so . . . We'll probably be a good family together."

"How old is she again? What's her name?"

"Tiara. She'll be seven this summer. Ronnie, do you think it's okay for me to get married? Is it okay? I mean, you guy's are going to have girl friends pretty soon. Y'all won't be thinking about me."

"Mom, if that's what you want to do. As long as I don't have to call him daddy. hee hee . . ." That's my little boyfriend. He's always on my side.

"Mom, did you tell pops you were getting married?" Matt asked with smirk in his voice. There he goes . . .starting. He didn't want to leave his dad out the picture, although his dad's been out the picture over ten years. Mike hasn't visited us one time since we've been living here in Seattle. I'm the one that kept my kids in touch with his ass.

"Noooooooo . . . IIIIII . . . didn't and why should I Matt? Stop being a turkey."

"I just asked." Matt laughed

"Yeah mom, we just wanted to know what dad thinks about you getting married". Ronnie laughed too. My boys! My babies.

Once Aaron closed that book between him and Patricia, everything between us went right into place. We were already set up as a household with me, him and Tiara. We just had to get it right by getting my boys home and getting married. I was sick and tired of my little rendezvous which ended up as nothing but sex. I told Aaron when I first met him, that I was waiting on the right man. I really meant it too. There's somebody out there just for me.

I hope I'm doing the right thing. I know Aaron wanted to have sex with me and I kind of pushed it on us getting married. He would have been just as happy having sex and us living together, but not for me. I want something different. I prayed that I'm doing the right thing. I hope he's the one. He has a lot of issues that I would like fixed, for instance, he doesn't brush his teeth and floss as much as I like. I'm so particular about hygiene, especially dental hygiene. I'm going to work on that. He's fixable.

Aaron didn't push me to have sex with him. He asked a couple of times but truthfully, he was a total gentleman and I appreciated that. Only thing is . . . I hope he's not marrying me just to finally get it. That's going too damn far. But I was willing to gamble on us. Maybe we will work out. We waited before we were intimate with each other. The wait was kind of exciting for me. I was anticipating our wedding night. This was so huge for me, to wait to be married first. I was waiting for my husband. Whow, I was being honorable and good. I was being wholesome.

It's been close to a year now since I had my new roommates. Tiara and Aaron has had me all to their selves without my boys. They hadn't had a chance to check us out, not really. They don't know how close we really are, my boys and me.

Somehow my aunt Hattie had my wedding all planned. Me and Aaron got married at my family reunion with everybody there. My whole family was there. They worked it in the program at our reunion. I didn't want all that, but it was okay. My uncle James married us. My brother Kenny walked me down the aisle. I looked beautiful. Momma told me so. He was a handsome groom. Mom fell in love with him along with every other female in my family. Aaron looked extremely good that night. He can be pretty damn charming too. My brothers all thought he was okay. Kenny thought he was a pretty boy.

"Kenny he's not a pretty boy."

"You sure Sharell? You know what they say about those pretty boys."

"Kenny everybody thinks you're a pretty boy."

"Sharell, nobody thinks I'm a pretty boy. Girl, you'll say anything."

"Yes they do, Kenny. They think you're fine."

"That's different! That's different."

"No it's not."

"Yes it is too. Pretty boys are gay. They're closet homosexuals."

"Boy, Aaron's not gay! Kenny! You ought to be ashamed of yourself."

"You know that for sure, Sharell? Well, as long as you're happy, that's what counts."

"He's not gay Kenneth . . . and yes, I'm sure."

As long as I've known Aaron, he's always been the macho type, he's never had a drink, and holier than thou, but he decided

C. Oakes

to drink on our wedding night. My uncles were ready to supply him with all and everything he wanted on our special day. They wanted to welcome him in the family, treat him good, let him know that he's one of us now. I didn't think it was a problem, him having a drink on our wedding day, but Aaron stayed up, stumbling around all night long. He looked wild. The more he drank, the more energy he had to make a fool of himself. He said he would come to our room in a minute.

I had waited over a year to be intimate with the right man. Tonight I was ready. The kids were in their own room getting to know each other, along with my other nieces and nephews. I figured they would stay up and play. I remember when I was up all night with my brothers and sister and cousins at these family reunions. We had fun.

Finally, this was my night. I'm going to make love to my husband on our wedding night. I wore a sexy white and black laced gown, I sprayed Oscar perfume in all the right places. My breath smelled like babies milk. I was ready and willing. I fantasized on all the things I was going to do to my own husband. I was going to make sweet love, tonight. I had been exercising, doing sit ups, crunches and squeezing it, then relaxing it. I didn't want my muscles to get sore cause I was going to give it to him. He just don't know what's he's getting. I positioned myself in the bed just right and I waited. I think I dozed off.

"Damn, what time is it? He should have come by now. I'm not going out to find his ass." I waited and I waited. I was up now, pacing the floor, feeling disappointed. "Where was he? What is he doing? Why isn't he here with me? This is our wedding night. How could he do this to me?" I finally went back to sleep, terribly disappointed. Approximately 7 am, the next morning, Aaron came stumbling in our room and he passed smooth out. He stinks. I undressed him and went back to sleep.

Later that day, he looked droggy and stupid.

"Sharell, I'm sorry. I got a little out of control."

"That's okay Aaron. I know my family. We drink and have fun. Did you enjoy yourself?"

"Yes! What kind of family is this? Man. They treated me so good. Your uncles! They welcomed me in the family right. I really enjoyed myself. Everybody was so nice and good to me. I had so much fun. Baby can you forgive me?" Then he went back to sleep.

"Yeah, I forgive you, that's the way we are. You married into a good family. They'll do anything for you." Actually, I was very disappointed. Fairytales just don't happen for me.

Later that day, when I decided to show my face at the family reunion, everybody was looking wanting to know the scoop. They already heard about my new husband. They knew he wasn't with me and something wasn't cool. Everybody saw how out of control and ugly my handsome prince had gotten. Momma got the word about Aaron, being up all night, stumbling and acting a fool, not being with me on our wedding night.

"Sharell, what did you do last night?"

"Momma, Aaron don't drink and for some reason he decided to drink last night, he was up all night drinking with everybody."

"I heard about it, he was pretty wasted. Girrrrl!"

"Yeah, he didn't come in till this morning, then he passed out. He's still in the room, passed out."

"Well, he was just having fun. You know how everybody is, especially your brothers."

"He enjoyed himself alright. The kids had fun. They're still sleep too."

"The bus is taking us to the mall, you want to go?"

"Naw, momma, I'll see you later."

C. Oakes

Chapter 29

Finally, my boys were home with me, along with my new husband and my new step daughter. The boys were excited about the new changes to our family. Aaron seemed ready to be the friend that'll teach them the computer and how to tinker with cars. I was ready to take Tiara shopping. No daughter of mine was going to be homely. She was going to look as good as me and my boys. I never had a daughter but I was ready to learn some new things, like braid hair. Plus I needed to make sure she comes up right. She has to know how to brush her teeth and floss. She's so cute.

Aaron had his own ideas for us. He wanted us to go to church at least three times a week. We went. My kids were now use to our church in Oklahoma and Alabama. They have big choirs and people got happy and shouted in church. I didn't know how they would react to our Seattle church. Our family was there pretty regularly. Actually, we were there for every opening. We sang without music and from the hymn book. The Pastor really enjoyed singing those old songs. He probably grew up on those hymns. I wasn't feeling it. I wanted to go to church, but I wanted a bigger congregation, a church outside of our little family. I guess the rest of the members didn't need any help right now. They'll be back sooner or later.

It's funny how things work out. The Pastor is a real scholar on the Bible. He's really a man of God. My kids grew in the word. They received understanding that blew me away. Matt would read scriptures then explain what he had read. I couldn't believe what I was hearing. I think it was because the congregation was so small, we had room to ask questions, it was more of an intimate, one on one atmosphere.

I even learned how to love God. I always knew I was suppose to love God but I didn't know how, so I asked God how to do that, how to love him. Then I got it. It's a gift, a blessing that comes to you. I don't know how it happened but it happened. I love God. I love Him so much. It's so good. I never want to live without Him in my life, ever again. I'll just have to ask for forgiveness, everyday, if that's what it takes. How did I not know Him? Now,

I understand those old hymns, and why old folk love those songs so much.

Pastor would walk through the neighborhood inviting people to church. They sure needed our presence because we were right behind low income, drug infested housing. They need God and the Pastor cause he was going to show them real love. Sometimes they would come to church, they show up a few weeks before they would drop off. But at least they came and they knew we were there.

Val is moving back to Oklahoma City. Shoot!

"Sharell, we've decided to move back to Oklahoma City."

"What! Why? There's nothing there. I thought you guys liked it here. Aren't the kids doing good in school. Seattle has good schools. Why would you leave and take them out of school like that? Val don't go." I was ready to cry. "What am I going to do without you?"

"Now Sharell, you've had me here with you over five years. My family needs me. My mother is getting old and she needs me. Phyl has all those kids and she needs me. You could always move back home yourself."

"Val, I can't move home. It's nothing there for me. What am I going to do without you here." I cried because she was my security blanket. I wasn't too worried as long as I had Val. I could always call her if anything went wrong and she could always call me. Although her sister Phylis was my best friend growing up, Val was truly my sister now. We could count on each other and now she's leaving me.

"When are you leaving?"

"It'll be another month or two before I'm ready. I've been paying my storage bill in Oklahoma City all these years and now I want my stuff. Girl, I'm ready to go home."

"Damn, that's not long. Do you need me to help you drive or anything?"

"Naw girl, Edward is driving now. He'll help me with driving, but Eddie's staying a little longer. He'll come in a few months."

"I guess I'll see you next summer or something, when I'm home visiting. I'm not ready to move home yet." To tell the truth, I was a little embarrassed to go home. I have nothing to show for my being gone. I'm basically broke. I lived paycheck to pay-

C. Oakes

check. I don't drive a new car. I haven't done anything significant since I left Oklahoma. I need to stay here.

"How's Aaron and the boys getting along?"

"They're doing good. Aaron's drinking, he wasn't doing that before I married his ass. I think it get's on the boys nerves a little cause he always want to have a family meeting when he's drunk, then we have to listen to him talk about nothing. Grand standing all night, for hours, when the kids have to go to school in the morning."

"Sharell, why do you let him do that? He wouldn't keep my kids up with that bullshit. Man, that's a turnaround. He was so nice when I first met him."

"He'll probably stop. Like I said, he wasn't doing that when I met him. He knows he can't drink."

"I hope so. You guys made a good couple. I wonder what made him start doing that?"

"He started drinking at the family reunion last summer. I didn't think it would cause all this. Now, he's drinking everyday. Aaron goes to church drunk. He needs to stop. He's different, he's not the man I married."

I finally stopped working in the clubs. I got a good job as a Flight tracker for a parcel service. It was really interesting. I enjoyed my job. I felt good about myself for the first time in years. I was paying bills on square income. Aaron's money helped but I couldn't understand why we didn't have more. I thought we should have been farther down the road. We kept separate accounts and I never had anything left after my pay check. Aaron never had anything anytime.

We had to move out of Johnny and Kathy's house because we were late every month. When I lived by myself, I was never late, now since I have a husband that has a good paying job, I'm late every month.

"What's going on?" I tried to talk with Aaron to get a handle on things. "We're getting evicted out of our apartment after only four months. I don't understand this."

"Aaron, let's set a budget. You can give me seven or eight hundred dollars every month and I'll pay the bills and put money up in a savings or something. We got to get our finances in shape."

"I don't need you to keep my damn money, Sharell. I got to

take care of my daughter. She has to visit her mother next month during spring break. I got to buy her plane ticket. I can't give you that kind of money right now."

"Aaron, your responsibilities comes here first. Your daughter can visit her mother another time when we can afford it. We are getting evicted again. We need a place to stay.

"Sharell, my damn responsibilities are with my daughter, she comes first."

Is this man a damn fool. I decided to let it go. I didn't want to fight. I thought I should ask the church for help. I went to Pastor Carter, maybe Aaron would listen to him. Maybe if he listened to Pastor, he could get his priorities in place and we could save our marriage. I was really tired of him. Something has to change. So I went before the church and ask for prayer and intervention in our marriage. But Aaron laughed. It's a joke to him.

It's been a over a year since I made that mistake, marrying Aaron. I'm trying to stay with his ass till our next family reunion. Since I got married in front of all my relatives, I didn't want to show up without him at the next reunion, but it's hard.

The last time he tried to kiss me I almost threw up. I thought I would be able to change him. I thought maybe I could get him to brush his teeth and floss, but you can't change a grown-ass man. Now, it's too late for me. I can't be intimate with him. He grosses me out. How can someone that was so fine, get so ugly? I've grown distant and he get's drunker and uglier.

I wanted another point of view. I decided to call my brother and ask him what he thought was going on with our finances.

"Kenny, I don't know what he does with his money. He get's paid good, when he goes to work. Most the time he out on sick leave. I don't know why, but they like him at the job. Then when he gets paid, he keeps all his money in his pocket. He don't want to put any up in a savings, he don't want to buy a house or a decent car. I don't know what he's doing with his money. He doesn't want to do anything with me that'll get us ahead. I don't understand."

"Sharell, you work? . . .You have a good job? He works, he has a good job? He's not on drugs or anything is he?"

"No, no, nothing like that. What is he doing with his money? We can't get ahead. We keep getting evicted. He's drinking all

C. Oakes

the time. I don't know what's going on. We're borrowing money from the church. There's no reason why we should be doing that. I'm the treasurer, now I'm writing checks to him. We borrowing money, we make good money, we shouldn't have to do that."

"Sharell, he's buying pussy. That's what he's doing."

"What? That's what he's doing? He's picking up girls?"

"Yeah, that's what his ass is doing. Just pay attention, you'll see."

That makes sense. I hated when he touched me. I wasn't doing anything with his drunk ass, that's for sure. I just can't. I can't handle his ass. But that makes sense. So he spending his money on girls and damn us. Now this is so ironic. I married a trick.

I decided right then I was going to leave Aaron. He had gotten besides himself, disrespecting me, he even had the nerves to hit Matt. He socked Matt in the jaw when he wasn't looking. We all jumped on his ass. Then I called the police and had him removed. I felt sorry for Tiara, she was so distraught and she had become so attached to me. I asked her to stay with me, but she left too, with her dad. They slept in the car and was back the next day. I wasn't putting Tiara out like that again.

I think Aaron was a little jealous of Matt. Matt's now a good looking teenager. He's going on sixteen. He has girlfriends calling and coming by. I don't know why he's jealous, Aaron has had his day. Now it's Matt's turn. Aaron would put Matt on punishment for weeks at a time. This shit was ending.

The savings for the church had dwindled below a hundred thousand. Aaron has a brother in law, Leo, that's a master builder. It's good to know good people. Leo came with his crew to help us. We began building until the funds were depleted. The church wasn't finished, but it was close and I felt easy that the money was spent the way it was meant to be used.

Okay, now it's my turn. I went to a community agency and got an apartment. I would pick the boys up from school and we would go to our apartment and just sit on the floor. We had our place and Aaron never knew it. I was waiting on the right time to move. I sure hated to leave Tiara like that, but I wasn't staying with her father.

I decided to leave the next Saturday Aaron was scheduled to

work. As soon as he left the house, we were up packing. It wasn't that I was scared to leave him, I wasn't ready to fight. I thought he would start a fight or make it difficult for us. He'll start some bullshit. We were singing and dancing and happy, getting out fast. Tiara was in her room crying and crying, she was being hysterical.

"Mommy, mommy, please don't leave me."

"Baby, I'm not leaving you. I'm leaving your father. I can't stay with him. I'm sorry." Tiara only got louder.

"Mommy, mommmmmmy don't leave me."

I started crying too. "Tiara I'm sorry, I'm sorry baby, but I can't stay."

Right at that time, Aaron pulled up. He saw the moving truck. We didn't say anything to him. I didn't want a damn thing from him. I even left my furniture because he had laid on everything and it had molded to fit his body. He was a regular drunk couch potato. I took my kids furniture. I took their bedroom sets, their tv's and their computer. I didn't want any parts of our bedroom set. So why was he up on the truck inspecting what I was taking? It was all my stuff.

"Sharell, you're not taking my computer. That's my damn computer."

"What? Aaron take the fucking computer off the damn truck." I couldn't believe he was that damn petty when I left all the living room furniture, the dinette set and my bedroom set. I didn't want any of that shit. I only took my kids bedroom sets. We were getting us new furniture.

As I drove away, Tiara screamed louder and louder. I thought she was coming out the window.

"Mommy, mommy please don't go, please mommy don't leave me." Tears were running hot down my face. I cried for days.

We were finally settled into our apartment. I had gone to a few garage sales and discount furniture stores to get us a few things. It was coming together. We didn't have the quality that I had before, but it was cute. I slept with Ronnie until I had my own bed.

The boys was happy. Their friends came by and it was comfortable without Aaron ready and willing to start lecturing.

"Ms Sharell, I couldn't understand why you were with that guy anyway. I mean, you're so nice and that guy was terrible.

He's ugly."

"You think he's ugly?"

"Yes ma'am. He use to drive around the streets drunk, burning rubber, messing with those girls on the streets. He did that all the time. I couldn't understand that when he had you at home."

"You saw him?"

"Yes ma'am we saw him all the time."

"Matt, Ronnie, you guys saw him doing that?"

"Yeah mom, we saw him. But we wasn't going to say anything. I didn't want to hurt your feelings like that. He use to pick up those nasty looking girls. It was embarrassing, mom."

I couldn't believe what I was hearing. Kenny was right. He said I would find out.

"Let me tell y'all something. I don't care how bad it may hurt my feeling, but always tell me things that I need to know, just like I'll always tell you, what you need to know, even if it hurts. If there's something you need to know, I'm going to tell you. What you don't know, could kill you. You understand?"

"Yeah mom. Okay. We won't keep those kinds of secrets anymore. But it was embarrassing, I'm sorry. I didn't know how to tell you something like that. He's sorry, momma. Drunk all the time."

"That's okay. Next time, just spit it out. Okay Ronnie?"

"Okay mom."

It wasn't long before the Pastor came to the apartment with Aaron begging for my forgiveness and to come back home. Aaron was trying to convince me that he quit drinking. At this point, I didn't care. All I could think was "I wish they would hurry up and leave." I couldn't believe they were there. Did they really think, after all I went through to get us out of that mess, begging for help, going through this housing agency, that I would go back to his ignorant ass. When I asked for help, it was funny, it was a joke.

C. Oakes

Chapter 30

We've been living by ourselves for a while now. Matt's graduating from high school in a few months. Ronnie is in middle school. They've grown so fast. Girls are all over the place.

I started back dancing. I needed the extra income, it's too hard by myself. There's no way I can pay these bill's with my little money. Then there's the prom and graduation. I have to buy clothes. Matt needs a little car. I needed the extra money.

I have a good day job with insurance and everything. The pay isn't that bad thanks to my new friend Mr. Murry. He's an engineer. I never knew how hard it is for black government contractors. Mr. Murry was a fighter, that fights hard for his share of government contracts. I'm writing government proposals. It's great, I really like what I'm doing. It's exciting. In fact, I'm leading my double life again. None of my daytime friends or associates know anything about my nighttime activities and vice versa. My co-workers wouldn't know how to handle me if they knew what I did after hours. I'm happy that I can still do it. It's been a while since I've danced.

I still have my shape and I don't look that much older. I had to get new costumes . . . a little bigger, but that's okay. I go by a different stage name now. I go by Leah. And I went to a club outside of the Seattle area, in Lynnwood. You know, just in case somebody comes in, I don't want to be embarrassed. I'd probably get fired. All you have to do is change your wig and name, then you're a whole new person. It's convenient, being a different person whenever the need arise. I definitely needed an alias with the squares and morals on my day job.

I see Aaron and Tiara sometimes. Aaron scares me. He shows up from nowhere, standing behind me at the grocery store, acting like it's a coincidence. I'm out to lunch with my friends and he's happens to stop at the same restaurant. Sometimes I see him jogging pass the office, like he's just out having an innocent jog. He comes by my house unannounced, like it's okay. I chews his ass out every time. He shrugs it off. He's sneaky and weird.

Matt started playing the keyboard and making beats for rap

groups. He's really good. I didn't realize he played the keyboard like that . . . until I heard the songs. . .then I knew. He's good! I'm proud of him. My boy's an artist that produces music. I asked him when did he start this, where did it come from. He says it was there all the time. He said all day long, he hears music in his head, then he plays it. I never knew that.

Ronnie does everything. I can't keep up with him. He boxes, plays football, plays the clarinet. He's joined all kinds of science and acting clubs. He joined the math club. I have to work two or three jobs to pay for everything. They've grown up.

The Green River killer's been out the news for a while. It's been a few years. There's all kind of stories, saying he's already in jail or dead. The jail story is the one everyone's leaning toward. But one of the dancers, Patty was murdered after leaving the club the other night. It was her last night working there, then she was quitting and moving west with her two year old daughter. This was really hard for me, because we were all there at the club, kicking it, the same night she was killed. It was real slow that night, I sat in the dressing room talking with Patty about her plans to move. She was so happy and excited about her life and where she was going. I felt bad that I couldn't be more help to the police when they conducted their investigation. I didn't notice any customers that night. I didn't notice anybody acting weird or suspicious. Hardly anybody there so I wasn't on the floor. We sat in the dressing room all night and talked.

Out of all the girls that worked with us, Patty was the most athletic. She was a very pretty blond, muscular and tall and she knew she could kick ass. That's what we couldn't understand how could someone get Patty like that. Well, the dirty dog, cut her tires. The dog must have been following her, cause when she stopped with her flat tire, he attacked and killed her. We were in shock. I think about her alot. I think about how a simple turn of events could be fate knocking at your door. She was leaving town in the morning. Patty wanted to make a little extra money before she left town. It could have been any one of us. We didn't think it was one of the Green River killers' crimes. Like I said, nobody's heard about him in years. It could have been the Green River killer. On the other hand, Patty said her ex was upset that she was moving. We don't know who did this and they don't know either.

C. Oakes

Matt wants to go to California and visit his dad after he graduates.

"Mom, I'm just going for a while, I'll be back."

"I don't know Matt. Your dad is so unstable. I don't think that's a good idea."

"Mom, I've lived here all my life. I want to go to California around my other brothers and sisters for a while. I want to get to know them better. I haven't seen Andy in years." Andy is their older brother. Andy's so sweet. It's hard to believe he's Mike's kid. "Mom he plays the keyboard like me. I want to make music with Andy."

"Why don't you stay here and go to school, you can join the reserves or something. In the reserves you can travel to different countries, see the world and they'll pay for it. It's a good opportunity."

"Mom, I'm not ready to start school again. I just got out. Dad's sending me a ticket to visit him for a while."

"I decided not to be the enemy. I wish you wouldn't, but it's okay, if that's what you just got to do. It's okay, Matt." I nodded at him and smiled to reassure my son. When I was young, I wanted to leave home too. "I'm going to miss you. Don't get to California and go crazy, you better call me. I'm not playing with you Matt, you stay in touch. Call often." I left the room before he saw me cry. I pouted around for weeks. I want him to know I wasn't happy.

Matt left me and Ronnie in Washington. My son was gone. He was ready to leave. I wasn't ready for him to leave us. We were lonely. With Matt gone, I felt so insecure. We had no family ties, nobody that I considered close. It was just me and Ronnie. Val and Jolynn moved back to Oklahoma a long time ago. I thought about going home. For now, I should send Ronnie there and I go later when I have more money saved.

I got to do something. Ronnie became the target for a local gang. They were coming to his school looking for him. One night he got shot in the leg, but luckily, the bullet just grazed his knee cap. Since Ronnie has taken boxing, he was ready to fight.

"Mom, I'm not scare of these guys around here. They can't whip me."

"Ronnie, I'm not saying you're scared or that they can whip

you, all I'm saying is . . .these guys have guns. They can damn sure shoot your ass. You'll be surprised how much a person can dislike you, and you'll never know it. Plus, it's just us, Ronnie. I need you. You're out there by yourself. Your brother's gone. You hung out with him and his friends, remember. All this mess could be about them. I can't let anything happen to you. I couldn't take it. Man, how could I live without my baby boy. . .I thought about it for about a minute. Damnit Ronnie. I'd rather be safe than sorry. You're leaving here."

It was after the first quarter of the 1996 school year when we left Seattle for Oklahoma City, where we have a wealth of family that has our best interest in mind. Ronnie could start back to church. He could focus more on school and graduating; and less on trying to stay safe and alive. Ronnie was not happy moving to Oklahoma and that's okay. Momma was way too strict for this city slicker and that's okay too.

I on the other hand wasn't ready to stay in OKC. I needed a more money. Momma didn't push it but she tried to talk logic and common sense to me.

"Sharell, you're never going to have enough money. So you just go with what you got. Make it work for you." Then she started trying to use her psychology on me. "I got all these kids. I can't keep up with all these kids." I know my mother a lot better than this. It's right up her alley to control these grand kids and make them stay home on weekends. She'll want to meet their girlfriends, meet their parents, then tell how unsatisfied she was with the whole family. She'll make them cut the yard and work around the house. Ronnie is a good kid, he won't give her any trouble.

I blocked everything she was saying out. "Mom, just let me do this." I didn't want to talk about what I was doing. I thought I could probably get a coffee stand set up like it is in Seattle. I thought if I go out until the end of the school year, I would have enough money saved to open up a coffee stand. It was do-able.

"Well when are you leaving?"

"I thought I would leave Monday evening sometime. I want to go to church with you."

"You're coming to church with me?" She was happy. "Okay, that'll be nice."

Sunday came and I was happy to be in my church. But I couldn't shake the sadness that was so apparent. There was a sad cloud over my church, actually over the entire city. It hadn't been long since the Murrah Building got bombed in downtown Oklahoma City and the hurt from the attack was still there hovering over the city. As soon as I got off the plane, I felt it. In Oklahoma City, it's hard to describe, but I could feel the sadness. Five members in my church were killed.

I could see people pointing at me. I could hear voices whispering, "Pumkin's here." That's my nickname. People knew me intimately, they were happy to see me. They wanted to see my son and know him. They wanted to talk with us and know what I've been doing. Ooowee, if only they knew.

The minister wasn't our regular Pastor. I guess my childhood Pastor was getting old. My Pastor was there, moving slowly along, and he even recognized me after I've been gone over twenty years. He remembered me. His patience was challenged because I thought he might have forgotten who I was. He sure let me know. "I know who you are. How you doing, baby? Good . . .Good." He walked out the sanctuary without waiting for my response, he was using a cane. My Pastor was getting old.

The new minister wasn't letting me out the door without talking with me.

"Hello Sister, how are you doing? Are you coming home for good? I'd like to have a talk with you."

"Well, sir, I'm leaving tomorrow evening. Maybe we can talk some other time."

"What time are you leaving tomorrow evening?"

"Evening Sir, tomorrow evening."

"Tomorrow morning is a good time for me, we can talk in the morning. 9 am.?" He nodded

"Okay. I'll be there."

That's nice. He wants to talk with me. I left the sanctuary and went to the Fellowship Hall to speak to all my other church family. This is nice. People that I grew up with were hugging and screaming, happy to see me. This is good. I forgot what it's like to be home and see everybody. Church was good. The choir was great. Ronnie liked our church.

The next morning, 9 am sharp, I was there to meet our minister. I didn't know what to expect, having a meeting with the minister and really talking with him. I said I would be there.

"Come in Sister. Have a seat." I sat down and the minister sat with me at a little round table. He didn't waste any time getting to his point. "Sister, I want you to come home and join the church."

"Well, actually, I feel like this is my church already."

He just smiled like he knew better. "I meant to say, reunite with your church."

"Sir, I have to leave again. I need to do a few things before I'm able to come home. I need to make more money before I can come home."

"Why? This is your home. Why do you need money to come home? Can't you make money here?" I looked at the minister, I sized him up to get a feeling, if I could trust this guy. I felt comfortable enough to trust him so I took a chance.

"Well sir, I work in a club."

He didn't flinch, he just nodded . . .okay! He acted like he was just one of us, like he was a normal person. Then I continued to bleed.

"I dance." I immediately started crying. This was the first time I really faced what I've been doing. How did I let this happen, for so long. I was suppose to be better. . . I continued. I've never faced the fact that I let my family down. But words weren't enough. No way could I say everything that wanted to escape from my spirit. I continued to trust him . . .to tell him my secrets. Whow, I couldn't believe I told somebody at my church that I danced for a living. My mother would scream. He didn't blink. But I sure did. I felt vulnerable. I hoped he wouldn't judge me. He handed me kleenex cause I was sure snotting now.

"Is that all you're doing?"

"Yes sir, that's all I'm doing. I didn't say it but my heart was ready to confess. I've done a lot more."   "Why do you feel you need more money before you come home. Just stop now and come home."

"I've been living this life. I don't have anything to show for it. I want something that I can come home with, so I won't be ashamed."

"Sister. I've met your son. You should never be ashamed.

C. Oakes

He's a fine young man."

"I thought maybe I could open a coffee shop, like they have in Seattle, you know to show for something that I've been doing . . . and I need more money to do that."

"What if you don't get a coffee shop. Will you still love God."

I looked at the minister. I was shocked at that question. "Sir I'm going to love God anyway. Regardless of my circumstances. I love God."

"How long do you need to be out there?"

"I don't know. I plan on coming home this summer, some time."

"Okay sister." The minister was looking deep in my eyes. "You go back out there and do what you do. But when you come home, I want you to slam that door shut and never look back."

I looked at the minister. This was the first time I've ever discussed me giving up the fast life and never looking back. I nodded in agreement.

Then he started to pray for me. He asked for forgiveness for me. He asked for direction for me. He asked the Lord to protect me while I was away. He told the Lord I had a discerning spirit. I didn't know what he meant by that but I know it was good for me. He continued to pray and pray. I cried because I was so sorry for my life. I was sincere, but I didn't want to stop. Not right now.

I've always wanted to quit and not have to do it again. But I've never considered not having that option. Dancing has been a trump card for me. I can draw a crowd. I've been dancing on and off since I was eighteen. Now, I'm in my forties. That's a long time. I've seen dancers work well into their fifty's making grand theft money. You'll be surprised how exercise will keep you young. If me or my boys needed anything, all I had to do is dance a few months. Me, being a single parent, I needed that dependable help from the strip clubs. I'm getting old now. I could probably dance well into my fifties, but there's nothing worst or sadder than an old dancer.

C. Oakes

Chapter 31

I gave up my apartment. All my things were in storage and now I'm renting a room from another dancer, Cheryl. Cheryl reminds you of the actress, Sally Fields, that played in The Flying Nun. She's a small brunette and real cute. But all the dancers are cute and thin.

She lives close to the strip club in Lynnwood. So it's convenient. Getting to work won't cost too much. I'm trying to save as much as possible. I haven't started to work yet. I'll go tonight. Cheryl said the laws have changed. She said there's a new 3 ft rule, meaning we have to stay at least 3 ft away from customers while table dancing.

"What! Cheryl, how does that work? How can we table dance like that? We won't make any money. That's our entire hustle."

I couldn't imagine us making money with regulations like that. They're trying to break the strip club industry. There's been a lot of problems with the people that owned the clubs. In fact, one of the owners was just released from prison. But damn, don't make us suffer.

"Don't they realize we have kids. We have goals, like going to school, starting businesses, this is supplementing income for the girls that are single parents." I was ranting now. "What are they trying to do to us?" I couldn't understand it. "Would they rather we all go on welfare and not work. At least we're working and pulling our own weight around here. Don't put the dancers like this. Gosh!" This was terrible. "So Cheryl, are the girls making any money?"

"Not really. Everybody's moving away. They're going to Vegas and Alaska to work. Some are going to Vancouver, they say it's real good there. It's terrible here. Washington is over. Jay Leno's been talking about us on television."

"You're kidding me. Jay Leno? Damn I wish I had of known this before I came way out here. I wish I called you first. Man, what are we going to do?" I couldn't believe it. I could have gone to Vegas.. .Vegas would have been closer. Shoot, I could have worked Oklahoma City. But I wouldn't do that to my family, embarrass them like that.

"Sharell, the money just dried up around here. The police are really crazy. They come in all week buying table dances. Then on Friday's, they go to the manager's office, look at our pictures on file, pick out who got tickets, then take them all to jail. It'll be about ten or more that they'll get."

"You got to be kidding me. I was only gone three weeks. All this happened . . . that quick?"

"I'm thinking of moving. Stormy and Liz are working at Cat's in Vegas. I'll probably go after my lease is up."

I kept thinking about my agreement with the minister in Oklahoma City. It was kind of funny. The minister asked me to come home and leave this lifestyle behind. . . and I said "No, not yet." But looks like I won't have much of a choice. What a coincidence. Maybe the Lord is shutting me down.

I got to figure out something. I promised I'd quit by this summer. Shoot, by then I could have saved a few grand. Now I don't know. I spent a lot of money getting my drivers license back. It was ridiculous. All those tickets, then my license was suspended, I was charged for everything. It cost thousands and it was all getting paid before I left Seattle. I wasn't going home without my drivers license. If I could only make that money back, would be great.

That night I went to work and didn't make a damn thing. I came home with less than a hundred bucks. By the time I paid for food and the cab ride, I had thirty dollars in my pocket. This was awful.

I had been sending all my money to Oklahoma City. I would buy money orders and mail them to my bank. Plus if Ronnie needed anything, momma would be able to get it without going through me. I know he need things. Michael Jordan has his own brand of tennis shoes now, and Ronnie needs those shoes.

"Mom, everybody's getting them."

"Well, you can get them if you want, Ronnie."

"Mom, you have to tell grandma. She won't give me the money."

"Why not? Why won't she give you the money, Ronnie?"

"Mom, guess what? All the kids are leaving school during lunch Friday to go to the mall to get some Michael Jordans. It's

C. Oakes

almost like a holiday. Mom, I want to go too. It's the first day that they're out. The mall's going to be packed."

"Ronnie, how much are they?"

"They're kind of expensive. They can be for my birthday."

"How much?"

"They're $150. These are the first editions Mom, they're going to be worth more than that in a few years. Mom, everybody's getting them during lunch tomorrow. Please mom."

"Ronnie, what kind of tennis shoes are worth 150 bucks? That's crazy."

"Mom, these are Jordan's. Have you seen them?"

"No, that's okay Ronnie, just don't forget, they're your birthday present."

"Okay Mom. Love you. You want to talk to grandma. You'll have to tell her I can get them. She won't give me the money."

"Okay put mom on the phone. Mom, give Ronnie two hundred dollars. He'll need it for Friday."

"Sharell, I know you're not letting that boy buy those expensive tennis shoes. That doesn't make sense."

"Mom, this money is for his birthday." I didn't want to explain my expenses to my mother, but that's the price I have to pay for letting her handle my money while I'm gone. She's going to be mom. Nosey.

I didn't stay in Lynnwood. There were undercover officers every night, giving tickets to girls for violating the new regulations. You would think that they had more important things to do, than buying lap dances, like catching the Green River killer. But we were easy targets and easy money for the county because girls needed to make money. So we lapped danced and hoped we didn't dance for an undercover cop and get a $200 dollar fine while making about fifty dollars a night. The whole state had changed it rules. They were killing us. Every night I was a nervous wreck.

I hustled up a plane ticket. I paid my storage bill in Seattle for a few months. Then I was out of there. I found a room in Las Vegas that wasn't on the strip or downtown, it was a regular hotel room, so it was reasonable. I was ready. I wanted to try Cat's. All my life I've been use to going in a club and being hired immediately. So I didn't think it would be a problem for me getting hired anywhere. I know how to make money. Any club should be happy to have me work for them. Plus, I still look young. I can pass for my late twenty's or early thirty's easily.

When I arrived at Cat's, I didn't feel that I belonged there. It was a new wave. The girls didn't seem like hustlers nor did they look like hustlers. They were straight Barbie dolls. They did a lot of pole dancing. They remind me of Texas with all the stages. The crowd was young and screaming. The managers looked like wrestlers or body builders. I don't think they knew one thing about a strip club or making money. They sold alcohol and that's a good thing for them. Girl's got tips on stage. They were good dancers. Maybe I'm use to a more trained audience. This looked like a huge bachelor party. Young guys screaming all over the place. Wild and drunk.

I went to the bar and asked for the manager. I looked like a million bucks but I sure wasn't ready for this manager's reception.

"Come in and have a seat. Where have you worked before?"

I positioned myself in the seat, looked him in his eyes and proceeded to let him know that I was definitely a pro. "I've worked all over, Florida, Seattle, Texas, Denver, Alaska, Hawaii. I've worked everywhere. I consider myself a professional dancer. I can draw a crowd and I make money."

He nodded. I thought we understood each other, at least on the same page. "Well, here, we have different standards. We have a weight limit, you look a little overweight for this club. Get on the scales."

"Excuse me!" I couldn't believe what I was hearing. "I'm a size 8. That's not what you would call overweight. Plus, I'm good. You don't know what you're talking about."

"I can only hire you for the third shift. If you're willing to take that shift, then I can hire you."

I was irritated. "What's that?"

"You're mainly work from twelve midnight until 8 am. We're open 24 hours a day."

"Okay," I pouted. "Is anybody here at that time? Can I stay now, since it's already 10 pm?"

"Yeah, that'll be fine. Tomorrow come in at midnight."

I felt old leaving the manager's office. I went to the dressing

C. Oakes

room and put on my best costume. It was white trimmed with rabbit fur. That's usually my moneymaker. I didn't say much I just listened to the other girls that were in the dressing room. I could tell they didn't make money by their conversations. Not like the money we use to make in Seattle. They weren't hustlers.

The customers were mostly young guys, like I said before, the bachelor party type. They made a lot of noise. There were only a few real hustlers, I could finally see them moving around, but the crowd wasn't trained. Not like older gentlemen that know how to treat a woman and have the means to treat a woman right.

The next night, I got to the club at eleven. I got dressed and was on the floor a little before midnight. This time I danced on stage. The wrestler looking manager was checking me out. He liked it. I know I looked good. Since it was a weekday, it wasn't the young loud guys there, it was older retired gentlemen. Just what I wanted. I was able to make a couple of hundred that night. I was glad for that money, but it didn't last long. It was probably one night out of a week that I made a little money. The problem is, Cat's didn't have any customers during those hours. This wasn't going to work.

Everything was terrible. I even started having nose bleeds because the air was so dry in Nevada. I've never had nose bleeds before, this was real bad. I didn't know what I was going to do. I started to seriously think about going home for good. I didn't belong in this environment.

I felt lonely. I felt lost. I didn't have anybody with me. It's better to travel with someone, never by yourself, especially in a place like Vegas, doing what I do for a living. I was tempted to turn a trick but I told the minister that I wouldn't do that. Guys would come in the club looking for dates. I was desperate, but I decided not to go that way. I hadn't felt like this since my days in Texas.

Was God telling me that my time was up out here. Does He move like this. That's the way I felt. Why all of a sudden, I couldn't make any money. It was like . . . overnight my livelihood got stripped away. This wasn't gradual, it was immediate. I was shut down. I know what happened. That minister prayed for me and the Lord is bringing me home. Whow. He's amazing. For some reason, I just know that's it.

This was so apparent. He's telling me it's over. Whow! Take what you got and go home.

I didn't want to go home. I didn't understand why but I just didn't. Why would I rather live in this filth and vulgar environment than to go home, where it's clean and people there, know and loved me. What was I holding on to and why. I had to search my heart as to why it's so hard for me to go home. I could say all the obvious reason, like, I need more money. But that's not it.

None of those questions were as hard as the main questions that I needed to ask myself. . . Where is Sharell after all this? Will she ever be normal? Will I ever fit in a square environment? Could I be accepted if somebody found out about me. It's very divulging to face yourself. To stop and look, figure out what happened and why, then what to do next. It was lonesome, because I didn't have anyone with me, that I could talk to that would help me figure it out.

After meditating and researching my life, my heart, my soul, I admitted that I did have someone with me, waiting for me to wake up from the dead. Sharell, the sweet, innocent girl that I use to know, has been there all the time, buried deep somewhere . . waiting to be released. She wouldn't come out and face the mess I had made of my life. What was I thinking. Why was I doing this to myself. It was time to wakeup. I'll be alright, thanks to God. All the years He's been protecting me. After looking back at everything, He's never left me or forsaken me. My God.

There was a song I use to hear, *I've Been To Paradise, But I've Never Been To Me*. Well, I've been to me, I just forgot who I was. I know it's not going to be easy peeling away all the life that I've lived. It won't happen overnight either, cause it's so much dirt that needs to be washed away. But one day, I'll find myself whole again. I'll be clean. I'll feel normal again, maybe become a real sister in church. It'll be nice to get to know me again. To be me. That sure sounds good. To feel my true heart. After all this time, it's going to be different finding out how I really feel about things, but I'm ready.

It's time. I'm coming home, just as I am.

THE BEGINNING

Foreword

I've been home a while now. Let's see, I came home, in 1997. I feel that I've adjusted well considering the length of time that I was "lost in space." It sure feels good to be home again, making a regular and honest living. I'm back, I'm really back. I rejoined my church. Everybody was happy to see me walking down the aisle, I was happy too. I think I started running into the arms of my church family. Man was I ready. They say, "The angels will rejoin when one comes home." I believe that.

Well, I haven't heard the "voice" since I've been home. I wonder if that's a good thing. Maybe God doesn't have a reason to send his Angel Seals to rescue my butt anymore. Maybe I have my head on straight for a change. I just want to say "Thank you." I wouldn't mind a little "Hallelujah . . you've made it, " whisper from the voice. That would be nice. I still wonder, who exactly was that, during those days. I know God sent his angels to protect me, I just want to meet them, without dying first.

You know, I don't know if this counts . . . but when my Dad was leaving this world. I heard him tell me that he wasn't going to make it, while he was in a coma. I did hear him. He told me clear as day, that he wasn't going to make it. So I guess I can still hear some voices. And I still have my keen sense of intuition. That's good. Most of the time, that's all you need. Because we all will get that strange feeling when something is wrong or when we're about to make the biggest mistake in our lives. We just have to learn to trust it and not be so hard headed.

Mom is still running things. She's something else. It's hard seeing your beautiful mom get older. I'm so thankful for this opportunity to spend some time with my mother. I worry about her. I'll be here for her. She's our queen.

I'm changing the subject now. When I came home, I thought I should do something with myself like volunteer work. That's just the right thing to do. I'm not going to be dead weight around here, so I joined our women's mission group. Can you imagine that? I visit the sick, send letters to women and men in prisons. Believe me, I know what a letter means to someone in prison. It's wonderful. We work and there's plenty of work to do.

I did open my restaurant that stayed opened, at the most, six months. It was a nice place and a huge challenge. Owning and operating a restaurant has always been one of my big dreams. I really felt that I could do it and I would be good at it. I can cook. I can build a customer base. I've done that so many times in strip clubs. So I thought this would be easy. But there are so many things that has to fit just right, like who owns the building. Are they going to be decent to me. My owners gave me a headache. I realized I didn't want a restaurant at all and that's okay.

Oh, before I forget. The Seattle Police Department caught the Green River killer in 2003. I was absolutely shocked to see it was somebody that I recognized from the clubs. He was what we called, "a regular." I never liked the guy. He seemed dorky. I never approached him for anything. When I think about his personality, I can see why the police let his sorry ass go during their investigation. He's a twit.

Matt never left California. He's into his music. In fact, he's pretty good. He's sold songs to some big time people. If you're into rapp music, you've probably heard some of his work. He has a lot out there. His granddad got him working in the construction business too, laying tile. He runs his own crew. He hasn't asked me for any money, so that's a good thing. I don't see him much. Hopefully, that's going to change. I got three grandchildren by Matt.

Ronnie moved to California too. He's been attending the University of Southern California in Sacramento. Ronnie is still an overachiever. He's acting. I think he's going to be the next Denzel. (I'm probably his biggest fan.) I see more of him because he has a son that lives here in Oklahoma. They both live close to Mike. By the way, Mike is like a brother to me now. He's calmed down so much, you wouldn't recognize him. The old geezer is still having babies.

Val still lives here in Oklahoma City with her husband, Eddie. The kids are all grown. The twins are in their twenties now. Time sure flies. Val has so many kids around her. Their house is the place where neighborhood kids hang out. Now it's the grand kids place to hang out. Val's so good. She's just like Phyl. Phyl's still with Keith with all their kids too.

Phyl's a soldier. She drives a church bus and picks up all the kids in her neighborhood. She has them lined up at her house doing homework. She checks their report cards. She gets on the corner praying for the bad ones. Phyl is something. She has guts.

Jolynn did get back with her husband. They had another kid before she left him for good. I can't believe that girl. She looks the same, hasn't changed one bit. She's doing good now, she's in church. We both quit cocaine about the same time. Jolynn's in the real estate business, drives a new jag. I'm proud of her. She's a hustler. Every blue moon, she'll give me a call.

I lost one of my best friends, since we were kids. After 26 years of marriage, Vicki, my brother's wife, died of cancer. I was blessed that I had a little time with her before she left. Kenny was amazing through those tough days. I have a new appreciation for my big brother.

Johnny and Kathy aren't together anymore. They remain good friends. When my boys go to Seattle to visit, they'll usually stay with Kathy. We're still like family. I'm glad when I hear from them. Kathy's in church, too.

Tiara has a little girl now. She sends me pictures. Aaron tries to stay in touch, but I'm finished with him. I love Tiara. She's still my stepdaughter. I can't wait to see her daughter in person. I know she as beautiful as her mom.

Lucky moved back to Oklahoma City too. He opened a little club on the eastside. After I was deep in my book, I had to address his actions toward me. He told me that he's not Lucky anymore. He's a new person and I should "get over it." I guess I should.

Oh yeah, I'm totally drug-free. No marijuana, nothing. I had been smoking weed since my early teens. I'm deep in my forties and I want to get older. Anyway, after I quit smoking weed, I couldn't figure out, for the life of me, what was the big deal. One thing for sure, I couldn't have written this book if I was still smoking that stuff.

After my restaurant awakening, I've had a few jobs. I've been working decent jobs, but I get laid off. The companies go bankrupt, every thing happens. These days, there's no job security anywhere and getting that pink slip is devastating. So I decided I would do something where I wouldn't have to worry about being laid off. I became an over-the-road truck driver.

Driving over the road has been fun. I'm not afraid of too much. The Lord's been taking care of me all this time. I grew up with snow and ice in Oklahoma City, so I'm not afraid of that either. Plus, I've had an opportunity to see this great country. These United States are absolutely beautiful.

Anyway, my friends and family have been getting on me about writing this book. I fought it for a long time. I wasn't ready to face it. I don't know why I decided to finally put my life on paper, but it turned out to be very therapeutic for me. There were a lot of issues that I needed to address. For instance, I finally stopped looking toward men for my happiness or to rescue me from life's hardships. If a person's not happy by themselves, how could they find happiness in someone else. True happiness and security is in the Father and accepting Jesus as the Christ. I still have issues and that's okay because I can stand on the Word. I'm much happier, that's for sure.

So, there I go driving across this country in this 18 wheeler, with my laptop, pouring my heart out. There's a time when we all change. We have to forget and move forward. We have to get over our failures. But most of all, we have to forgive ourselves. As long as we are holding on to the pass, or letting our past stagnate us, God can't move us to the next level.

I use to have a problem revealing my pass. Telling someone that I was once in prison, made my stomach hurt. Boy, it kept me from pursuing a different career. I was so afraid that during a background check, prison would pop up, then I wouldn't get the job anyway. So why bother with a job search. Then telling someone I was a dancer. Man, that was really hard. Getting over that was the most difficult thing I could do. But if I couldn't tell where I've been, how could I be a witness to God's awesome power and His love. He not finished with me. There's no telling what might happen in my life.

When God opens a door for you, who can move you? Doesn't matter where we've been. I was listening to a recent radio talk show when the host ask the men in his listening audience, "When it came to other men in their woman's life, How many is too many?" He was asking the men, what was their limit, at what point would they have to say, "No. I can't. You're not good enough.

You've fallen below my standards." This was only entertainment to him, but he was talking about women that have already been abused by life. It was terrible. We all fall short. That's a fact.

I'm so glad that God doesn't have limits. I'm so happy that God is deeper than our minds and our flesh. I was giving an opportunity to turn my life around. I don't know why He allowed me to live, but He did and I thank Him. I'm not the perfect child of God. He's still working on me. He's still making me, molding and developing me. Hopefully, I will continue to grow.

So when you see a women or girl, on the streets, lost. Be mindful of what you think, be careful not to judge too harshly. Pray for her. Reassure her with a smile. For all you know, she could be a saint in training. My pastor use to say, "When we know better, we do better."

Learn to love and trust God.

Praise for *A Long Way Home*

Cassandra, You got a bestseller. I could not put it down. . . This is a book of survival and redemption. I love this book.

> Dr. Ann Allen, OKC Public School

In *A Long Way Home*, you will experience the growth of Sharell and her homeys... although Sharell did test the limits, she evolved into a wonderful woman in the end. Never losing sight of what was important in this life... This is a must read for all who have walked in the wrong path. It's never too late.

> Shelia Reynolds
> Oklahoma City (Via California)

Boo, you have a bestseller on your hands. Sharell and I took *A Long Way Home* together and it was a hell of a trip. Your creative story telling was fluid, and it quenched my thirst as Sharell dehydrated and suffered through her worst. Through her eyes, I was a passenger on a white water roller coaster ride I did not want it to end, but was pleased it did and how.

> Kevin Anderson, Poet

Cassandra . . .it was wonderful. It was enlightening. I never knew things like that really happened.

> Nicy Bishop, Ft. Polk

Every preacher needs to read this book. Cassandra Oakes is a very talented writer who tells the story of how an innocent, fun-loving girl can get caught up... Expect the full ride. I believe this book should be a part of every serious evangelistic college seminary course.

> Cynthia Calloway, M.Ed., LPC

I read the book in just a few days... I was especially drawn by the writing style...it is clear she had an angel watching over her.

> Donny Beechum, 442 SCMS/GUMD

Cassandra, I can whip your butt. I never knew . . . You got a good book, girl, and I'm very proud of you.

> Your Brother, Kenny

C. Oakes

CPSIA information can be obtained at www.ICGtesting.com
Printed in the USA

268801BV00001B/4/P